Mr. Tompkins Inside Himself

Also by George Gamow

One Two Three . . . Infinity

Puzzle-Math *(with Marvin Stern)*

A Planet Called Earth

A Star Called the Sun

Mr. Tompkins
Inside Himself

Adventures in the New Biology

GEORGE GAMOW
AND
MARTYNAS YČAS

With illustrations by George Gamow

THE VIKING PRESS / NEW YORK

Library of Congress catalog card number 67-20297
Printed in U.S.A. by Vail-Ballon Press, Inc.

Parts of this book are based on material previously
published in *Mr. Tompkins Learns the Facts of Life*
by George Gamow, published by Cambridge University Press in 1953.

To the memory of Pat Covici

" . . . Oh solve me the riddle of living,
That age-old, tormenting riddle,
That many a head has brooded over,
Heads in hieroglyphic bonnets,
Heads in turban and black mortar board,
Periwig heads and a thousand other
Poor, perspiring heads of people—
Tell me this, what meaning has man?
From where is he come? Where does he go?
Who dwells up there on starlets golden? . . . "

—H. HEINE, *The Sea and the Hills,* translated by Frederick T. Wood. (Boston: Chapman and Grimes, Inc., 1946.)

Acknowledgments

It is the authors' pleasant duty to thank those who have helped with the preparation of this volume: Dr. R. W. G. Wyckoff, Laboratory of Physical Biology, National Institutes of Health, for an electronmicrograph of bacteriophages; Dr. M. Demerec, Department of Genetics, Carnegie Institution of Washington, for a photomicrograph of fruitfly chromosomes; Charles Lehman, Los Alamos, New Mexico, for an anthropomorphic photograph of the Maniac; Dr. J. Z. Young, University College, London, for a photomicrograph of a cat's cerebral cortex; Dr. M. H. F. Wilkins and Dr. W. Fuller, Kings College, London, for a photograph of the X-ray diffraction pattern from a fiber of DNA; and Dr. David S. Smith and the *Revue Canadienne de Biologie* for an electronmicrograph of a cross-section of aphid muscle. Thus, if one takes the illustrations literally, Mr. Tompkins has the chromosomes of a fruitfly, the brains of a cat, and the muscles of an aphid. But, considering the basic similarity of the structural elements of all living things, it really doesn't matter much.

We thank Miss Luanna Love and A. A. Ayres for some of the drawings; Chapman and Grimes for permission to quote from a translation of Heinrich Heine's *The Sea and the Hills;* Harper & Row and *The New Yorker* for permission to quote "A Bitter Life" by John Updike; and Yale University Press for permission to quote from John von Neumann's *The Computer and the Brain.*

It is our particular pleasure to express our gratitude to Mrs. Beatrice Rosenfeld of The Viking Press for her help and advice in the preparation of the manuscript. On many occasions we have tried her patience sorely.

G. G.
M. Y.

Contents

Illustrations

Introduction

Cyril George Henry Tompkins is a teller at a large city bank. His work is tiring and requires close attention, and after hours most of his fellow employees try to relax by watching television or going to a movie or reading detective stories. But not Mr. Tompkins. He prefers to stretch out comfortably in a big armchair with a book or magazine on popular science, which would plunge him into the mysterious realm of atoms, stars, and galaxies, far away from his daily tasks. In spite of his interest, it has frequently happened that after an hour or two the page would begin to blur before his eyes, he would yawn, and his head would lean against the back of his soft armchair. This did not mean, however, that he had abandoned the scientific topics he was trying to follow. His vivid imagination carried him through his dreams into fantastic worlds. The dreams were often odd and grotesque, but in one way or another they fitted the facts he had read about. Hence he was better able to grasp the meaning of the words he had been reading by seeing the unusual events they described with his own eyes.

Mr. Tompkins's interest in science was fortified by his domestic life. Once he had attended a series of popular lectures on physics given by a professor of the local university. Mr. Tompkins became acquainted with the professor, then met and married his daughter Maud, thus getting the opportunity to learn more physics in the family circle.*

*The previous adventures of Mr. Tompkins in the world of physics can be found in a book written by George Gamow and published in 1965 by Cambridge University Press under the title *Mr. Tompkins in Paperback*.

Guided by his father-in-law, he first developed an interest in pure physics. Gradually, however, both the professor and he realized that biology, which for centuries had fascinated and baffled both scientists and philosophers, was at last making giant strides forward. The finest details of the living body were revealed and their workings were becoming understood in terms of the atoms of which they were made. So Mr. Tompkins began to study the subject.

His first excursions into biology were described by George Gamow in *Mr. Tompkins Learns the Facts of Life,* published by Cambridge University Press in 1953. Since then biology has entered a "golden age," with one important discovery following another. As a result much of Mr. Tompkins's earlier biological explorations has become obsolete. We have therefore prepared this new and enlarged volume, in which we have attempted to give the reader a broader view of biology, including recent developments in molecular biology, through Mr. Tompkins's self-education about one of the great achievements of our time.

GEORGE GAMOW
MARTYNAS YČAS

Christmas 1966

Mr. Tompkins Inside Himself

» 1 «

Through the Blood Stream

THE large waiting room of the New Memorial Hospital was cool and comfortable. The patients were sitting in somewhat strained poses, waiting for their turn to be called for inspection. Some of them were trying to distract their thoughts by glancing through magazines; others were just staring into space. Once in a while a stretcher rolled past, pushed by a white-clad attendant; everybody's eyes automatically followed the procession until it disappeared at the far end of the corridor.

Mr. Tompkins picked up the latest issue of *The New Yorker,* but the subtle humor of the cartoons, which he usually enjoyed, did not seem to affect him now. Yesterday he had felt quite all right and full of life, but this morning, during breakfast, he had glanced through a newspaper account of a lecture on cancer. The article described in vivid words how the usually regular and well-coordinated processes of cell division in living tissue can sometimes get out of hand, producing ugly malignant growths, and leading ultimately to the complete destruction of the organism. The author had compared these destructive tendencies of certain aggressive cell groups, which appear now and then within the peaceful commonwealth of normal cells constituting a living organism, with similar phenomena in the field of sociology and world politics, and suggested that in both cases the only cure known at present is the use of the scalpel or the sword.

"Sure," agreed Mr. Tompkins, "to hell with all this appeasement business. *Si vis pacem, para bellum!*"

But later at the bank, thoughts about the grim possibility of aggres-

3

sive cell division just would not leave his mind, and all the while, as he cashed checks, he felt that something unusual was going on in the organized community of cells which he called his body. His head was heavy, his respiratory organs seemed to work under unusual strain, and he felt an ache in all his joints.

As he had also completely lost his appetite, he decided to make use of his lunch hour for a visit to the dispensary of a large city hospital, which was fortunately just around the corner. He wanted to make sure that no aggressive cell groups were operating in his body. There was a long waiting line, so he picked up a magazine from the central table and settled comfortably into the last vacant armchair. He felt quite relaxed now, and a few minutes later the magazine fell softly to the marble floor at his feet.

Suddenly all the people in the waiting room straightened in their seats and turned their heads toward a tall man in a snow-white laboratory gown, who had just walked in through the door of an adjacent office. Mr. Tompkins knew this man very well through photographs which appeared now and then in the city's newspapers. It was Dr. Streets, the world-renowned authority on abnormal cell growth. Noticing Mr. Tompkins, who was almost hidden from sight by an enormously fat lady sitting next to him, Dr. Streets rushed toward him with wide-open arms.

"Oh, my dear Mr. Tompkins, what in the world could have brought you here?"

This was very strange since, though Mr. Tompkins might well know of this famous figure of the medical world, Dr. Streets had no reason whatsoever to know Mr. Tompkins.

"I came here, sir," said Mr. Tompkins, feeling the eyes of all the other patients concentrating on him, "to check the mitosis rates in my cells, and to find out if there is any neoplasm formation or any danger of metastasis." (He thought that by using this scientific language he would have some excuse for being examined ahead of all the others.)

"Oh yes, of course," said Dr. Streets, becoming suddenly quite serious. "We can get inside your body and have a quick look around at various cell communities to be sure they are behaving in the proper way. It shouldn't take too much time, provided one knows what to look for."

"You mean," said Mr. Tompkins with a chill running down his spine, "you want to open me up?"

There was a violent feeling of suction. . . .

"Oh, no," said Dr. Streets soothingly, "it won't be necessary unless, of course, we find something wrong. I am just going to inject you into your own blood stream, so that you can see for yourself the various cell colonies from which you are formed. The round trip through your main circulatory system takes not more than half a minute but, of course, since we shall have to change our linear dimensions, the time scale will change too, and we shall be able to make the examination in quite a leisurely way."

As he spoke, Dr. Streets put his hand into a pocket of his white gown, pulled out a large hypodermic syringe, and pointed its long shiny needle toward Mr. Tompkins. There was a violent feeling of suction, and for a moment Mr. Tompkins felt just as if he were a camel trying to squeeze itself through a needle's eye. Then something pinched his arm above the elbow, the suction turned into pressure, and Mr. Tompkins was forcibly ejected into a rapidly flowing mass of some slightly yellowish transparent fluid. For a moment he felt like an inexperienced diver who had jumped by mistake from a high diving board and was making desperate motions with his arms and legs to come to the surface. But, although this did not get him anywhere, he did not seem to feel any lack of air, and his lungs seemed to function quite normally.

"What a dirty trick!" said Mr. Tompkins. "He must have turned me into a fish!"

"You don't need to be a fish," said the doctor's voice near him, "to be able to breathe inside your own blood stream. After all, it carries all the oxygen supply needed for the respiration of your body cells. But if you feel uncomfortable floating in the plasma, why don't you climb up on this erythrocyte and have some rest? It is just as comfortable for travel as the proverbial flying carpet."

It was only now that Mr. Tompkins noticed a large number of disk-shaped bodies, pinched in the middle, floating in the fluid stream. They were about two feet thick and fifteen feet in diameter, and were painted bright red, resembling one of the inflated rubber rafts on which downed airmen await rescue in the ocean. Climbing up on one of them with the help of the doctor, Mr. Tompkins felt that his miseries were over.

"Aren't these erythrocytes, as you call them, simply what are known

Mr. Tompkins felt that his miseries were over.

as red blood cells?" he asked, stretching out beside Dr. Streets on the soft, velvety surface.

"Exactly so," was the answer. "In fact, *erythros* means 'red' in Greek. The material which gives them that bright red color is known as hemoglobin and is a complicated chemical substance possessing great affinity for oxygen. When the blood stream passes through the lungs, these red blood cells adsorb large amounts of oxygen and carry it along to various cell colonies in the body. In fact, although erythrocytes occupy less than fifty per cent of the volume of the blood fluid, they can adsorb seventy-five times more oxygen than can possibly be dissolved in the plasma itself."

"Must be a tricky substance," said Mr. Tompkins thoughtfully.

"So it is," agreed Dr. Streets. "And, as a matter of fact, biochemists have had to work hard to learn its exact composition. If you use this lens, you can see how complicated its structure actually is."

"You mean I can see the separate atoms forming the molecule?" asked Mr. Tompkins with surprise.

"Sure you can. At our present scale you are just about two microns tall. That means that the atoms will look to you like little spheres a few tenths of a millimeter in diameter. A simple pocket lens would be enough to see the structure quite easily. Just look at those little pimples covering the surfaces you are sitting on."

Mr. Tompkins took the lens from the doctor's hand, stretched out on his stomach, and examined a hemoglobin molecule attentively. It looked like four long ribbons, loosely tangled around flat disks.

"What looks like a ribbon," explained Dr. Streets, "is the protein part of hemoglobin, called globin. The disks are heme, the business part of the molecule, and they also give it the red color. As you can see, they are symmetrical structures built around a heavy atom of iron located at the center. The iron atom is surrounded by a group of four nitrogen atoms and twenty carbons. Outside are attached hydrocarbon chains sticking out in all directions like the tentacles of an octopus. If you watch carefully, you can see that the oxygen molecules are caught by the iron atoms like flies on a fly sticker. Some of the oxygen molecules keep breaking loose from time to time, but they are caught more frequently than they escape."

"If the oxygen is caught by the heme, what is the purpose of the globin?" asked Mr. Tompkins.

"Before I answer that question," replied Dr. Streets, "perhaps we

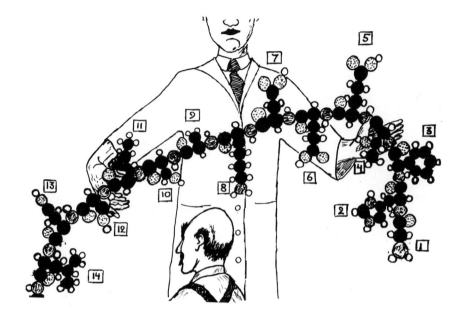

"It looks rather like a charm bracelet with pendants of different shapes hanging on it." (The "pendants" in this immature form of the hemoglobin molecule are: [1] glycine, [2] histidine, [3] phenylalanine, [4] threonine, [5] glutamic acid, [6] glutamic acid, [7] aspartic acid, [8] lysine, [9] alanine, [10] threonine, [11] isolucine, [12] threonine, [13] serine, [14] leucine.)

should examine the globin more carefully. Your body would not be alive unless it were mostly made of protein, and to understand what life is you have to know what a protein is. Globin is a very good example of a protein for beginners. Let us step through the lens and pull out one of these tangled globin ribbons to see what it looks like."

They did so and, grasping the tangled ribbon in two places, the doctor stretched out the ribbon like a rubber band.

"To me," said Mr. Tompkins, "it looks now rather like a charm bracelet with pendants of different shapes hanging on it."

"That is the general idea," said Dr. Streets. "The pendants, as you call them, are known among biochemists as amino acids, and are various kinds of rather simple organic molecules possessing special snaps which fasten them to each other, thus forming sometimes very long chains. In this particular protein, for example, there are four such chains, two of which each have 146 amino acids from one end to another, and two

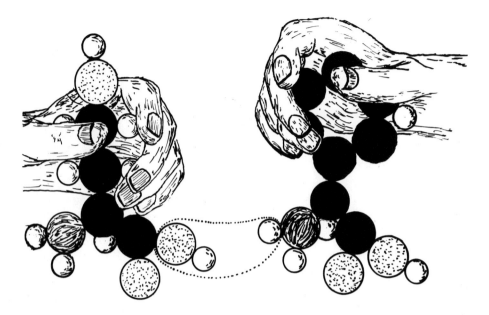

Every amino acid has one carbon atom, to which two snaps are attached.

with 141 each. That is why the protein molecule looks so complicated."

"How do these snaps operate?" asked Mr. Tompkins. "I am sure that they do not look like those used by tailors and dressmakers."

"I can show you easily," said the doctor, extracting from his pocket two molecular models made of colored wooden balls. "I built these models the other day to use at a lecture I gave for the hospital personnel. Every amino acid has one carbon atom, called the alpha carbon, to which two snaps are attached. One of the snaps is called by chemists an amino group, something related to a molecule of ammonia."

"You mean," said Mr. Tompkins, "the rather smelly stuff my wife uses to remove dirt from window panes?"

"Yes, she uses ammonia dissolved in water. Ammonia is a nitrogen atom with three hydrogen atoms around it. If one of the hydrogens is removed, and some more complicated configuration of carbon atoms is attached in its place, you get a more complicated ammonia which is called an amine.

"Now here is the other snap attached to the same atom as the amino group. It is a carboxylic acid; a carbon atom which holds on to two oxygen atoms. One of these oxygen atoms also has a hydrogen atom attached to it. This is why chemists call the entire molecule an amino acid; it has both an amino and an acid group on it.

"If you look at the atoms more closely, you'll see a hydrogen atom on the amine, and an oxygen and hydrogen on the carboxylic acid group. Putting the two together, we get $OH + H \rightarrow H_2O$, or water. So if I push the amino group of one amino acid against the acid group of another, I force out a water molecule and at the same time the amino and acid groups join up and snap the two amino acids together. Other amino acids are snapped on in the same way, and we get our long chains.

"You can also see," said Dr. Streets, "that although each amino acid has these two snaps, the rest of the molecule is not always the same. Two more chemical groups are attached to the alpha carbon in addition to the two snaps. One of them is always a hydrogen atom. Depending on what the other group is, the amino acids have different properties and are given different names. The ten amino acids forming the part of the chain which I hold between my hands are glycine, histidine, phenylalanine, glutamic acid, again glutamic acid, aspartic acid, lysine, alanine, threonine, serine, and leucine."

"Such complicated names!" said Mr. Tompkins. "How can the biochemists remember them all?"

"Well, fortunately, although one can synthesize thousands or even millions of different kinds of amino acids, nature uses only twenty of them in building protein molecules."

"I suppose," said Mr. Tompkins, "that we are urged to eat protein-rich foods so that we can incorporate them into our bodies without having to take the trouble of making proteins ourselves."

"Not at all," replied Dr. Streets. "If this were to happen, the consequences would be strange indeed. What you are depends on the kinds of proteins you have. If you could incorporate foreign proteins, you could gradually change yourself into a chicken by eating chicken. Fortunately, the chicken proteins you eat are digested—broken down into amino acids. From these you form human, and specifically Tompkins's, proteins. Thus you are in no danger of becoming someone else by eating him. It is true that at times many people have thought otherwise. Cannibals and other primitive people ate brains of men or hearts of lions to become wiser and braver. But, alas for them, their stomachs broke everything down to the same amino acids, whether they ate heroes or cowards. Of course, they may actually have become braver by thinking they were braver. A psychiatrist might tell you more about this."

"I am not sure I follow you," said Mr. Tompkins. "If proteins are all made of the same twenty amino acids, why aren't they all the same?"

"The differences between various proteins depend on the order in which the twenty amino acids are arranged in the sequence. It is something like using the twenty-six letters of the alphabet. Depending on how you arrange the letters, including, of course, the spaces and punctuation marks, you can write sentences, long letters, and volumes of books. Each protein has to carry out a definite function in an organism. The instructions on how to do it are given by the order in which the amino acids follow one another."

"Here I have," continued Dr. Streets, taking out of his pocket a typed sheet of paper, "two recipes which I copied from a cookbook."

He read: "Ham and potato cakes. Combine one cup mashed potatoes, one cup ground cooked ham, one tablespoon of chopped parsley, half a teaspoon of grated onion, one-eighth teaspoon of pepper. Shape into flat cakes. Dip lightly in flour and sauté in bacon drippings.

"Plum pudding. Sift one cup sugar. Beat until soft one-half cup butter. Add the sugar gradually. Blend these ingredients until they are creamy. Beat in six eggs. Mix one cup raisins, currants, and pecans. Sprinkle lightly with flour. Combine with two cups of bread crumbs, two teaspoons of cinnamon, half a teaspoon of cloves and half a teaspoon of allspice. Stir into the butter mixture. Bake in a greased pan at three hundred seventy-five degrees for about one-half hour.

"Each recipe contains just a few hundred letters but, depending on the way you arrange them, you get quite different dishes.

"In the same way, the hemoglobin which I hold in my hands helps erythrocytes carry oxygen to the lungs; insulin, which is made of fifty-one amino acids, regulates the utilization of sugar in the organism; and vasopressin, only nine amino acids long, shrinks the walls of the blood vessels and increases the blood pressure. The whole living organism represents a complex chemical factory containing innumerable compounds of different kinds which make it work."

Mr. Tompkins looked thoughtful. "I see now how the same amino acids can form different proteins. It takes a cook, however, to read a recipe and carry out the instructions. Who reads the instructions written in the proteins?"

"Various molecules read the instructions and behave accordingly," replied Dr. Streets. "Watch this." He let go of one end of the globin, and it snapped back into a strip of folds and curls. "Depending on the way the amino acids are strung together, the protein will fold or curl up in different ways. So we can have protein molecules of many different shapes. Depending, in part, on their shapes, proteins can aggregate to form larger structures. Muscle proteins form thin filaments which make it possible for muscle to contract. Another protein forms hair. Still another kind forms an elastic film which is the surface of the red cell on which we are sitting. But probably the most important thing proteins do is to catalyze chemical reactions in our bodies.

"Because a protein molecule may take on all sorts of complicated shapes, it can have a cavity into which another molecule can fit. The structure of such a molecule may then become so distorted that it breaks, or, again because of distortion, it may react more readily with another molecule. Since a single protein molecule can cause many molecules to react without itself changing in any way, we say that such a protein catalyzes a reaction, and call it an enzyme.

"The presence of various enzymes decides which chemical reactions will occur. For example, in your stomach and intestines enzymes catalyze chemical reactions which digest, or break down, food into simple compounds your body can use. Inside cells, enzymes break down nutrients to yield energy, convert sugar into fat, synthesize amino acids, and so on. Proteins, in short, determine what you do and, quite literally, what shape you are in."

"To get back to the hemoglobin we are looking at," said Mr. Tompkins, "what is the protein doing here?"

"A number of things. The most important is that when the heme is combined with the globin, an oxygen molecule can become attached to the iron atom of the heme. Heme alone cannot do it; the globin has to change the distribution of electrical charges around the iron atom to make this possible. The exact distribution depends on the shape of the globin molecule. In fact, the globin is very precisely designed in this respect. As you see, the giant hemoglobin molecule actually consists of four protein chains, each of which has a heme attached. When one of the hemes picks up an oxygen molecule in the lungs, the distribution of charges changes, as does the shape of the globin. The remaining three hemes then have an increased affinity for oxygen, which helps to ensure that the hemoglobin becomes saturated with oxygen. On the other hand, when the blood reaches the tissues, it is important that all the oxygen be liberated. At first the hemoglobin gives up its oxygen with some difficulty. This does not matter, because at this point it is carrying an ample amount of oxygen. But after part of the oxygen is gone, the shape of the globin changes back again, so that the last of the oxygen comes off more easily where it is most needed."

"There is more to this hemoglobin than I had thought," said Mr. Tompkins, as he followed Dr. Streets back through the lens and settled himself comfortably on the erythrocyte.

"There is more to most proteins," said Dr. Streets, "and we are finding out remarkable things about them all the time."

"Say," said Mr. Tompkins, "what is sticking to this heme? It looks very different from an oxygen molecule." Dr. Streets took the lens from Mr. Tompkins's hand and examined the object carefully.

"Oh yes," he said, "it is a molecule of carbon monoxide. You probably picked it up from your cigarette, or perhaps from the fumes of motor traffic."

Seeing the alarm on Mr. Tompkins's face, the doctor hastened to explain further. "Carbon monoxide is indeed a dangerous substance produced by incomplete combustion of carbon. Like oxygen it has a great affinity for the heme iron, and while it sticks to the heme the hemoglobin cannot pick up oxygen. So if you have inhaled a large amount of carbon monoxide your blood cannot carry sufficient oxygen, and you suffocate. In your case, however, there is no special need for alarm. In our modern cities there is always some carbon monoxide from traffic and industry. This is not especially desirable, but you are not worse off than the rest of your fellow citizens."

The two men were so involved in their conversation that they did not notice that the broad stream through which they were previously floating had narrowed to a small channel, and that their erythrocyte was gliding along its slippery semitransparent walls.

"Here we are!" said Dr. Streets, looking around. "We have entered one of the small capillaries supplying blood to the thumb of your left hand. These large lumps of protoplasm lining the walls of our capillary channel are the living cells of your own flesh."

"Oh!" said Mr. Tompkins, who had already seen microphotographs of cellular structure, "they look exactly as they should. And, I suppose, the darkish bodies near their centers are the nuclei?"

"Right," said the doctor. "And, speaking of cancer, you notice that these particular cells are quite normal. Cancerous cells are characterized by a special growth pattern, and in some cases by abnormally large nuclei, and usually can be easily distinguished under the microscope from normal healthy cells. The trouble is, of course, that in order to diagnose cancer in its early stages one would have to examine millions of cells to be absolutely sure. But I hope that we shall soon be able to develop some method which will permit us to do so in a quick and inexpensive way."

"I see," said Mr. Tompkins, who had begun to feel a little short of breath. "I hope you will have such a method soon. But it seems a little stuffy here."

"Sure it does," retorted the doctor. "After all, the blood stream with which we are traveling comes here to give away its oxygen content to the cells, and to take carbon dioxide and carry it away from your body. Watch how the oxygen molecules are becoming detached from the body of our erythrocyte and sticking to the walls of the capillary. They will then diffuse through these walls into the lymph (the liquid surrounding the individual cell), and then into the cells themselves. At the same time, the carbon dioxide accumulated in the cells is draining into the blood stream, where it is partly dissolved in the plasma and partly attached to the molecules of the hemoglobin. As the hemoglobin is losing its oxygen, it is turning purple, the color of venous blood. So our trip back to the lungs is not going to be pleasant."

"I should say not," said Mr. Tompkins, feeling his lungs nearly bursting. "Isn't it silly that I must almost suffocate in order to keep my own thumb breathing?" He certainly did not feel too well, and black spots were floating before his eyes. He seemed to be losing touch with reality, and the black spots seemed to become bigger and bigger.

"Must be cellular nuclei," thought Mr. Tompkins. "Oh, no! It looks more like heads with sailors' caps on. This does look like a submarine. Am I joining the navy, or what?"

"Two hundred fathoms," said a husky voice from nowhere, "and still going down. Darn these jammed valves!"

"I hope they know about it at the base," said another voice. "They'll surely do something about it."

"Oh yeah!" screamed somebody in semi-hysterics. "No, brother, there is no way out of Davy Jones's locker!"

Suddenly the body of the submarine was whirled round violently as if caught in a giant whirlpool. People and instruments were being thrown about all through its narrow interior, and Mr. Tompkins found himself

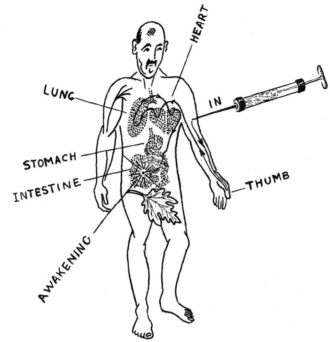

Route of Mr. Tompkins's travels through his blood stream.

clinging to the base of the periscope. For a moment he saw the face of the doctor, a chalk-white face. . . .

"Hold on!" whispered the doctor. "We have just entered the right ventricle of the heart and are heading into the pulmonary artery which leads to the lungs. There will soon be enough air for everybody!"

When Mr. Tompkins had recovered his senses, the air, or rather the plasma, was indeed quite clear. He was lying on the same erythrocyte, tightly embracing the doctor's leg. Their erythrocyte was again floating smoothly through a narrow channel, but there were no cells crowding the space on the other side of its transparent walls. On the contrary, it seemed quite empty except for swarms of what Mr. Tompkins first thought to be little flies or fleas, dashing through it in all directions.

"Atmospheric air," said Dr. Streets, pointing with his long finger.

"You mean we are out of my system?" asked Mr. Tompkins hopefully.

"Oh, no," said the doctor, "we are still in your circulatory system, but we are now passing through one of the capillaries of your lung, to get rid of the carbon dioxide, and take in a new supply of oxygen. The free space across the wall of the capillary is called an alveolus, and is just one of the air pockets, or bays, which line the inside surface of the lung. Each time you breathe, the lung and all its alveoli are filled by the fresh air from the outside so that venous blood can get its new supply of oxygen."

"You mean that these tiny fleas are actually air molecules?" said Mr. Tompkins.

"That's it. But remember that on our present scale, which is roughly one in one million, simple molecules like those of oxygen or nitrogen are about one-tenth of a millimeter in diameter. No wonder you mixed them up with fleas, considering their fast, dashing movements. See how many of them get through the walls of the capillary and attach themselves to the red blood corpuscles. By the time the blood finishes its passage through the lungs and enters into the aorta it is ready again for the new trip across your body."

"I don't think I should like to make that journey again," said Mr. Tompkins, who had not yet recovered from his unpleasant experience.

"But you should!" retorted the doctor. "You haven't seen much yet; in fact, you were delirious throughout most of the long trip from your thumb to the lungs. Besides I haven't yet had a chance to look into the question about which you came to me, and to diagnose your condition."

"All right," said Mr. Tompkins reluctantly, "but perhaps we can get hold of an auxiliary oxygen tank."

"We can do better than that," said the doctor. "As soon as conditions become really uncomfortable we'll simply get you out of your system. But you'd better get ready for a rough ride now, as we are just going to enter your left heart."

"What do you mean, left heart?" asked Mr. Tompkins, baffled. "I thought the heart is always on the left."

"That is correct, and I should rather have said, left half of your heart. You probably do not know that the human heart, which is essentially a pump driving the blood through the body, is actually a double pump. The right half of the heart pumps blood from the body through the lungs and back into the left side of the heart. Then the left side pumps blood through the body and back again into the right side of the heart. Both pumps, complete with valves and so on, are independent, except that both are driven by the same muscles. In fact, when you were an embryo, you had two really separate hearts, which gradually fused into one organ before you were born.

"But hold on now!" Their erythrocyte was now behaving very much

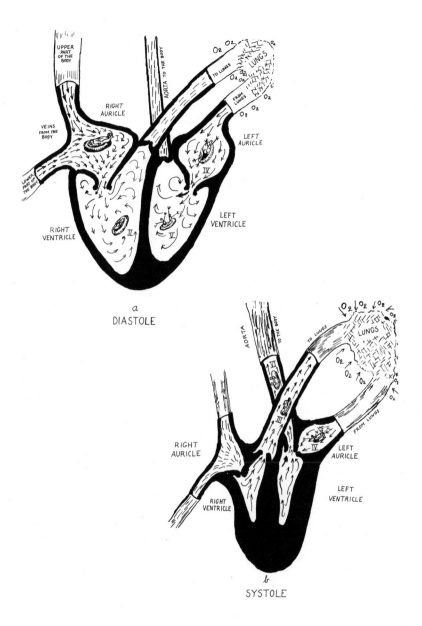

a
DIASTOLE

b
SYSTOLE

Their erythrocyte was now behaving very much like a canoe riding the rapids of the Colorado River.

like a canoe riding the rapids of the Colorado River, and Mr. Tompkins had quite a difficult time trying not to be thrown off into the swirling plasma. They rushed through a narrow opening into the left auricle (the entrance chamber of the heart) and then through another valve into the left ventricle itself. A second later the heart contracted, and their erythrocyte was forced out again through the exhaust valve of the heart pump.

"Well," said the doctor, making himself comfortable on the soft, velvety surface, "now we can have a long chat about things. Is there anything in particular you would like to know?"

"I'd like to know first of all," said Mr. Tompkins, "whether or not this thing we are riding on is alive."

"It's a difficult question," said Dr. Streets. "The answer is probably yes, but with some reservations. The fact is that red blood corpuscles are constantly being born: they live their life, and finally they die when they are three to four months old. In a normal person about ten million erythrocytes die and are replaced every second. The breeding place of erythrocytes is the red marrow of the bones, where they are produced by the steady division of special cells, known as erythroblasts. But before they get out into the blood stream their nuclei decay, and a cell without a nucleus is only half alive. In particular, they completely lose the ability to reproduce themselves, since cell division is a process governed completely by the nucleus. All they can do now is carry the loads of oxygen from the lungs to the body cells, and the loads of carbon dioxide from the body cells to the lungs, thus supporting the life of the entire cellular colony."

"Like oxen or mules," remarked Mr. Tompkins.

"Yes, very much so," agreed Dr. Streets, "and as load-carriers they are, of course, completely indispensable."

"Are they deprived of their reproductive power," continued Mr. Tompkins, "so that their sex instincts do not interfere with their work?"

"Maybe, maybe," said the doctor reflectively, "although, of course, there are many species (frogs, for example) where erythrocytes retain their nuclei all the time while in circulation. Again, in the case of a man who for some reason or other has lost a lot of blood, immature erythrocytes with nuclei are poured into the blood stream to support the dwindling cargo traffic. So it really doesn't make much difference. When erythrocytes die they are disintegrated in your liver and spleen, and their remains are removed through the urine and the feces."

"But what about the white blood cells?" asked Mr. Tompkins. "Do they carry some special load through my body?"

"Oh no," said Dr. Streets, "the white blood cells, or leucocytes, have nothing to do with the Transportation Department. They are rather members of the National Guard, and their job is to protect the cell community from outside invasion. Like all good soldiers, they always possess a brave nucleus. We also call them phagocytes, or 'cell eaters'— in Greek *phagos* means 'eating'—since they attack and eat up most of the invading foreign cells. If you look around, you will notice a few of them floating through the blood stream and maintaining law and order. If they notice a bacterium, they will attack it right away, envelop it with their protoplasm, and devour the invader in less than half an hour. If the invading bacteria are not in the blood stream but some-where in the lymph between the body cells, phagocytes force their way through the walls of the blood vessels and 'get their man' all the same. The trouble is, however, that, in order to catch the bacterium, the phagocyte must pin it against some solid wall, such as the wall of a blood capillary; or else several of them have to attack the bacterium from different sides. If you look this way, you will see how it is done." Look-ing in the direction of Dr. Streets' finger, Mr. Tompkins noticed sev-eral phagocytes which had cornered a bunch of bacteria and were get-ting ready to devour their prey.

"If the bacterium floats in the middle of the blood plasma," continued the doctor, "it is very difficult for a single phagocyte to grab it; about as difficult as it is for you to catch with your teeth an apple floating in a bucket of water. That is because most bacteria possess rather tough skins, the so-called capsules, which make them as slippery as the bobbing apple. However, the phagocytes are helped in their job by complex chemicals known as antibodies, which appear in the blood during each bacterial invasion, 'softening up' bacterial skins as well as neutralizing the poisonous substances or toxins excreted by the bacteria into the blood stream."

"I take it," said Mr. Tompkins, "that these antibodies are not living creatures, since you refer to them as chemicals."

"Quite right," agreed Dr. Streets. "Like so many other chemicals in your body, they are proteins. The amusing thing about them is that they are produced in the organism only when it is attacked for the first time by some bacterium or other. At the time such an attack occurs, special white blood cells begin to produce antibodies specially suitable for defense against that particular invader. They are, so to speak, tailored for each type of invader, and fit it as a key fits a lock. Of course, since antibodies are proteins, and therefore much smaller than bacteria, they fit not the entire bacterium, but rather various chemicals which compose the surface of the bacterium. Antibodies are also produced against various proteins which are poisons, or, to speak more generally, against most large foreign molecules. We may consider antibodies as another example of a protein which is so folded that the substance against which it acts, in this case called the antigen, fits tightly against it. When combined with an antibody the foreign poison is made harmless and is quickly eliminated, and a bacterium is either killed or becomes an easy prey to phagocytes.

"It is likely that an organism possesses, to start with, proteins for making the antibodies which can be quickly molded into any suitable form. You might imagine, as an example, a locksmith's shop with a large collection of uncut keys. When the locksmith is called on to open a new and complicated lock, he would probably use a skeleton-key which can be adjusted and fitted into the lock by trial and error. This may be a lengthy process, but, once it is done, a locksmith can easily produce any number of keys answering the same purpose. And, if he is shrewd enough, he will keep a sample of that key in case he meets with an identical lock sometime in the future."

"Isn't that what doctors call immunity against the disease?" asked Mr. Tompkins.

"Just so," was the answer, "and to produce such an immunity as a preventive measure, we inject into a person a certain amount of dead or inactivated bacteria or virus, which, not being able to multiply, can cause no harm, but can still induce the organism to work out a suitable antibody to be used in case of actual invasion. This method . . . Oh, wait a second!" And Dr. Streets broke off, rising to his feet and trying to catch something floating through the plasma past their erythrocyte. "I think I can now diagnose your illness."

He was holding between his fingers a slippery object about the size of an apple.

"Is that a bacterium?" asked Mr. Tompkins.

"Oh, no! On our scale a bacterium would be as large as a dog. What you see here is a virus particle, and I would bet my professional pride that this is nothing else but the influenza virus."

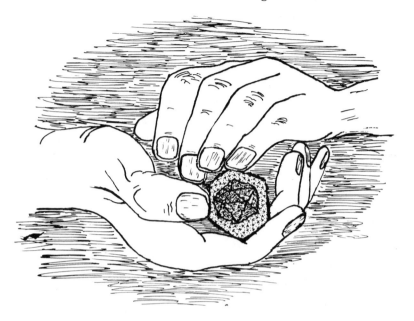

Nothing but the influenza virus . . .

"Oh, 'flu,'" said Mr. Tompkins with relief. "So there is nothing to worry about!"

"Well, sometimes one can have a nasty case of 'flu.' But I think you will be all right, and if you look here I will show you why."

With these words, Dr. Streets pulled at the object he held in his hands, and it easily separated into two parts. In his left hand was a round body with a rather rough-looking surface, and in his right a semicircular shell into which the other part had previously been fitted.

"You see now," said the doctor, "this sphere is the influenza virus, a monstrously large molecule built from many millions of atoms. You must have heard, of course, about the viruses, which lie halfway between living and nonliving matter, and are sometimes called 'living molecules.' While bacteria can be considered as a kind of plant, secreting poisonous substances into the body of the organism they attack, viruses are the living poisons themselves. We may consider them as regular chemical molecules, since they always have a strictly defined atomic structure, but on the other hand we must also consider them as being alive, since they are able to multiply in unlimited quantities. Many diseases, such as influenza and poliomyelitis in man, foot-and-mouth disease in cattle, and mosaic sickness in tobacco plants, are due to viruses, not to bacteria. And when you are attacked by a virus disease your organism learns how to produce the antibodies which can cope with that emergency. This is fortunate, since as yet we have nothing like penicillin which would act on viruses. The empty shell which I hold in my right hand is the antibody for the influenza virus, which covers it up and renders it inactive. Look how closely the surface details of the virus particle fit into the corresponding details on the inner surface of the antibody; this is the key-lock relationship I was talking about before. These antibodies float in large quantities through your blood stream, catch the virus particles, clog them into clusters, and later eliminate them from your system. Since this particular virus particle, and a few others which I have noticed floating by, are already taken care of by the antibodies, I would expect that your 'flu' will not develop into anything serious. I don't think you need even stay in bed."

"I think I like that key-and-lock analogy," said Mr. Tompkins reflectively, "but I don't quite see who is the locksmith. Who makes them fit?"

"I don't see it too clearly myself," said Dr. Streets, "and I doubt whether even my good friend Linus Pauling, of the California Institute of Technology, who is an ardent advocate of the key-and-lock analogy, can tell you more about it. The fitting is apparently done by attractive forces between the atoms in the invading particles and those in the attacking skeleton-key antibody. I admit that it seems at first sight almost unbelievable that simple atomic forces can produce such remarkable structures, but you may begin to think differently if you remember the fantastic shapes of stalactites and stalagmites, which are produced by nothing but a water solution of calcium salts leaking through cave ceilings."

Dr. Streets carefully fitted the influenza virus back into its antibody shell, so that it would not cause any harm, and released it into the blood stream.

"Aren't these antibodies going to attack me, since they must consider me to be a foreign body?" asked Mr. Tompkins with some trepidation.

"You are in no danger," replied Dr. Streets, "since you can scarcely be considered foreign to your own body. They might attack me if I stayed here long enough, but since I am, so to speak, a single particle, and do not multiply, it will take a long time to raise the alarm."

"Why should my antibodies distinguish between you and me?" asked

Mr. Tompkins in astonishment. "We are both human, are we not?"

"Unfortunately—from the medical point of view, that is—not all individuals of the same species are alike. This makes it impossible to transplant organs from one individual to another, unless, of course, they happen to be identical twins. Antibodies recognize that the transplanted tissues are different and attack them as a foreign body. This is because the sequence of amino acids in some proteins differs somewhat from one individual to another. Sometimes it is indeed possible to transplant a comparatively simple kind of tissue; as for example blood. However, even in blood transfusions one should be very careful to select the proper type of donor."

"Oh, the blood groups," said Mr. Tompkins. "I never thought that problem was connected with the disease-fighting agencies."

"It certainly is," said Dr. Streets. "If, by some mistake, you had injected into your blood stream the blood of a dog or a pig you would become seriously ill, since your antibodies would start a violent and devastating campaign against the alien erythrocytes. You might even die from thrombosis, as the doctors call it, if the debris of the battle clogged the capillaries and prevented the circulation of blood.

"What actually happens is that an individual antibody molecule has several places which fit the antigen. By attaching itself to two different red cells, it acts as a glue, preventing the red cells from moving apart, or, as we often say, clumping them.

"Now, within the same species the blood is sometimes interchangeable, but not always. Human red blood cells may have on their surfaces blood-group substances called A and B. These are long chains of amino acids and sugar molecules, somewhat as proteins are long chains of amino acids. The red cell may carry blood-group substances A or A and B or B or none. In the latter case we say a person is of blood group O. The blood group of a person is inherited from his or her parents.

"A person who lacks one of the blood-group substances has an antibody against that substance. For instance, if a person is of blood group B, his blood contains antibodies against A; if he is of blood group A, he has antibodies against B; if he is of blood group O, he has antibodies against A and B; but if he is of blood group AB, he has no such antibodies."

"This I fail to understand," said Mr. Tompkins. "Why should a man of, say, blood group B have antibodies against A if he has never been injected with red cells carrying substance A? I thought you said antibodies are only made against a foreign antigen to which the body had been exposed, such as a virus."

"I do not understand why this should be so myself," replied Dr. Streets, "but we do know that there are two kinds of antibodies. One is made only in response to a foreign substance. But there is also another kind, which is present irrespective of whether you have been exposed to the foreign substance. The antibodies against the blood-group substances are of the second kind."

"How does an organism know that a substance is foreign, so that it can begin making antibodies against it but not against its own substances?"

"This again we do not know, but we do know that it regards a substance as 'self' and not 'foreign' if it has been exposed to it very early in life, before birth. If a chicken, for example, has been injected with a foreign antigen while still in the egg, it will not make antibodies to it either then or, within certain limitations, later. It now regards the antigen as part of itself. In the same way, we believe, a human embryo has the capability to make antibodies against both blood-group substances A and B. If it is of blood group O, it continues to make them. If, however, during early life it has red blood cells of type A, it ceases to make antibodies against it, because it recognizes that blood-group substance A is 'self,' and similarly if it has cells of type B, it ceases to make antibodies against B. Thus it always makes antibodies against the blood-group substances it does not have.

"From the practical point of view, if blood from an A-donor enters the system of a B-recipient, the anti-A of the recipient's plasma will attack the erythrocytes of injected blood. This fight may often be fatal to the patient. If a blood transfusion takes place between two persons of the same blood type, no harm will follow."

"I see now why they use plasma," said Mr. Tompkins. "If the red blood cells are absent no fight can take place."

"You are nearly right, but not quite," said the doctor. "Even if the blood which is injected has no erythrocytes, it still contains in solution the antibodies which would attack the erythrocytes of the recipient blood, unless, of course, the donor is of AB type. The point is, however, that, by mixing the plasma obtained from persons of different blood types in a proper proportion, one can prepare the so-called pooled plasma, in which the concentration of both antibodies, though not exactly zero, is sufficiently low not to cause any harm. But I am afraid

I am getting too technical, and we'd better spend the rest of our time in surveying the other wonders of the blood stream. I still have to show you some hormones and vitamins."

"Are they also living molecules?" inquired Mr. Tompkins.

"Oh, no," said Dr. Streets. "In many cases they are rather simple, and some of them can be synthesized from inorganic chemical compounds. Hormones, for example, whose name was derived from the Greek word *hormao*, meaning 'to stir up' or 'to excite,' are sometimes built from as few as a couple of dozen individual atoms. They are not the high executives of life, being more like orders or instructions sent out by these executives—sheets of paper marked with ink carried around by couriers, but absolutely necessary for the smooth functioning of the business. If you take my lens and inspect the plasma floating past your palm, you may be able to see some of these particles."

Following the doctor's advice and watching carefully the passing parade of the inhabitants of blood plasma, Mr. Tompkins soon noticed a very interesting object. Under the lens it looked like one of the dragons seen in the streets of Chinatown during the New Year's celebration. But it was less than one millimeter long and (as Mr. Tompkins counted) was formed of only twenty-two atoms.

"This is a molecule of epinephrine, or 'scary hormone,' which is produced by certain glands near the kidneys every time a person is frightened. Being rapidly carried by the blood stream through the entire

A molecule of epinephrine, or "scary hormone."

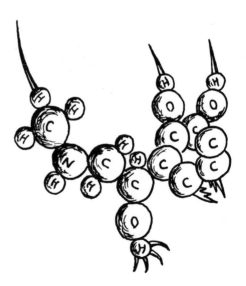

body, this hormone speeds up the action of the heart, causes the blood vessels to contract—thus increasing the blood pressure—and induces the release of sugars from the liver, providing the immediate source of extra energy for escaping the danger. The one you have just seen is probably left over from the moment when you were scared by believing yourself on a sinking submarine. There are also many other hormones in all walks of life such as, for example, secretin, which induces certain glands (the pancreas located just below your stomach) to produce digestive juices at a higher rate, testosterone, the male hormone that makes a man a man, the estrone that makes a woman a woman."

"But what about vitamins," asked Mr. Tompkins. "Are they in my blood stream too?"

"I am pretty sure of that," replied Dr. Streets, "since I believe your wife gives you the right sort of meals. Vitamins, as you probably know, are obtained from the proper foods and are absolutely necessary for health. A man needs more than a dozen different vitamins, all of them comparatively simple substances which in many cases can be produced synthetically from inorganic material. You must certainly have heard about vitamin C, which is present in spinach, green peppers, orange juice and tomato juice, and so on. Unless you get about sixty milligrams

Vitamin C, found in spinach.

of that vitamin every day, you are liable to get scurvy: your gums begin to bleed and your teeth become loose. On the other hand, the lack of vitamin A—found in butter, fat, and fish oils—causes a scaly condition of the eyes and night blindness, whereas vitamin D (found in cod-liver oil) serves to prevent rickets, a disease involving malformation of the bones and unsatisfactory development of the teeth."

"You mean that I am all set as far as vitamins are concerned if I have a normal diet?" asked Mr. Tompkins.

"Quite so. In most cases taking more is not necessary unless there are special reasons for it, although usually it does no harm except to your pocketbook. However, there are two vitamins, A and D, which in really large doses are poisonous. Eskimos know that the liver of the polar bear should not be eaten, since it contains enough vitamin A to be fatal. But you can certainly find all the information about vitamins in any book on food and nutrition. You'd better look around now, since we are entering one of the villi of your small intestine.

"Here is the place where the blood absorbs the digested food you ate this morning, in order to carry it around to all the cells of your body. If you look through the thin transparent layer of cells separating us from the 'inside of your insides,' you will notice a brownish mass of what was once bacon and eggs. It is now completely broken down by the digestive enzymes. The food you eat consists essentially of three chemical types: proteins, carbohydrates, and fats. The three types of enzymes known as protease, amylase, and lipase attack respectively these three main food components, turning them into much simpler substances. Heavy protein molecules are broken up into much simpler amino acids, carbohydrates are turned into sugars, and fats are split into glycerine and fatty acids. All of these substances are soluble in water and diffuse through the thin walls into the villi. Once inside, amino acids and sugars get into the blood capillaries and are immediately dispatched to all parts of the body, where they are expected by the hungry cells. The distribution of the products of fat digestion is, however, much slower. Instead of choosing fast transportation through the circulatory system, they recombine again into tiny fat globules and move in a horse-and-van fashion through the lymphatic system. Lymph, as I mentioned before, is a fluid very similar to blood plasma which fills the spaces between the tissue cells. It forms a waterway system as intricate as the channels in Florida's Everglades, where only the native Indians can find their way. And, like the Everglades' network of waterways, it is mostly stagnant water with very little or no current."

"Did you say," asked Mr. Tompkins, who had hardly been listening to Dr. Streets' later remarks (which had got a bit dull anyway), "did you say that there is still some bacon and eggs left on the other side of the villi's walls? Since I've gone without my lunch I certainly shouldn't mind eating my breakfast all over again."

And, before the doctor could hold him back, he dived from their erythrocyte, and was already making his way through the thin layer of villi-cells separating him from the inside of his insides.

"Come back!" shouted Dr. Streets in despair. "You will be eaten up by your own digestive enzymes.

"Too bad," he added, seeing that all his attempts were to no avail, "I should have told him about ulcers—when a man digests his own stomach."

Mr. Tompkins was walking ankle deep in a slushy substance which reminded him by its consistency and color of an unsurfaced country road after heavy rain. These remnants of his breakfast did not look at all appetizing, and his hunger was completely gone. Suddenly he saw in front of him a large number of very strange animals playing happily in a muddy pool. They had big round bodies and short stocky tails, and reminded Mr. Tompkins of some kind of giant tadpole.

"I don't believe it!" said Mr. Tompkins to himself; "I can't possibly have frogs living in my stomach, marshy as it is."

"They will never grow into frogs, they are phages," said a voice near him, and Mr. Tompkins saw the tall thin figure of a man wearing patent-leather riding boots, a red-and-gold embroidered jacket, and a shiny black opera hat.

"Besides, the extensions that you probably believe to be their tails are not tails at all but rather the stings with which they attack the bacteria they live on.

"I am Herr Max, the famous phage trainer," his new companion introduced himself. "Phages, as you may know, are a special type of virus, a living molecule which feeds on bacteria. The particular breed of phages you see here attacks *Escherichia coli*, or simply *E. coli*, as we usually call them—peaceful bacteria which can be found in quantity in everybody's intestines. I breed the phages here for my genetic experiments, and this particular strain is known as T_1. There are also

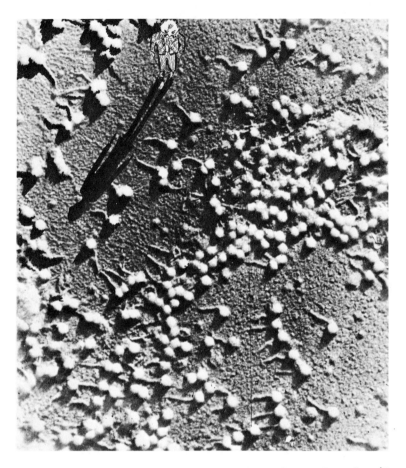

They looked like giant tadpoles. . . . *(Electronmicrograph of bacteriophages by Dr. R. W. G. Wyckoff, National Institutes of Health, Bethesda, Maryland)*

six other strains, four of which have tails, or rather stings, and two which don't."

"I never knew molecules had tails!" said Mr. Tompkins incredulously.

"And why not?" asked Herr Max. "If molecules are big enough—and each of these here contains many millions of atoms—they can afford a luxury like a nice long tail. Of course, we can't yet write an exact structural formula for this particular chemical compound, but when such a formula comes to be written, it will certainly show a long chain of carbons, oxygens, and hydrogens extending from the main body of the molecule."

"But how do you know that these things are chemical molecules?" insisted Mr. Tompkins. "Why don't you also believe that real tadpoles, or even dogs for that matter, are single molecules too?"

"You can't crystallize dogs, can you?" said Herr Max with a smile.

"What do you mean, crystallize dogs?" asked Mr. Tompkins sheepishly.

"I mean one can't form a crystal in which dogs (all of the same breed and age, of course) would play the same role as water molecules in an ice crystal. This has been done, however, with some of the viruses, and I am sure it can be done with all of them, including these phages. Thus, for example, a virus attacking tomato plants and known as tomato bushy stunt virus crystallizes in the form of large and beautiful rhombic do-decahedrons—crystals with twelve faces. You could put such a crystal on the shelf in a mineralogical museum together with feldspar and amethyst, and nobody would know that it is a colony of living organisms. And in a way it isn't, since, inside the crystal, the virus molecule behaves just like any other chemical molecule. Now dissolve that crystal in a bucket of water, and spray it over a tomato plot. As soon as the virus particles find themselves within the cytoplasm of the plants' cells, they will begin to multiply rapidly. And, if you collect the sick plants and separate the virus from their leaves, you may get truckloads of the same beautiful rhombic dodecahedrons."

Seeing the look of astonishment on Mr. Tompkins's face, Herr Max decided to elaborate a little.

"I am afraid," he said, "that I have not been quite fair with you. It is quite true that viruses can exist as crystals, but from the point of view of most chemists they would not be regarded as single molecules. They are actually composed of one or more kinds of proteins, and also of genes, which are molecules of something called nucleic acid. In spite of this it is nevertheless true that a virus particle can also be regarded as a single molecule, because its component molecules of protein and nucleic acid are arranged in an absolutely fixed order with respect to each other. Otherwise viruses would not form crystals. So let us say that a virus is a supermolecule made of giant molecules, just as an ordinary molecule is made up of atoms."

"Do viruses multiply by division, as cells do?" asked Mr. Tompkins.

"No, they can't. Since they are molecules, with each atom in its proper place, they cannot grow or multiply like ordinary living organisms. When a virus particle gets into the substance of a cell in which it can live (and they are very choosy in selecting their hosts), the viral genes sneakily instruct the cell to make viral proteins and viral nucleic acids instead of cell proteins and cell nucleic acids. It is as if the government of a state were to be secretly taken over by a foreign power. Since the government would continue to issue laws and orders in the same way as before, the citizens wouldn't know the difference and would continue to obey them without question. Here what is different is that while the instructions look the same, their intent is different. Everything is now done for the benefit of the foreigner. The citizens, however, do not realize this until it is too late.

"Incidentally, this is the reason it is so difficult to fight viruses with antibiotics. Bacteria have their own molecular machinery for making more of themselves and since this is slightly different from our machinery, it is possible to jam it without at the same time jamming our own cells. But since it is our own cells which make the viruses, it is very difficult to stop their production without hurting our own cells. We have no 'wonder drugs' against viruses such as we have against bacteria.

"Thus the virus-infected cells make virus components instead of their own, which, when ready, come together and form a virus particle somewhat in the same way as a crystal is formed. Therefore, all viruses are fully grown the moment they are born, and all of them are exactly alike.

"Viruses, of course, do their hosts no good, although some are worse than others. When one of these phages here gets into the body of *E. coli*, and begins to multiply at its expense, the bacterium is entirely eaten up in the course of twenty minutes. Its skin breaks up, and a flock of several hundred young phages comes out ready to attack other bacteria. Here, take a look."

With these words, Herr Max led Mr. Tompkins to what was once a beautiful *E. coli* bacterium. But there wasn't much left of it except its original shape, and its entire body was nothing but a wriggling mass of T_1 phages.

"Br-r-r . . . how disgusting!" remarked Mr. Tompkins, involuntarily raising his hand to his nose. "It looks like a piece of meat that was left out of the icebox when the family went off for a summer holiday."

"Such is life," said Herr Max philosophically, using the butt of his long whip to push the phages about. "Oh!" he exclaimed suddenly. "If

I am not mistaken, here is a case of a very interesting mutation. Now I can start a new *T*-strain.''

And, forgetting about Mr. Tompkins, Herr Max stepped into the wriggling mass of phages and inspected each one with the greatest attention. Mr. Tompkins, who had no desire to follow him into the dissolved bacterium, and was feeling a little sick, decided to try to find his way back into the blood stream. He was, in a way, sorry that he had given up a comfortable ride on the erythrocyte for a slushy walk in his intestines.

Suddenly he felt a sharp pain in his leg and saw a giant leech biting his calf.

"Must be a protease or amylase," he thought, kicking it off with the other foot. "I really have got myself into a mess. There is no food left to speak of, and my digestive enzymes are getting wild with hunger. Better get out of here!"

But it was too late. The enzymes attacked him on all sides, and a couple of particularly bold lipases were already hanging tight on the fleshy part of his chin.

"Ouch!" exclaimed Mr. Tompkins, and suddenly woke up.

A stout lady in the next chair in line turned her sympathetic eyes to him.

"Does it hurt much?" she asked. "I get bad pains too, and they make me scream. The doctor I went to see last week told me that unless I take care of myself . . . but you won't be interested in all the details. What's your trouble?"

"An attack by a flock of hungry proteases, amylases, and lipases," said Mr. Tompkins. He was just beginning to realize that he was back in the hospital waiting room.

"That's a new disease to me," said the lady, "but I hope the doctor will help you."

But Mr. Tompkins was already off his chair, walking briskly toward the exit.

"There is no point in waiting for an ordinary doctor's diagnosis," he thought, "when the great Dr. Streets himself has told me that I've got nothing more than a touch of 'flu.' Besides, I mustn't be late at the bank."

» 2 «

Muscle Beach

DURING the summer Mr. Tompkins had a few weeks' vacation from his work at the bank coming to him. He was looking forward to staying home or going to the University Library to bury his nose in books that would tell him more about the nature of life. But Maud ruled otherwise; she wanted to go to a beach where she could enjoy swimming and stretching out for hours on the sunlit sand to get a nice tan. As usual, she won the argument, and, following the advice of a friend, they selected a small and quiet seaside resort located on the southern tip of Cape Cod and only an hour's drive from Boston. Arriving there they found that the place was perfect. True, it had only one good restaurant, one drugstore, and not a single movie theater. But the view was beautiful, the sand soft and warm, and the water very invigorating.

The next morning Maud, in her elegant new swimming suit, and Mr. Tompkins (who did not care much for swimming), in his light shorts and a short-sleeved shirt, made their way to the beach. After taking a swim, Maud smeared her skin with lotion, stretched out on the sand, and covered her face with a wide straw hat. Mr. Tompkins, who much preferred soft armchairs to beach towels, lay for a while on his back watching the seagulls floating in the blue sky above him. He had brought with him the latest issue of *Scientific American,* which contained an article on the mechanism of muscle contraction, and he was trying to concentrate on it. But his position was not too comfortable

33

A man with snow-white hair, flexing
his muscles at the water's edge.

for reading, and the magazine was knocked out of his hands a couple
of times by a big ball thrown by children playing on the beach. Finally
he put aside the magazine and turned over to take a nap. . . .

But he didn't seem to fall asleep, so he got to his feet and strolled
along the shore, watching the surf running on the sand. When he came
to a more deserted part of the beach, he noticed a man with snow-white
hair flexing his muscles at the water's edge. In contrast to his elderly,
though alert face, his bulging biceps would have made the best athlete
envious.

Overcoming his shyness, Mr. Tompkins approached the man and
said, "Excuse me, sir, but are you by any chance one of those scientists
who, as I have heard, come here during the summer months?"

"Yes, young man," said the elderly athlete. "In fact I live here all
year long and work with my assistants on a very important problem:
the functioning of muscles."

Feeling the friendliness in the voice of his new acquaintance, Mr.
Tompkins decided to continue the conversation. "Well, what about
muscles?" said he. "There are strong people and there are weak people;
it all depends on their training."

"If you think so, jump!" said the man.

In high school Mr. Tompkins had devoted much time to athletics, and, disregarding the strangeness of the request, he soared well over a foot into the air.

"Not bad," said his new friend. "It is just about one-fifth of your height. But do you know that frogs can jump three times their length, grasshoppers about eighteen times, and fleas close to a hundred?"

"Curious," said Mr. Tompkins, "but what is the importance of this fact?"

"Oh, but it is very important for understanding the functioning of muscles. If you measure the height of the jumps of small and large animals, not in terms of their size but in feet and inches, you will find that they all can lift themselves from the ground to about the same height: something between six inches and two feet. Of course, there are some exceptions, because the structure and the length of legs varies among different species; an elephant cannot jump at all, whereas the kangaroo soars up several feet."

"But what is the reason for this, Professor?" asked Mr. Tompkins.

"First of all, do not call me 'Professor.' Everybody here, rightly or wrongly, calls me 'Saint.'

"To return to muscle, this fact can be explained by a simple law of mechanics first formulated by Sir Isaac Newton. The motion of your limbs is caused by the contraction of your muscles attached to the bones of your skeleton. When you move your feet in walking or jumping, lift your hand or move your fingers as you do, let us say, when writing a letter, the muscles contract and produce the desired motion. Since the muscles can only pull but not push, another muscle has to bring the bones back to their original position. They therefore usually occur in pairs on opposite sides of the bone. For example, there are two muscles connecting your shoulder bone and your elbow, which run on opposite sides of your upper-arm bone. One, known as 'biceps,' runs along the front part of the bone. The other, 'triceps' (sometimes referred to as the tennis muscle because it is useful in the back stroke), runs along the other side of the bone. The motion of the skeleton is caused by contraction of one of the 'cepses' and the relaxation of the other."

"But still," said Mr. Tompkins, "why can all the animals, big or small, jump to about the same height?"

"This is very simply explained by Newtonian mechanics," said Saint. "Suppose you have two animals similar in their skeletal structure, one of them, let us say, a flea, and another a frog. A flea is about one-tenth of an inch in size while a frog may be about three inches—that is, some thirty times longer, thirty times wider, and thirty times taller. Thus a frog weighs about 30 × 30 × 30, or 27,000 times more than a flea. When both jump, their muscles contract, producing the energy necessary to lift them to a certain height above the ground. How much energy is produced in each case? In cross-section the frog's muscles are 30 × 30, or 900 times larger than those of a flea, so, if the pull produced by contraction per unit of the cross-section is the same in both cases, the pull exerted by the frog's muscles is correspondingly larger. Also, since frog muscles are 30 times longer than those of the flea, their shortening in length will be 30 times greater. Therefore, we may conclude that the energy delivered by the contraction of a frog's muscle will be 30 × 900, or 27,000 times larger than in the case of a flea. But, as I told you before, this much larger energy must lift into the air a 27,000-times larger weight. According to the laws of Newtonian mechanics, the height to which a given body can be lifted above the ground is directly proportional to the available energy and inversely proportional to the weight of the object. Thus the ratio of the heights to which a frog and a flea can jump is 27,000/27,000, or 1. This means that a frog and a flea should jump to the same height, provided that their muscles liberate the same amount of energy per unit cross-section and per equal contraction. Since the facts indicate that this is at least approximately correct, we must conclude that the muscles of most animals, be they fleas, frogs, kangaroos, or men, have identical properties.

"This is true not only of muscle. As I once wrote: 'Four decades of research have left no doubt in the author's mind that there is only one life and living matter, however different its structure, colorful its functions, and varied its appearance. We are all but recent leaves on the same old tree of life; even if this life has adapted itself to new functions and conditions, it uses the same old principles over and over again. There is no real difference between the grass and he who mows it. The muscles which move the mower need the very same two substances for their motion as the grass needs for its growth: potassium and phosphate, the two substances we put on our lawn as fertilizer so as to have something to mow—a strikingly simple demonstration of the basic unity of living nature. So, in principle, it does not matter which material we choose for our study of life, be it grass or muscle, virus or brain. If we dig deep enough we always arrive at the center, the basic principles on which life was built and due to which it still goes on.' "

"What do you mean when you say, if we dig deep enough? In fact, how do you go about finding out something about muscles?"

Saint appeared to hesitate a little, then said, "Would you like to visit my laboratory? It will be easier to show you how things are done rather than draw pictures on the sand."

When they arrived at the laboratory, Saint led Mr. Tompkins into a room full of beakers, flasks, and the usual laboratory paraphernalia.

"It will be best to start, I think," he said, "by demonstrating to you a most primitive example of contraction. We begin by taking a muscle apart into its constituents. Having done this, we then try to put it together. It is like taking a watch apart and putting it together again. Once you do this, you begin to understand how it works."

"When you speak of breaking a muscle down into its components, you mean breaking it down into the cells which make it up?" asked Mr. Tompkins.

"No, here we break it down in a much more fundamental way. We dissolve it in a suitable salt solution, which means it is broken down into the molecules of which it is composed. We then separate the different kinds of molecules. Having done so, we try to put the molecules together again and make a muscle."

"This seems a rather tall order. Have you succeeded?"

"Shall I say that we have gained some insight. Let me demonstrate. The basic structure of muscle is made of two proteins: myosin and actin. Here these two proteins are dissolved in the proper solvents. I now mix them together." He poured some of each into a beaker, and drew the mixture up into a syringe. "Now watch this. I shall squirt the mixture from the syringe into the proper salt solution, and form a thread."

Mr. Tompkins watched as the thread formed. "Curious," he said, but without much conviction in his voice.

Saint noticed this and smiled. "The actin and myosin have combined to give what we call, rather obviously, actomyosin. This is the substance which contracts in muscle. Now I will add a drop of something, and the thread will contract."

Mr. Tompkins now watched with more interest. As Saint had predicted, the thread began to contract and slowly shortened.

"Quite a feat," said Mr. Tompkins.

"I am glad you think so," said Saint. "My collaborators and I have worked many years to achieve this."

"What is this thing that you added to make your actomyosin contract?" asked Mr. Tompkins.

"That was a bit of ATP, the reverse of Parent-Teachers' Association. ATP is the universal carrier of energy in the body, a sort of biological gasoline. It is used to make muscles contract, propagate a nerve impulse, synthesize compounds, pump waste products from the blood into the urine, and so on. Not only is it the universal energy carrier in human bodies, but in all bodies, quite literally, from cabbages to kings. So when ATP is broken down in the 'engine' of actomyosin, a part of the energy that was in the ATP causes actomyosin to contract."

"Where does this ATP come from?" asked Mr. Tompkins.

"It is produced by using the chemical energy contained in the food you eat, and it gives the energy back when needed, in particular when you want to move the various parts of your body."

"Oh I see. This is like a steam engine or a gasoline motor," said Mr. Tompkins, "which uses the chemical energy of burning fuel and then turns it into mechanical energy."

"In a way yes, but living organisms do this in a much more rational way than heat engines. Since time immemorial, people have burned fuel to keep warm and for cooking food. In these cases the heat produced by burning was what they wanted. For doing mechanical work they used their own muscles, or the muscles of domesticated animals.

"Then a couple of centuries ago, according to the story, while watching the top of a boiling teapot jumping up and down, James Watt conceived the idea of turning heat into motion. A new era then started in technology. Heat engines now pull trains, propel boats, operate various kinds of power plants, and so on."

"But isn't it true," said Mr. Tompkins, "that I am also some kind of heat engine? After all, I heat up and perspire when I do physical work."

"It is true," answered Saint, "that when food products combine with oxygen in your muscles some heat is produced, but this is incidental so far as the action of your muscles is concerned. An electric motor also gets warm partially because of the friction of its parts, partially because of heating of the wires; however, it is not this heat but the electric current which produces the power. Now birds and mammals have taken advantage of this incidental heat and have developed methods for keeping their bodies at a constant temperature, since this is useful in many ways. For instance, it makes it possible for them to be active in winter, when other animals like snakes and frogs are torpid. Unlike birds and mammals, such 'cold-blooded' creatures change the rate of their body activities as the outside temperature changes. A fish in the ocean entering the warmer Gulf Stream will begin to swim somewhat faster. Taking advantage of this, a friend of mine once constructed what he called an 'ant-thermometer.' This is a simple, flat, narrow ring with an ant running round and round it. The warmer the air, the faster the ant runs. Thus, using a stop watch, one can measure the temperature. Of course, it is not a very reliable instrument, but it was built just for fun.

"But to get back to muscles, in 1824, a young French military engineer named Sadi Carnot showed that the maximum efficiency of heat engines—that is, the fraction of available heat which can be turned into mechanical energy—is proportional to the temperature difference between the hottest part of the engine, let's call it the 'boiler,' and its coldest part, the 'sink.' If one runs a heat engine between the boiling point of water and the melting point of ice, the maximum efficiency will be only twenty-seven per cent. Since temperature differences within the human body hardly exceed one degree, if you were a heat engine, your efficiency would be no more than one per cent, and you would have to consume some thirty times more food to have enough strength to move a finger!"

"But why are heat engines so inefficient?" asked Mr. Tompkins. "After all, I've heard that heat is the motion of the molecules forming material bodies. Isn't this the same kind of energy as that of a flying bullet?"

"A bullet is a good example," said Saint. "Suppose you have a bullet lying quietly on the table. There is a lot of molecular motion inside it, and the particles oscillate around their equilibrium position with high kinetic energies. Now you put this bullet into a rifle and shoot. In this case you add the kinetic energy supplied by the gunpowder to the kinetic energy of the thermal motion. But although these are the same kinds of energy, they are, so to speak, differently arranged. In the case of thermal motion the molecules move in all possible directions with rather widely varying velocities, whereas the additional velocities supplied to each of them by the gunpowder are all equal and strictly parallel for all molecules. Thus the bullet flies straight to its target. Now, when the bullet stops after hitting the target, the velocities of the originally organized motion become random and add to the previously existing random thermal motion. The bullet becomes hotter."

"Well, naturally," commented Mr. Tompkins. "But what has it to do with the low efficiency of heat engines?"

"Very much," said Saint. "In heat engines you start with fuel, be it wood, coal, or oil, consisting of highly organized molecular configurations with an energy content determined by well-defined interatomic forces. By burning the fuel you obtain heat, which, as I have just explained, is an extremely disorganized motion of the burning products, or a natural disorder, so to speak. After doing this, you attempt to turn this orderless random motion into the orderly motion of the engine's pistons, levers, and wheels. Since the orderless motion is much more probable than the orderly one, it is not an easy job and you must pay a high price for it. It can be done, however, by bringing a part of orderless system to a state of orderly motion, at the cost of permitting the rest of it to become still more orderless."

"I see your point," said Mr. Tompkins. "But why can't our engineers eliminate the heat stage in designing their various gadgets?"

"They try. But do not forget that organic evolution is a few billion years old, while engineering development started only a few centuries ago. Your muscles, as well as all other parts of your body, are chemical, or rather electrochemical, devices and therefore much more efficient than the steam engines of good old James Watt. But already we have flashlight batteries that produce electric current without much heating and fluorescent lamps that don't burn your fingers when you touch them."

"But what about getting mechanical work without heat directly from the internal chemical energy of different compounds? Can it be done at our present engineering level?" asked Mr. Tompkins.

"Yes, we have made at least a start on that problem," said Saint, leading Mr. Tompkins to a table with an odd-looking gadget on it.

"This is the so-called 'mechanochemical engine' developed recently by three scientists working at the Weizmann Institute of Science, in Israel. It operates on the difference in concentrations of a salt—in this case, lithium bromide—in two beakers, A and B, put side by side. If you connect the two beakers, the process of spontaneous diffusion will distribute the salt equally between the two beakers. The trick is to get work while this is taking place. What you do is take a string made of a protein called collagen, of which leather is made. When this string is dipped into the salt solution, it contracts, and can be used to pull something. Next, the string is put into pure water. Now the salt mole-

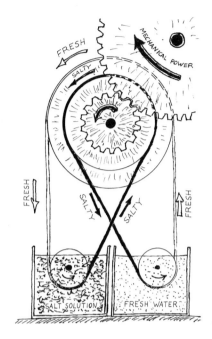

How to get mechanical work out of two beakers of water.

cules have a large space in which to redistribute themselves, so they are washed out of the string, and the string relaxes. This, of course, transfers some salt into the fresh water. Then it goes back into the salt solution, contracts, back into water to relax, and so on. So it works just like a piston, moving wheels. Actually it is so arranged that the motion of the wheels themselves moves the string from salt to water and back. Eventually, of course, the salt concentration in both beakers becomes equal and the engine stops."

"Is this the way muscle works?" asked Mr. Tompkins.

"In a general way, yes," replied Saint. "Muscle works by taking advantage of what we call a chemical potential that resides in ATP. To explain this I should show you what an ATP molecule looks like. There is no need to go into the atomic details; it is enough to know that it consists of a rather complicated organic molecule called adenosine, to which three phosphate molecules are attached as follows: adenosine-phosphate-phosphate-phosphate. Instead of ATP, which stands for adenosine triphosphate, we can write it as A-P-P-P."

"It does look a bit complicated," said Mr. Tompkins.

"If you put ATP into water," continued Saint. "The following reaction takes place, especially if certain enzymes are present.

$$A\text{-}P\text{-}P\text{-}P + H_2O \rightleftharpoons A\text{-}P\text{-}P + P$$

What happens is that one of the phosphates breaks off, giving a compound we call ADP, or adenosine diphosphate. Some ATP is also formed from ADP and phosphate by a reverse reaction, but the long arrow shows that ATP breaks down much more rapidly than it is formed, so that once an equilibrium is reached, there is much more ADP than ATP. We therefore say that ATP has a spontaneous tendency to degrade itself to ADP. Just as the collagen machine does work when salt and fresh water mix, so muscle does work using the energy released when ATP passes to the state of ADP and phosphate."

"Clear enough," said Mr. Tompkins. "So what is the problem about muscle that remains to be solved?"

"Our problem is to find out what sort of machine it is that can extract work from this reaction. After all, you know that salt dissolves in fresh water, but it takes some ingenuity to build a machine to make use of this. Nature has shown extreme ingenuity in constructing the machine called muscle."

"But you have already showed me how actomyosin contracts," said Mr. Tompkins.

Saint smiled. "This is just the beginning. It is true that our actomyosin will contract, rather weakly, when we add ATP to it. But real muscle is much more than just a lump of actomyosin. It is much more because it has to do more. It has to contract strongly and rapidly and then to relax for the next contraction. It must contract only if a nerve tells it to do so. It has to make the ATP that provides it with its energy. And finally, do not forget that in time all the molecules of muscle break down and have to be replaced, so that a muscle has to know how to make all the proteins and other things of which it is composed. Perhaps the best way to understand muscle is to look at it, starting first with the naked eye and then at higher and higher magnification, until we reach the individual molecules.

"In your body, muscles come in all sizes, and besides being connected to bones so they can move the body, they are supplied with blood vessels that bring food and oxygen and remove waste products. They are also connected to nerves, which signal from the brain to tell a muscle when to contract. However, whatever its size and function, a muscle, like every other tissue of the body, is made up of cells. Muscle cells are long and thin, and are referred to as muscle fibers. You can easily understand the structure of muscle if you think of a muscle fiber as a cable, which in turn is made up of thinner cables, which in turn are made of even thinner cables of the size of large molecules. In this respect it is rather like the cables that support our suspension bridges. Here, take a look first through this low-power microscope."

"There are curious bands running crosswise in the muscle fiber. What are they?" asked Mr. Tompkins.

"They are the key to how a muscle works," said Saint. "Before I start to explain, take a look at the next preparation. Here the muscle fiber has been frayed out to show the next smaller fibers, the myofibrils. They are long, and about one micron thick."

"I see that the myofibrils are banded, just like the muscle fibers," said Mr. Tompkins.

"Quite right. The reason the muscle fibers show the banding—we call it striation—is because the bands of the myofibrils are themselves banded, and the bands are aligned, or 'in register,' throughout the muscle fiber. The striations consist of broader, darker bands, interrupted by thinner, lighter bands. One of the bands has a dark line, called the Z line, running through it."

"Very curious," said Mr. Tompkins. "And you say that the bands hold the secret of how a muscle contracts?"

"Well, a large part of the secret. To see what the bands mean, we need the magnification of an electron microscope, as shown in this photograph of a bee's wing. If you will follow me into the next room, I can show you how it is made."

He unlocked a door and led Mr. Tompkins into a small, windowless room. Standing there was an instrument about the size of a desk, with what looked like a television tube and a rather formidable-looking console full of dials, switches, and indicators.

"So this is it," said Mr. Tompkins. "I have often heard of the electron microscope, but this is the first time I have ever met one. Is it true that it is so powerful that you can see atoms with it?"

"No." Saint smiled. "Not quite. But you can see the larger protein molecules, and this is impressive enough. The things you can see with this microscope are at least a hundred times smaller than the smallest things you can see using an ordinary light microscope."

The myofibrils are themselves banded. *(Electronmicrograph of the flight muscles of a bumblebee taken by Dr. D. E. Philpott, Marine Biological Laboratory, Woods Hole, Massachusetts; photograph of Dr. A. Szent-Györgi taken by George Gamow.)*

"Is this because it is so difficult to grind good lenses for the light microscope?" asked Mr. Tompkins.

"No," replied Saint, "it has nothing to do with our technology, but with the nature of light. As you of course know, light consists of electromagnetic waves about one micron long in the visible range, several microns for infrared, and a fraction of a micron for ultraviolet. If the body is considerably larger than the wavelength of the light used to observe it, you get a good image, showing its detailed structure. But if the body is smaller than the wavelength used, then diffraction occurs, and you see only a diffused spot with a diameter comparable to the wavelength of light. If you want to paint the wall of your house, you naturally use a large brush. Artists painting murals or large pictures use much smaller paintbrushes, smaller than the details depicted in the picture. But if you want to paint a miniature—say, the face of a lady on a medallion one inch in diameter—you have to use extremely thin brushes, since a single stroke of an ordinary paintbrush will cover a good part of the area to which you are limited. Biologists have tried to use ultraviolet microscopes with quartz lenses which are transparent to ultraviolet. In this case you cannot see the image, but you can photograph it. But this improves the situation only by a factor of two or three. A greater step forward was taken when the electron microscope was invented, and now we can see the detailed structure of much smaller bodies.

"In an electron microscope one uses not light waves, which cannot show the structural details of biological bodies smaller than the wavelength of light, but beams of electrons which, at the velocities at which they are used, still behave as particles without the annoying effect of wave diffraction. Of course, in the case of electron beams one cannot use ordinary glass lenses, and you have to develop special 'magnetic lenses' to deflect and focus them. This is attained by specially designed magnetic coils which influence the motion of electron beams in a way similar to the effect of glass lenses on the beams of light rays in ordinary optical microscopes.

"Now when we want to use the electron microscope, we put the specimen we want to look at into the path of the beam. Some parts of the specimen absorb more electrons than other parts, so we get an image, somewhat like the image we get by shining light through an ordinary photographic negative. We can see the electron image on a fluorescent screen, or we can photograph it.

"To illustrate the detail that can be seen with the electron microscope, here on the wall you see three photographs. The first one was taken by Dr. H. Fernández-Moran, the founder of the Venezuelan Institute of Neurology, who had to flee abroad in a great hurry when the dictator Pérez Jiménez, who financed the Institute with government funds, was deposed in a *coup d'état*. It has the comparatively small magnification of only 5000 times and represents a cross-section of the retina of a butterfly's eye. The white spaces are the cross-sections of the air-conducting channels.

"The second photograph, taken by L. W. Labau and R. W. G. Wyckoff, corresponds to magnification by a factor of 37,500 of a crystal formed by particles of southern bean mosaic virus, each particle being 250 angstroms (Å)* in diameter. But the real McCoy is the third photograph, taken by my good friend Dr. Robley Williams, of the University of California, with a magnification of about 500,000 times. You can see

* One angstrom is equal to 0.00000001 centimeters (10^{-8} cm.).

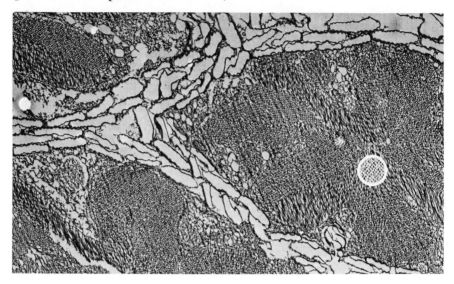

Electronmicrograph of the retina of a butterfly's eye.

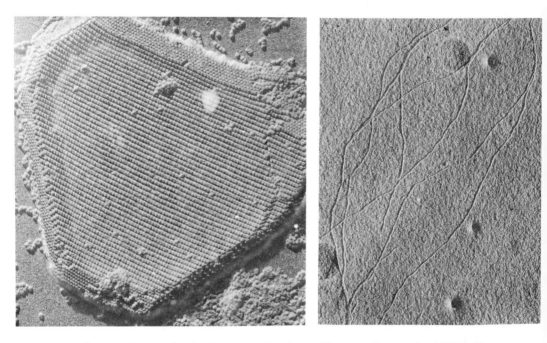

Electronmicrograph of a bean mosaic virus. Electronmicrograph of DNA fibers.

the single threads of deoxyribonucleic acid, which form the chromosomes and are the carriers of hereditary information.

"It is all really rather simple; all you need is about fifty thousand dollars to buy the microscope, and then you must learn to operate it."

"Could I put my finger under this microscope and see what it looks like at such a high magnification?" asked Mr. Tompkins.

"I'm afraid it would not be a good idea. There are some details I have not explained to you yet. First of all, the flight of the electrons must not be impeded, so the whole system has to be at a high vacuum, just as your television tube has to be evacuated so the electrons are not deflected from their track. You must also remember that we see the object by transmitted electron 'light.' Our specimen, therefore, has to be sliced on a machine like the one the butcher uses to slice sausage, except that the slices it cuts are only a few atoms thick. The last difficulty is that most biological objects are too transparent to electrons. To see anything worthwhile, we must 'stain' it in a special way, by adding salts of some heavy metal, such as uranium. The metal atoms are absorbed in some parts of the specimen but not in others, and since they are opaque to electrons, we get a much better contrast in our picture.

"So you see that looking through an electron microscope is not like examining an object with a hand lens. What you see has to be carefully interpreted. That's why it is often better to build a model, based on the information obtained by many experts in this field."

Saint continued. "I have compared a muscle fiber to a cable made of smaller threads, the myofibrils. When we use an electron microscope, we see that the myofibrils are themselves made of still smaller threads, the fibrils, which are of two kinds: thick and thin. The thick and thin fibers interpenetrate, but neither kind runs all the way through the fiber. They are, we say, interdigitating, like the extended elegant and slim fingers of a lady's hand placed between the extended thicker fingers of a man."

"Oh, I see now what the bands I was looking at are. The darker bands are where the two kinds of fibrils overlap; the light bands are where there is only one kind of fiber."

"Precisely. You may notice that the fibers are arranged in a very regular way; six thin fibers always surround one thick one. In cross-section, the electron microscope reveals a beautiful hexagonal pattern."

"What are these fibrils?"

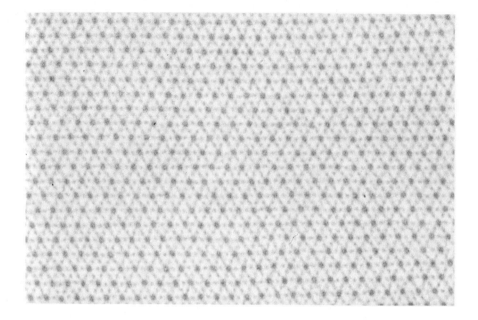

Electronmicrograph of a section of aphid flight muscle. *(Courtesy of Dr. D. S. Smith and the* Revue Canadienne de Biologie.)

"The thicker fibers, which have a diameter of 160 Å are composed of myosin; the thinner ones, 50 Å, are actin."

"Just the things you showed me contracting in your beaker."

"Yes, indeed," replied Saint. "And now you can begin to understand how muscle contracts. As has been pointed out by the eminent British scientist Hugh E. Huxley, since no single fibril runs all the way through the fiber, if the fibrils were able to slide over each other, they could shorten the whole fiber and thus make it contract. It is rather like two caterpillars facing opposite ways and crawling over each other. If you fasten a thread to the tail of each, they would, in effect, shorten the thread and do work. Of course, two fibrils can do very little work, but there are vast numbers of them in a muscle. Hercules, you will remember, was quite strong; yet he did it all with little fibrils."

"But if so, why was the contraction so weak in your beaker?" asked Mr. Tompkins.

"When you make an actomyosin fiber artificially, the arrangement of the fibrils is random, and most of them were not properly aligned with respect to one another. They are more like a mass of caterpillars crawling in all directions and mostly canceling out one another's efforts. Here in muscle, each is in its proper place."

"But what makes them align themselves so neatly?"

"We cannot answer that completely as yet, but the work that muscles perform apparently has something to do with it. The muscles I have been showing you are called striated; these muscles are needed for sudden and hard work. There is, however, another kind, called 'smooth muscle.' Smooth muscle lines internal organs such as the bladder and intestines, and has to perform slow, prolonged contractions. You cannot see striations in it, because the fibrils, while more or less in parallel, are not sufficiently in register with each other. An interesting experiment shows, however, that you can line up the fibrils of smooth muscle and thus transform it into striated. If the bladder of a dog—still in the dog, of course—is frequently distended and collapsed artificially by filling it and emptying it with fluid, striations begin to appear in the originally smooth muscle of the bladder wall. Housewives who make taffy at home experience something like it. If you keep pulling taffy in one direction, you line up the molecules in the direction of pull, continuously making the taffy stronger and harder to pull."

"Your explanation of the fibrils sliding over each other seems reasonable enough," said Mr. Tompkins, "but it seems to me you have slurred over a rather important point. This sliding is all very well, but how do the fibrils do it?"

"This should teach you a lesson," said Saint, "about coming to a research laboratory. We have research laboratories because there are still many things we do not understand, and your question is one of them. The results of research do seem to indicate to some people that the rods of actin and myosin are a sort of ratchet mechanism. It is as if the rods had notches and grooves in them, so that if they are moved forward, they latch on to one another and will not slide back. In fact, at the highest powers of the electron microscope, we see little knobs on the myosin fibrils which may be part of such a ratchet mechanism. We do know that to move an actin molecule one notch, one ATP molecule has to break down, and that a muscle fibril moves fifty to a hundred notches a second. Although I'm not convinced we really understand what makes the fibrils move over one another, of one thing I am certain: our ignorance won't last long, because many people are working on the problem."

Mr. Tompkins felt impressed that he had set foot, so to speak, on the very frontier of knowledge, but was still determined to pump Saint for further information. "You mentioned before," he said, "that muscle has other things to do besides contract. Can you tell me what is known about these other things?"

"Oh, yes," replied Saint, "we do know something about them. They are concerned with how the muscle makes and properly distributes ATP, and how it receives a signal from its nerve, ordering it to contract. This is done by miniature plumbing systems. But to understand this you have to know a bit more about how a cell is constructed.

"You might imagine that the simplest possible cell is just a mass of cytoplasm or a solution of protein in water. But that is too simple; if this were so, the contents of a cell would just leak out into the surrounding fluid, and the cell would die. To prevent this, cells are covered by a membrane made of special proteins and fats. It is only a few molecules thick, but is quite impermeable, somewhat like a rubber balloon. Of course, it has to let some things through, such as food, water, gases, and so on. So there are tiny holes in it, shaped to allow some things to pass, and some not. As a matter of fact some of the holes in the membrane act as molecular pumps, pumping such things as sugars and amino acids from the outside in and concentrating them for the cell to use.

"This membrane is extremely important for life. When a cell dies, one of the first things that happens is the membrane becomes leaky. You have noticed, no doubt, that when your wife puts beets into cold water, the water stays clear, but when she kills the beet cells by boiling them, the red color inside the cells leaks out and the beet water reddens."

"Funny," said Mr. Tompkins. "Now that you mention it, I know I have seen it happen many times, but I have never thought anything of it."

"We often fail to notice the familiar," remarked Saint, "even though it is important. The permeability of cells has a lot to do with surgery, for example. Some of the anesthetics, such as ether, paralyze nerves which keep you conscious. They do this by dissolving in the fatty part of the cell membrane and changing its permeability.

"Until rather recently, we thought that the membrane covered only the outer surface of the cell, but now we know better. Under the electron microscope we can see that the cell is riddled with very small tubes

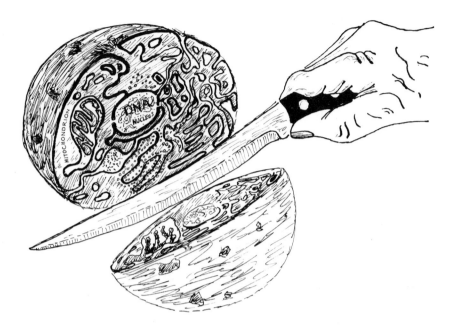

The cell is riddled with very small tubes or channels. . . .

or channels, which open out at the cell surface, somewhat like channels in a Swiss cheese or a sponge. These channels are also lined with the same or similar membranes as the outer surface of the cell. In some places the channels balloon out to form sacklike bodies called 'mito-chondria,' or expand to surround the chromosomes and thus form the cell nucleus. In most cells the channels continually open, close, pinch off, and reunite. Briefly, we can say that because of this infolding, the outer surface extends far into the interior of the cell."

"What is the purpose of all this infolding?" asked Mr. Tompkins.

"There are several purposes," answered Saint. "In general, one may say that this infolding of the membrane is a method the cell uses to form little bodies or organs inside itself. Perhaps you will understand better if I give you one example. Between the fibers of the muscle cell there are the objects called mitochondria. These are the power plants of the cell. But, of course, they do not generate electricity, but rather make the ATP which powers the cell. All cells have mitochondria, but there are more of them in such cells as muscle which have to work hard."

"They do not look terribly impressive to me," said Mr. Tompkins.

"But I will take your word that they are important. Why do they look like bags?"

"They actually are bags, made by folding up the same sort of thing that covers the outside of the cell. A mitochondrion is a double membrane; it resembles a ball that has been pinched in and whose inner part had then grown into a series of folds. I will open one of these biological power plants for you, so you can see how it is organized inside," said Saint.

The inner walls of the mitochondria are folded to provide room for the enzymes that make ATP.

Mr. Tompkins examined the structure with interest. The entire inside was covered by a regular mosaic pattern, which glowed faintly with beautiful pink, yellow, and blue colors.

"The mosaic," explained Saint, "is made of enzymes. Some of the red ones contain a heme very similar to the heme of hemoglobin. Others have a yellow pigment called riboflavin, which, by the way, is vitamin B_2. The blues are copper atoms, also attached to enzymes."

"Why is the pattern so regular?" asked Mr. Tompkins.

"For these enzymes to function well, each enzyme has to be next to another enzyme in correct sequence. So they are organized into little groups which are attached to the inside walls of the mitochondrion. The walls are folded to provide room for more of these enzyme units."

"What do the enzymes do?"

"Primarily one thing; they make ATP. That is why we refer to them as the powerhouse of the cell. They do some other things, of course: they burn or make fat as circumstances require, for example. Very important little things, these mitochondria.

"If you examine a muscle fiber in an electronmicrograph, you will see that leading from the mitochondria there are tiny channels, called the 'sarcoplasmic reticulum,' which lead to and envelop the myofibrils—sarcoplasmic reticulum, hybrid Graeco-Latin, means 'fleshy net.' Thus the mitochondria make ATP, and this ATP then moves down the plumbing system to supply the myofibrils with energy."

"Most ingenious," said Mr. Tompkins. "But how is the ATP actually made?"

"We are back to chemical potential," replied Saint. "Without boring you with the details, the general idea is as follows. The various foods you eat, such as sugar, are compounds that can be burned to carbon dioxide and water; but if this were done, all you would get would be heat. The body has to trap the chemical energy to make ATP. So sugar is first broken down to compounds which react with phosphate spontaneously. Then some of the hydrogen and carbon atoms of these molecules unite with oxygen to form carbon dioxide and water. Some, but not all. The remaining parts of the molecules which are linked to phosphate have trapped some of the energy of the atoms which united with oxygen. Such phosphates are now 'high-energy' compounds, and their energy can be used to make energy-rich ATP. It's quite complicated in detail, and due to various recycling processes eventually all the carbon and hydrogen atoms can be burned and used to form ATP. But this brings to mind another function of the plumbing system in your sarcoplasmic reticulum. It makes it possible for you to incur a debt."

Mr. Tompkins was not sure he understood all this, but at Saint's last sentence his banking interests were immediately aroused. "A debt?" he asked.

"Yes. No doubt at times you have run hard and long, till you were gasping for breath. Even after stopping, you continued breathing hard for quite a while. During your run you incurred an oxygen debt, which you had to pay back after you stopped your violent exercise. The debt was negotiated by your sarcoplasmic reticulum.

"During your run your mitochondria were burning sugar as fast as they could to make ATP for your muscles. However, for this they need oxygen, and the blood supply, even with the accelerated pumping of the heart, could not supply oxygen fast enough to make all the ATP your muscles needed. The sarcoplasmic reticulum provides a temporary answer. As I just told you, it contains enzymes which can partially break down sugar without using oxygen, to the stage of lactic acid. This yields only one-eighteenth of the ATP that could be obtained by breaking down the sugar completely, but as there are a lot of these enzymes, a lot of sugar can be broken down, and a lot of ATP made. So you can run, for a short time, faster and longer than your heart and blood can supply the necessary oxygen. The excess lactic acid moves out of the sarcoplasmic reticulum into your blood stream, and this, of course, can go on for only so long. When you stop, the lactic acid is taken up by the mitochondria, which burn it in the normal way to carbon dioxide and water, using oxygen. So you pant for a while to repay the oxygen debt and then return to normal. This may not seem important to a bank clerk, but if you have to flee for your life in a jungle, you will see that the ability to incur an oxygen debt may be quite important."

"And what is the other plumbing system you mentioned?" asked Mr. Tompkins.

"It has to do with the problem of getting all the fibrils to contract at the same time when a nerve impulse arrives."

"I have always thought that a nerve is merely a sort of telegraph wire, which signals from the brain what the body is to do," Mr. Tompkins observed.

"You are right in so far as signaling is concerned. But a nerve signals somewhat differently from a telegraph wire. A telegraph wire takes the energy that is put into it at one end and delivers what is left of it at the other. A nerve delivers only the signal, not the energy."

"How is that?"

"You might visualize a nerve as a detonator cord such as is used by military engineers. You ignite it at one end, and the explosion propagates itself because of the chemical energy stored in the cord, quite independently of the properties of the original signal," explained Saint.

"But a detonator cord can transmit only one impulse and is gone. Surely a nerve does better than that."

"Of course. To continue with the analogy, the detonator cord is consumed by the impulse, but the nerve immediately builds it up again, ready for the next impulse. What actually happens is this. The surface of the nerve cell is covered by a thin membrane made of protein and fat. In this sheath are molecular pumps, whose exact working we do not understand, but which we do know pump sodium ions from inside the cell to the outside. The result is that the inside of the nerve becomes electrically negative with respect to the outside. You can think of such a fiber as a long cylindrical condenser charged with negative electricity on the inside and positive electricity on the outside. When the nerve fiber is disturbed at one end, it becomes permeable to sodium, the positive and negative charges come together, and the electric polarization in this section vanishes. This causes, however, a similar discharge in the neighboring section, and then again in the next one. As a result, depolarization processes run along the fiber from end to end—just like a detonation running along a primer cord. This is the nerve impulse, as you can see from the diagram here. But right behind it, the nerve

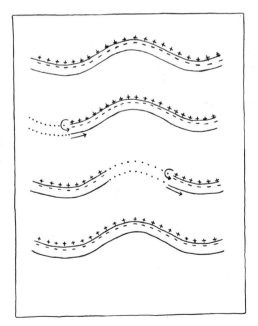

Depolarization travels along the nerve fiber like a detonation running along a primer cord.

cell is rebuilding the resistance of its membrane, which then pumps out sodium ion, using the energy of ATP, thus producing a potential difference as before, and the nerve is again ready to transmit the next impulse. So you see that a nerve impulse is, in a way, an electrical impulse, but rather different from the impulse carried by a copper telegraph cable."

"But it still does the same thing; a signal is a signal," Mr. Tompkins insisted.

"Yes, but there is also another difference. A copper wire will transmit a signal whose strength depends on the potential difference between its two ends. Not so the nerve fiber. If the excitation is too weak, no signal is transmitted, because the membrane resistance does not break down. But if it is stronger than a certain amount, this discharges the 'condenser,' and a maximal signal is transmitted. If the excitation is still stronger, the signal does not get stronger. It is like a loaded pistol. If you do not put enough pressure on the trigger, no shot is fired. If you put enough pressure, you fire a shot, but pulling harder on the trigger does not make the bullet go faster.

"There is still another difference. After each impulse, the nerve fiber has to rebuild its membrane resistance, so for about a thousandth of a second it cannot transmit again. The maximum rate that a nerve can conduct impulses is around a thousand per second.

"As a result of all this, a nerve really transmits information by frequency modulation, or FM. It is the number of impulses per second coursing over the nerve that is important, not the size or amplitude of the impulses. The amplitude is always the same. If a nerve is telling a muscle to contract more strongly, it signals more frequently, not with more violent pulses."

"I suppose," said Mr. Tompkins, "that nerve fibers are spliced together like wires to make longer connections."

"The splicing is chemical," answered Saint. "At the end of a nerve fiber there are little chemical factories, which release a substance whenever an impulse reaches them. This substance then stimulates the next nerve, and so on. The junction of two nerves is called a synapse. There are similar junctions between nerves and muscles and also other organs. These junctions are very important, and much research on them was done by the South American Indians long ago."

"You mean they actually conducted research on muscle?" asked Mr. Tompkins in surprise.

"In a way, yes. They were interested in the practical problem of paralyzing the muscles of animals they hunted, and discovered a plant product called curare. When they smeared their arrowheads with it, their victims became paralyzed and often died because the muscles involved in breathing would not function. Studies on curare have been very valuable to us in elucidating how nerve stimulates muscle. Curare, curiously enough, does not actually prevent a muscle from contracting, as you can show by stimulating a curarized muscle with a weak electric shock. Nor does it prevent a nerve impulse from traveling nor the nerve ending from releasing the chemical which stimulates the muscle. It numbs, so to speak, that part of the muscle cell which is sensitive to the stimulating chemical. Curare is sometimes used medically if it is necessary to put some muscle temporarily out of action."

"If a nerve," said Mr. Tompkins, "releases a chemical which stimulates a muscle, what makes a muscle stop contracting? Is there another chemical like a brake which says 'stop'?"

"No," replied Saint, "there is an enzyme that destroys the chemical in less than a thousandth of a second, and you are all set to go again. Here again there is a 'practical' application, but this time it was not the South American Indians who made the discovery. The so-called 'nerve gases' developed for use in chemical warfare prevent this enzyme from functioning; hence all nerve endings become full of the stimulating chemical and the victim dies in convulsions. As you see, there is no end to the benefits of science."

Mr. Tompkins detected a note of sarcasm in Saint's voice, and decided to change the subject.

"How fast does a nerve impulse travel?" he asked.

"This varies a great deal," answered Saint, "and depends mainly on how thick the nerve fiber is, and whether it is covered by a fatty sheath we call myelin. In the thickest myelinated nerves the conduction speed is around three hundred feet a second, but in some small fibers it may be as low as a couple of feet per second—in round numbers between ten and two hundred miles per hour. These are rather low speeds which at times may present a bit of a problem to the organism. In some cases it is quite important that all parts of muscle contract at the same time. For example, downstairs in some tanks you will find some interesting animals called squids, who are the original inventors of the jet engine. Their body is surrounded by a muscular sheath called a mantle, and when this contracts, a stream of water shoots out in one direction, while the squid shoots off in the other. Here all parts of the mantle have to contract as nearly simultaneously as possible. As the signal to contract comes from one point—the squid's brain—the nerve impulse which stimulates the mantle muscles must travel fast, and the squid, therefore, has very thick nerves leading from the brain to the mantle. These nerves are such large cells that it is much easier to study them than to study the usual nerve fibers. That is why you find so many squid here; they are a great favorite of my neurophysiological colleagues.

"But this brings us back to our question: how do you get not only a whole muscle, but also all the fibrils of a single muscle fiber to contract at the same time? It would not do to have the impulse arrive at different times at different places, so that some fibrils finish contracting while others have just begun to contract and others are already relaxing. At least, this would never do for a muscle which has to act quickly.

"We now know that the remarkable property of transmitting an electrical impulse over its membrane is not confined to the nerve cell. All cells, apparently, can do so; it is only that nerve cells do it so much better and faster. So when a nerve impulse arrives, it sets up an electrical wave at the surface of a muscle cell, where it propagates in a manner quite like an electrical wave on the surface of another nerve cell. But now the signal has to reach the myofibrils and tell them to contract. This is done by another plumbing system, called the transverse system. The surface of the muscle cell is indented and forms very narrow tubes which run from the surface to the Z lines of the myofibrils. The muscle cell is riddled with such channels, in addition to the channels of the sarcoplasmic reticulum. When a signal travels over the surface of a muscle cell, it also enters the tubes of the transverse system and hits the dark line called the Z line. It is only at the Z lines that a signal can cause the myofibril to contract. The Z line, incidentally, is made of a protein called tropomyosin, which is like a string tying together the bundle of fibers."

"You say cause a fiber to contract? What actually happens?"

"Here again we are not sure of the answer. At present the best idea is that when an electrical impulse hits the Z line, calcium is liberated around the fibrils. This calcium sparks the breakdown of ATP, as a spark plug sparks the burning of gasoline in an engine. The fibers then slide over one another and the muscle contracts. The other plumbing system we spoke about, the sarcoplasmic reticulum, has a substance called 'relaxing factor' with a great affinity for calcium. This quickly soaks up the calcium, the fibers slide back to their original position, and the muscle relaxes. At least, so some people think."

By this time Mr. Tompkins felt that as an amateur he had had enough. Besides, he did not want to impose further on Saint's time, nor did he wish Maud to wake up and find him gone.

"Thank you very much for your kindness," said he, shaking Saint's hand.

"Nagyon örvendek megismerni," answered Saint in a language unfamiliar to Mr. Tompkins, who wondered whether it was the language used in Paradise.

As Mr. Tompkins stepped out on the sidewalk a rather corpulent tall and blond man approached him.

"Mr. Tompkins, I presume!" he said as he held out his hand. "I am very glad to meet you, being, as it were, your creator, or, to be more exact, the author of the books in which you made your debut to the reading public. My friends call me Antonovich and since you are in a way my progeny, you may also do so."

Mr. Tompkins beamed. "Of course, I am so glad to meet you. I just had a very interesting conversation with Saint. A most remarkable fellow."

"Remarkable is the word," replied Antonovich. "There are innumerable stories told about him. He has worked on muscle here, but shortly after the First World War he discovered vitamin C in his native Hungary and was later awarded the Nobel Prize for this achievement. When he first separated this new substance, properly enough from paprika, he was not sure of the chemical formula, but he knew it was a kind of sugar. He reported his discovery in the British scientific publication *Nature,* and called his miraculous substance ignose—'ign' stood for ignorance, and 'ose' is the standard ending of all chemical names of sugars. At that time the editors of *Nature* were serious people, but unfortunately without a molecule of humor in their cerebral cortices. They asked Saint to find a more suitable name. 'Godnose' was the next suggestion, but, needless to say, this also proved unacceptable.

"As a young man, he took a comprehensive examination for a degree in medicine at a Belgian university. The examining committee, like most such, was lazy and careless in framing its questions.

" 'Name twenty diseases,' read one question.

" 'It is better to know the cure for one than the names of twenty,' wrote the candidate for his answer. The other questions were no better, and he failed his exam. Returning to Budapest, he passed the equivalent examination with distinction. In 1937, when he had been awarded the Nobel Prize for Medicine, the Belgian university, quite understandably, felt embarrassed at having failed so notable a candidate. They solved this problem by awarding him an honorary degree, Doctor Honoris Causa. But enough of this. I am just on my way to lunch. There is an excellent restaurant called 'Stepashore' located just off the fishing harbor. It serves wonderful seafood. Will you join me?"

"I would be delighted," said Mr. Tompkins.

"Tell me what you learned from Saint about muscles," said Antonovich after they were seated at a table with a view of the harbor.

"Oh, he showed me many beautiful photographs of muscle fibers taken through the electron microscope. They look like a bunch of thicker and thinner threads which he called myosin and actin respectively. They are aligned in a regular pattern and can slide past each other in opposite directions. If the actin threads slide into the empty spaces between the myosin threads, the muscle contracts; if they slide out, the muscle expands. He said that the actin threads crawl along the myosin threads and vice versa, just as caterpillars crawl over one another in opposite directions."

"I must confess," said Antonovich, "that I do not like this caterpillar analogy. Caterpillars crawl by using their numerous legs, which are operated by small caterpillian muscles. Now, how do these tiny caterpillian muscles operate? To be logical, one should say that these micromuscles are formed by still smaller micro-caterpillars, who in their turn have micro-legs and micromicro-muscles. And so on, and so on, beyond any limit."

"So what do you suggest instead of caterpillars?"

"Intermolecular forces. You know, of course, that if one puts a thin glass tube, a capillary, into a beaker with water, the water will rise in the capillary in defiance of the pull of gravity. If you put the same tube into a beaker filled with mercury, the level of the mercury in the tube will be depressed. One says that the water wets the glass, whereas the mercury does not. From the molecular point of view, the phenomenon depends on the cohesive forces between the molecules of liquid and the molecules of the tube, and the interrelated cohesive forces. The molecules of water are attracted more strongly to the molecules of glass than to one another and try to establish a larger contact area with the glass. Thus, the water column climbs up the glass tube until its increasing weight stops further motion. The opposite situation exists in the case of a mercury and glass interface, where mercury atoms prefer the company of their own kind rather than that of glass molecules. Although, speaking about capillary forces, one usually has in mind the interface between liquids and solids, as in the preceding two examples, surface forces also exist at the interface between two solids. Forces of a generally similar kind also exist at the interface between various jelly-like materials constituting the cells of living beings. The caterpillar analogy, like all analogies, is good up to a point, but ultimately it is at the level of the interactions between atoms or molecules that we must seek a true understanding of muscle action."

"But aren't these kinds of forces too weak to explain muscle action?" asked Mr. Tompkins.

"They are quite strong," replied Antonovich. "For example, the surface tension at the water-ether interface is 10.7 dynes per centimeter; at the water-benzene interface, 35.0 dynes per centimeter; and at the water-carbon tetrachloride interface, it is 48.0 dynes per centimeter."

"What is this dyne?" asked Mr. Tompkins.

"A dyne is a unit of force in the metric system; in the units you are more familiar with, a dyne per centimeter is about 5.5-millionths of a pound weight per inch."

"It is not very much then," commented Mr. Tompkins.

"True, but you must have heard from Saint that the myosin and actin rods are very thin: 160 and 50 angstroms respectively. An angstrom, you will remember, is one hundred-millionth part of a centimeter, so there are about 2.5 hundred million angstroms to an inch. If the average diameter of the rods is a hundred angstroms, then the total length of the borderlines wiggling between the actin and myosin rods per square inch of muscle cross-section is about five hundred million inches, or one thousand miles. So, even if we assume that the surface tension on the interface between myosin and actin is only one dyne per centimeter, one square inch of muscle cross-section will be able to lift the weight of one hundred pounds."

"That is Herculean!" exclaimed Mr. Tompkins.

By this time the oysters had arrived. "Is it not strange," commented Antonovich, "that oysters have such big ears? Have you not heard the verse?

'Which noise anoise an oister?
Each noise anoise an oister
But noisy noise anoise an oister most.'?"

"Must be the heat," thought Mr. Tompkins, and indeed it did seem quite hot.

The lobster duly came, and Antonovich continued his explanations. "The crustaceans," he said, "are much like you, but their skeletons are on the outside rather than inside. For small animals this provides certain mechanical advantages. You see . . ."

But by now it was unbearably hot. The restaurant, the waitresses, the boats in the harbor seemed to fade away. Mr. Tompkins felt an irresistible urge to sleep. Instead, he was surprised to find that he had just awakened.

"Had a good sleep, Cyril?" he heard the joking voice of Maud saying. "You know you've slept in this position for over two hours, and the sunshine here is rather vigorous."

"No, I was talking to a Saint," said Mr. Tompkins.

"Nonsense!" Maud laughed. "You slept like a baby. Have some of my lotion; it will soothe your burning skin."

And Mr. Tompkins gladly followed her advice.

» 3 «

The Heart on the Wrong Side

THE cable arrived in the morning and was very laconic. It read: "Taking transatlantic jet. Will be home by dinnertime. Wilfred." Like many mathematicians, Wilfred, the only child of Mr. Tompkins and Maud, was very absent-minded and forgot to give the flight number or arrival time. He had been away from home for over a year, working on his Ph.D. thesis at a large foreign university.

The telegram was quite a pleasant surprise. Wilfred had never been a good letter-writer, and his letters were infrequent, short, and uninformative.

"Wonderful!" exclaimed Maud. "Now we will learn all about his life over there. I will broil him a juicy steak for dinner tonight; he loves steak!"

They telephoned the international airport, located about one hour's drive from the Tompkinses' home, and found that two transatlantic jets would be arriving that afternoon about one hour apart. So Maud decided that she would drive over to meet the earlier plane, and if Wilfred was not on it she would wait for the second. Mr. Tompkins decided he would stay home and try to read a new semipopular book on proteins which he had bought recently. He was struggling with a description of levo and dextro amino acids and did not want to drop his reading. After Maud left, Mr. Tompkins picked up the book, but the presentation of the subject was complicated and not too exciting, and, stretched in his comfortable armchair, he closed his eyes. He did not even hear the door open and was awakened only when a familiar voice said, "Oh, Dad! Can't you do anything but sleep?"

Mr. Tompkins opened his eyes and saw his son standing in front of him.

"Welcome home!" said he. "But where's your mother? She drove to the airport to pick you up."

"Oh! She probably met the wrong plane, and as I didn't know I was to be met, I took the bus. I hope she'll be back soon."

"Oh, these women!" said Mr. Tompkins. "They always mix things up. But do sit down, and tell me how things are."

He looked at his son attentively and was surprised by the changes which had taken place in the boy since he had left home. Instead of an athletically built boy always ready to burst into laughter, Wilfred now was a thin fellow with sunken cheeks and a sad look in his eyes.

"Have you been sick?" inquired Mr. Tompkins with hidden anxiety.

"Not what the doctors would call really sick, but I've been in poor shape lately."

"Well," said Mr. Tompkins encouragingly, "this must be the result of too much studying and the poor food in the dormitories. Your mother is going to broil you a fine steak tonight. We will fix you up if you stay home for a while."

"I cannot eat steak or any other kind of meat," said Wilfred sadly. "I live on butter and vodka."

"But what has happened? Can't the doctors fix up your digestive trouble?"

"No, it is out of their power—at least for a long time to come. The only man who could have helped was an Indian guide from the upper Amazon river. But he is dead now."

"This makes no sense to me!" said Mr. Tompkins. "What medical help can you expect from an Indian guide, unless he is a shaman, of course? But from the medical books I've been reading lately, I understand that witchcraft is efficacious only for treating psychosomatic diseases."

"Well, let us start from the beginning," said Wilfred. "Soon after I arrived at the University, I met a charming, beautiful, out-of-this-world girl called Vera Sapojnikoff. I think I mentioned her name in one of my letters. She is the daughter of a very rich man of Russian extraction named Ivan Titovich Sapojnikoff, who owns numerous shoe factories and a series of retail outlets through which he sells his goods. After a rather short acquaintance, I came to the unshakable conclusion that Verochka is the only girl in the world for me, and she felt exactly the same way about me. So we started to talk about marrying after my graduation, and about home, furniture, and our future children. She is very fond of children and hoped to have many of them. But there was a difficulty. Although Mr. Sapojnikoff did not object to my occasionally taking Verochka out to dances and concerts, he was absolutely against marriage. He wanted to have a business-minded son-in-law who could later take over his enterprises, and not a mathematician who was interested in topology, or 'analysis situs,' to use a more technical Latin term, and who could never be interested in improvements of shoe production, in antitrust laws, gross receipts, installment sales, amortizations, and all that sort of thing. But what can a topologist understand about such complicated matters?"

"What is this 'topology'?" asked Mr. Tompkins, whose scientific curiosity strangely outweighed his concern over his son's personal troubles.

"Well," answered Wilfred, looking somewhat unhappy that his father seemed to take more interest in abstract mathematical problems than in his romance, "topology is the branch of geometry that deals with the properties of bodies in spaces of any number of dimensions which remain invariant with respect to any deformations made without cutting them."

"Speak more clearly, my son," said Mr. Tompkins. "Recently I have been interested in many problems of science and also of mathematics, which, as Bertrand Russell has written, is not a science but an art. Can you give me some examples of topological problems?"

"All right," said Wilfred. He realized that he was using language that was too technical. "Suppose you compare a European football and an American one. The first has a perfectly spherical shape and is supposed to be kicked by the foot. The second is an elongated ellipsoid, and you are supposed to carry and throw it by hand, except when the rules allow you to kick it. But, deforming it by stretching or shrinking its leather surface, you can change this ellipsoidal American football into a perfectly spherical European football. This can be done because within the limits of 'analysis situs' all stretchings or shrinkings are permissible, but you may not cut the surface with a knife. Take another example: a bicycle tire and a doughnut. The first has a large space in the middle, whereas the second has a comparatively small one. Here

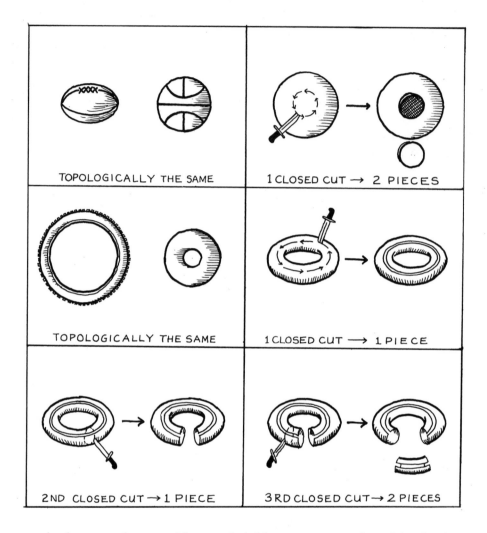

TOPOLOGICALLY THE SAME

1 CLOSED CUT → 2 PIECES

TOPOLOGICALLY THE SAME

1 CLOSED CUT → 1 PIECE

2ND CLOSED CUT → 1 PIECE

3RD CLOSED CUT → 2 PIECES

again, however, by stretching or shrinking, you can make a bicycle tire look like a doughnut or a doughnut like a bicycle tire. But do what you will, you cannot transform a football into a tire or a doughnut.

"There is also another great difference. If you stick a knife into the surface of a football, be it American or European, and make a cut along a closed line, the ball will fall into two separate parts. But if the object is a tire, you cannot separate it into two parts with a single closed cut, and even if you make a second cut the tire may still remain in one piece. Only a third cut will inevitably make two objects out of it.

"So one of the simplest things topology tells us is into how many pieces a given surface will fall after it is cut a given number of times."

"Looks to me like a kindergarten game," commented Mr. Tompkins. "Why is it important?"

"You yourself quoted Russell," retorted Wilfred, "as saying that mathematics is not a science but an art. Will you tell me why art is important?"

"Oh, but art," said Mr. Tompkins, "gives pleasure to people who look at pictures or listen to verses or music."

"Right you are!" remarked Wilfred bitterly. "But getting pleasure depends on whether one feels the beauty of art. I know a number of people, Vera's father, for example, who do not give a damn for art, be it painting, poetry, or music!" And he leaned back exhausted in his chair.

Fatherly instincts overwhelmed Mr. Tompkins, and he felt that he had led the conversation in the wrong direction. "Well, tell me more about Vera," said he. "How was she before you left for this trip?"

"I have not seen her since our engagement was broken."

"Your engagement was broken!" exclaimed Mr. Tompkins. "But why?"

"Because," said Wilfred sadly, "I was too much involved in mathematical problems and did not realize their possible biological consequences. As I told you, I was working on problems of topology, particularly on the Möbius twist, invented a century ago by the Swedish mathematician Möbius."

"What is a Möbius twist, and how could it result in breaking up the engagement of two young people who are in love?" asked his perplexed father.

"Let me have a piece of paper, a pencil, scissors, and some glue," said Wilfred.

Though rather astonished by this request, Mr. Tompkins provided the required materials. Taking the piece of paper, Wilfred cut from it a ribbon a couple of inches wide and, twisting the ribbon a half-turn, glued the ends together to form a ring.

"This is a Möbius ring," said he. "Unlike other rings, which have two sides, an inner and an outer one, it has only one side. You cannot paint this ring white on the inside and black on the outside or make it of silver and gold-plate it on the outside, because it has only one side, and if you begin painting it, starting from some point on either side, and go all the way around, you will find that the entire ring becomes the same color."

"I can understand, of course," said Mr. Tompkins, "that engagement and wedding rings play an important role in marriage, but how could a Möbius ring have broken your engagement to Vera, and put you in the state you are in now?"

"It was all due to her father objecting to our marriage because I could make no contribution to his shoemaking business. However, one sleepless night it occurred to me that making right and left shoes required two sets of machinery. Couldn't one make them all for the left foot, let us say, and then turn one-half of them into right-foot shoes by using some topological trick? This would surely reduce the cost of production."

"But what has the Möbius twist to do with it?" asked Mr. Tompkins, getting interested.

"Well, you see," said Wilfred, "if you go around the Möbius ring, objects change their 'parity,' as the physicists put it today. Let me demonstrate this using the twisted band I have just made for you."

He took out his fountain pen and sketched on the Möbius ribbon

It is not advisable for a matador to run around a Möbius surface.

a picture of a matador facing a bull, with a scarlet muleta and a sharp sword in his hand.

"You know, of course," he said, "that a surface, according to Euclid, has no thickness, so that drawings made on one side of it are just as visible if one looks at them from the opposite side. It would be better in this case to use transparent cellophane. As I have drawn it now, the matador is facing the bull in the correct way and has every chance to put his sword through the bull's heart. Now imagine that the matador bypasses the bull and takes a run around the Möbius ring and returns to the arena. When he returns to the original spot and faces the bull again, he notices that he is standing on his head. This, of course, is no way to fight a bull. But since the matador cannot leave his two-dimensional surface, he must turn 180 degrees in the plane, in which case he will have turned his back to the bull. Again not very convenient for fighting the bull. Thus it is not advisable for a matador to run around a Möbius surface!"

Mr. Tompkins was very much disturbed; his boy, who had always been so bright before, now seemed to be talking nonsense.

"But what has all this to do with your break-up with Vera?" he asked.

"Oh, quite a lot," answered Wilfred. "You will have noticed that after the matador has traveled around the Möbius twist, he has become the mirror image of what he was before. Well, one sleepless night I conceived the idea that the Möbius twist, well known in the case of surfaces, could also exist in three-dimensional space. According to the famous German mathematician Bernhard Riemann, who lived about a century ago, three-dimensional space can be curved in the same way as an ordinary two-dimensional surface. In fact, Einstein's entire general theory of relativity is based on Riemann's geometry. If there are Möbius twists in two-dimensional surface geometry, as I have just demonstrated to you with this paper strip, there should also be similar twists in three-dimensional space which turn objects traveling around their vertices from right-handed modifications to left-handed ones. Also I remembered reading that a biological expedition to the upper region of the Amazon River had found two kinds of snails, whose shells were mirror images of each other. Could it be that there is a Möbius twist axis crossing the surface of the earth somewhere down there? There, the two kinds of snails might have been originally identical, but could have become mirror images of one another because some of them had migrated around the Möbius vortex.

Two snails that look like mirror images of each other.

"If this were true, one should be able to turn left-handed gloves, shoes, and automobiles manufactured in Great Britain into their right-handed replicas merely by sending them around the Möbius vortex.

"The next morning I appeared at Mr. Sapojnikoff's factory, and after two hours' waiting was admitted to his luxurious office, where six telephones sat on his otherwise empty, ping-pong-table-sized desk.

" 'Have a cigar,' said he. 'It is a real Havana—Castro or no Castro. What have you to say?'

" 'Sir,' said I, 'I suppose that you are aware of the fact that each man as well as each woman has two feet: a right one and a left one.'

" 'So what?' asked Mr. Sapojnikoff, taken by surprise.

" 'Doesn't it make the production of shoes more expensive because two different sets of machinery are required to manufacture right and left shoes?' I asked. 'Wouldn't it be simpler if one could produce shoes for only the right foot or the left?'

" 'And let all the people jump on only one foot, or what?' grumbled Mr. Sapojnikoff, now persuaded that I—the candidate for his daughter's hand—was really nuts.

" 'Not necessarily,' I told him. 'The point is that recently I've been working on the mathematical possibility of the Möbius twist in three-dimensional space, a space which is, after all, quite similar to a surface except that you have three coordinates, X, Y, and Z, instead of only two. I won't take your time trying to explain what you certainly will not understand, having had no mathematical training. But I can state that according to the basic laws of mathematics, such a three-dimensional Möbius twist, turning right-hand screws into left-hand screws, may exist in the space surrounding our globe. In fact, there is some evidence that somewhere near the upper basin of the Amazon River the axis of the Möbius twist intersects the surface of the earth.'

" 'Oh,' said Mr. Sapojnikoff, who in spite of his business-oriented mind also had a vivid imagination, 'you mean that if you bring a left-foot shoe around this vortex, as you call it, it will become a right-foot one?'

" 'Yes, that is exactly what I mean,' I said, 'and I have to show you a two-dimensional model to demonstrate my point.'

"Since I knew that, like Hemingway, Mr. Sapojnikoff took an interest in bull fighting I had brought along a model of the Möbius strip with the bull and matador, just like the one I have just shown you. The old man was delighted when he understood the dilemma of the matador, who faced the choice of turning his back to the bull or fighting while standing on his head.

" 'Oh-ho-ho-ho!' he roared. 'That's, as we say in Russia, to get between Sila and Korob! Will you leave this model here to beautify my desk?'

" 'Sure I will,' said I, not daring to tell Mr. Sapojnikoff that the tale of Scylla and Charybdis is known also in other countries.

"Suddenly becoming serious, Mr. Sapojnikoff said, 'Wonderful, my future son-in-law! Go ahead with your plans. I will finance your expedition to this *Chorta na Kulichky** spot, and, if your theory turns out to be correct, we will throw a big wedding for you and Verochka, with a lot of this French drink they call champagne, and, of course, with a gypsy chorus! If you prove your point, I will also make you a junior partner of my firm.'

"Happy as could be, I walked out of the old man's office and spent a divine evening with Verochka, who looked more beautiful than ever that night.

* Russian equivalent of Shangri La.

"Well, when I was boarding my plane to Brazil, both Verochka and her father came to the airfield to see me off, and he handed me a box filled with all kinds of right-foot shoes—a hiking shoe, a tennis shoe, a woman's stiletto-heeled shoe, and even a child's slipper. He also brought a contract pertaining to my future junior partnership in his firm, which was to be signed if my experiment turned out to be successful. The jet engines roared, and I was off to win Verochka's hand.

"Arriving at the estuary of the Amazon River with the box of shoes, I organized an expedition of about a dozen natives to go around the mysterious Möbius vortex up the river. Each member of my group was given only one shoe, a right-foot one, which he or she had to wear, while the left foot was to remain bare. After some exercise, everyone got accustomed to that practice, although the woman who came along with us to cook, and had to wear a stiletto-heeled shoe, continued to feel rather uncomfortable.

"Our expedition up the Amazon was led by an old Brazilian guide named Situsianos, who had discovered the two kinds of snails in that region, and who was the only man in Brazil who knew his way around that God-forsaken part of the country.

"A motor launch brought us and our provisions to the spot indicated by Situsianos, and we were put ashore with the captain's promise to come back for us in a week. And so into the steaming jungles we went. The porters were bent under their loads of provisions and stumbled along on their one-shoed feet. Only I, wearing a pair of heavy hiking boots, and the old guide, who refused to put on any shoes at all, felt comparatively comfortable. I will not take your time to describe all the misery of this perilous voyage—heat, humidity, mosquitoes, snakes, more heat, more mosquitoes. . . . The woman took off her shoe and insisted on carrying it, but I did not feel that this would make any difference. Many of the men followed her example, and I told them that it was okay, as long as they did not lose their precious shoes. A week later we returned to the point of departure, and set up camp to await the return of the motor launch. Everybody felt relaxed, and I ordered all the members of my group to put their shoes back on. But, damn it, when I looked at the group surrounding me I saw that all of them were still wearing right-foot shoes just as they had before we started! The Möbius effect did not work, and the expedition was a complete failure. My calculations were apparently wrong. I knew then that Verochka would never become my wife, and

All of them were still wearing right-foot shoes. . . .

was ready for a moment to make a Möbius strip out of my belt and to hang myself on the branch of a tree. In disgust, I ordered all the members of my small group to take off their shoes and to throw them into the river. They did so with great delight, and their shoes became delicacies for the alligators swimming near the shore.

"The motor launch arrived on time, and in a few days I returned to civilization. When my plane landed at the airport, both Vera and her father were awaiting my arrival.

" 'Well, let me see the shoes,' said Mr. Sapojnikoff anxiously.

" 'I fed them to the alligators because they did not change to left-foot ones. I must have made some mistake in my topological speculations, and there is no such thing as a three-dimensional Möbius twist,' I told him.

" 'Oh, no!' murmured Vera faintly.

" 'I am very sorry, sir,' I continued, 'that I caused you all these troubles with my fantastic theory, and I think that it would be only fair if I returned to you unsigned our preliminary partnership contract.'

"So, producing the rather battered document from my pocket, I handed it to him.

" 'Very strange,' said Mr. Sapojnikoff after glancing at it. 'I cannot read it.'

" 'Mirror-writing!' exclaimed Vera. It *was* mirror-writing. Things had changed after all!

"In a flash the explanation of the alleged failure dawned on me. Nothing was wrong, and every right-foot shoe that the members of the group carried along had turned into the left-foot variety. But I also had become left-footed and left-handed, and, having changed myself into my mirror image, I naturally could not notice the same change in the shoes.

" 'Feel my heart,' I said to Vera. 'No, not here; my heart is now on the other side.'

" 'I will love you just the same,' said Vera happily.

" 'Too bad about the shoes,' said Mr. Sapojnikoff, 'although I am cheered by the fact that the shoes I manufacture are made from the best leather that money can buy, so that even the alligators of the Amazon river consider them delicatessen items. But I guess that this document and an X-ray photograph of your chest may be considered as a sufficient proof. Thus we will sign the partnership agreement as soon as the document is retyped, and I will announce your engagement to Vera at the party which my wife is planning to give tonight in your honor.' "

Mr. Tompkins was very surprised by his son's story. "But why didn't you let us know about your engagement?" asked he, feeling somewhat offended.

"Oh, we just decided to spring that on you as a surprise and wait until the arrangements for the wedding had been made. You see, there were still a few months left until I would get my Ph.D., and we decided that we would be married immediately after that."

"So what is wrong?" asked Mr. Tompkins.

"Well, everything went to pieces, because although I had become well educated in mathematics, I had learned nothing about the basic laws of biochemistry. The engagement party that night started very gaily, but toward the end of it I got involved in a conversation with one of the guests, a young biochemistry professor. I told him about my trip around the Möbius vortex in the upper Amazon River, during which the right-foot shoes became left-foot ones. His face grew serious, and he asked: 'Tell me, have you recently had any digestive troubles?'

"The question seemed to be rather out of place, but I decided to tell him the truth. 'Yes,' I said, 'since my return from Brazil I do feel some discomfort in the intestines. During the flight home our stewardess gave me some sandwiches for lunch. Although the cheese sandwiches seemed not to be too bad, the ham sandwiches caused trouble. It seems that I cannot digest meat, sugar, or starches of any kind, and have to live entirely on a diet of fats. The only other item I seem able to tolerate is vodka, of which I have been liberally partaking tonight. I suspect this must be the effect of the native food I ate during my trip through the Brazilian jungles.'

" 'Look,' said the biochemist, 'I don't want to spoil your party, but could you come to my office at the University sometime tomorrow for a test?'

"I did not pay much attention to what he said, but I made the appointment, and rejoined the party just in time to hear Verochka's father's words: 'Ladies and gentlemen! Stop the noise for a minute, since I have to make a very important announcement. Today our beloved daughter Vera became engaged to be married to the great mathematician Wilfred Tompkins, here on my right, whose wonderful discovery has made the manufacture of shoes much easier and cheaper!'

"He removed a silver slipper from his daughter's foot, filled it with champagne, and drank it in one gulp down to the heel. All the guests followed suit with this old-fashioned Slavic custom, and the party became wilder and wilder, gayer and gayer. . . .

"The next morning I remembered to turn up at the University's biochemical laboratory, to be examined by the man I had met at the party. First of all he put his hand on my chest and found indeed that my heart was beating on the right side—that is to say, on the wrong side. As you know, the correct position of a human heart is on the left side of the chest.

" 'This looks very serious,' said the biochemist. 'You really became a mirror image of yourself during that trip up the Amazon. Your heart is on the right side, that is, on the wrong side of your chest; your liver is displaced on the wrong side too, and intuitively you probably part your hair on the opposite side of your head from other people?'

" 'Well, what is wrong about that?' asked I. 'If I buy a new pair of shoes, I can put the right-foot shoe on my left foot and vice versa, and will feel just as comfortable. And I can use my comb in such a way as to have my hair parted on the same side as other people do.'

" 'That's quite correct,' said the biochemist, 'but there is a much more serious problem. If you will come to the blackboard here with me, I will explain to you what is the matter.'

"Taking a piece of chalk, the biochemist proceeded to draw for me two simple figures.

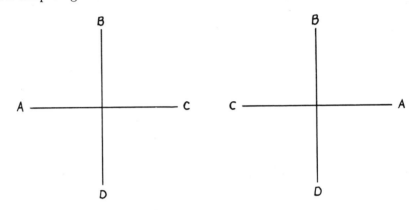

" 'Here, you see, I have arranged four different letters around a point. The two arrangements are the same, except that the positions of A and C are interchanged.'

" 'Elementary,' I said.'The second figure is merely the first figure reflected in a mirror.'

" 'Of course. As a mathematician you will notice that there is no way to rotate the second figure within the surface on which it is drawn so that it can be superimposed on the first. You can, of course, lift it out of its surface, turn it around, and then superimpose it on the first. But this requires a three-dimensional space, or one dimension more than we used to draw the figure. Within the limitations of two dimensions the two figures are not the same.'

" 'Precisely,' I answered. 'It is the same as when I had to take three-dimensional right shoes into the fourth dimension in order to turn them into three-dimensional left ones.'

" 'Since you are a mathematician,' continued the biochemist, 'all this does appear very elementary to you, but let's explore the bio-chemical implications. Your body is made of organic molecules, all of which contain carbon atoms. Now a carbon atom has, as we say, a valency of four, which means it can attach to itself four other atoms or chemical groups. Such molecules are not imbedded in a plane, but exist in three-dimensional space. The carbon atom sits in the middle of a tetrahedron, with the four groups at the apexes. If two or more of the four groups are the same, then no matter how they are arranged it is always possible to rotate the figures so that all molecules become identical. To put it in another way, the mirror image is identical with itself except when all four items are different. But of course in practice it often happens that four different groups are attached to a single carbon atom, so that there are a very large number of organic compounds which exist in two forms, right-handed and left-handed, or dextro and levo, as we say. Their two kinds of molecules are mirror images of each other. There is no way of rotating one to make it identical with the other, unless, of course, you operate in four-dimensional space.'

" 'I see it now,' I said. 'My right-handed molecules have become left-handed, and my left-handed ones have become right. But what difference does that make?'

" 'In ordinary organic chemistry it makes no difference. Right- and left-handed molecules have exactly the same properties, such as solubility, boiling point, or the energy required to synthesize them. Since they are the same, when an organic chemist synthesizes such a compound, nature does not know the difference and half the molecules come out right-handed, half left-handed.'

" 'So what is the problem?' I asked.

" 'The problem,' answered the biochemist, 'is that you are not an ordinary mixture of organic compounds. Right- and left-handed molecules are identical in all respects except in their relations to individual molecules, which can always distinguish between the two. Look at it this way. A man usually has two feet, so a combination of right and left shoes is okay. But suppose you have a one-legged man with a right foot. He can only use a right shoe, and can tell it at once from a left. Now it is an extraordinary fact that any given compound of this sort in our bodies has molecules of one kind only, like a crowd of men each of which has only a right foot. This means that our bodies distinguish between right- and left-handed molecules, just as a single foot distinguishes between right and left shoes.'

"As a mathematician, I could see at once how extraordinary it was that a living body should be made of only one of the mirror images of molecules, even though the probabilities of formation are the same for each.

" 'How come this is so?' I asked him.

" 'There is no difficulty in understanding the situation once you have a body with a predominance of one kind of molecules. The other kind of molecule will not react properly and will be eliminated on the principle "the majority wins and takes all." The problem is how such a body could originate in the first place. This is one of the great mysteries of the origin of life, and there seem to be only two possible ways it could have happened. One way can be called the hypothesis of the "primeval Adam," which maintains that billions of years ago a single molecule somewhere on the earth learned how to replicate— that is, to produce an identical model of itself—and it just happened to be a levo variety. Thus, as a result of replication, there originated billions upon billions of identical replicated "primeval Adams," all of them formed from the levo kind. When, much later, through the process of evolution, sexual differentiation took place, the primeval Eve appeared. But being made, as you know, from Adam's rib, she also was levo. Thus the entire living world, plants and animals, now is levo and not dextro.

" 'Another theory, which I like better, is that there were two anti-worlds of primitive living beings: one levo and one dextro. Since levo and dextro beings were mutually indigestible to each other, they fought a mortal fight, and the levo variety won. Thus we are all levo creatures.'

" 'Terrible!' I exclaimed. 'This means that I am a dextro animal and poisonous to everybody else!'

" 'This isn't so bad,' answered the biochemist, 'since cannibalism is now out, in our country at least, and nobody will eat Wilfred Tompkins chops. On the other hand, though, ordinary pork or lamb chops will not be assimilated by your digestive organs. But I am sure that your future father-in-law can build a biochemical factory which will produce dextro steaks, chops, sausages, and whatever you wish. One could shape dextro proteins to look exactly like the food you get in restaurants, and you would not notice any difference. But you must be sure that your future wife does not taste the food she cooks for you.'

"The biochemist paused for a while, looking at me with great sympathy. 'However,' he said, 'there is another problem, which cannot be helped now. I suppose you and your future wife plan to have children?'

" 'Oh, yes! Verochka loves children.'

" 'Then I regret having to tell you,' said the biochemist, 'that dextro sperms cannot fertilize levo ova. Thus there is no chance that you will have any children.'

" 'But Verochka wants to have several children!' I said.

" 'Sorry,' said the biochemist, 'but it will take a long time before we learn how to synthesize the deoxyribonucleic acid which forms the chromosomes and regulates heredity. And even when we solve that problem—as I am sure we will—the synthetic children will have no relation to their parents. So you might just as well adopt a few babies.'

"It occurred to me, however, that the situation was not really as desperate as all that. In fact, I laughed at his suggestion.

" 'No problem,' I said, 'I will merely go through the Möbius twist again and everything will be reversed back to normal.'

" 'Of course,' said the biochemist.

"The atmosphere of tension cleared right away, and we continued our scientific conversation in a relaxed mood.

" 'What particular compound in my body is causing me all this trouble?' I asked.

" 'Well, it is not fats, as you have observed. Neither is it alcohol. These compounds do not have carbons to which four different chemical groups are attached, so they exist in only one form, and you can still use them. Sugars and starches can exist in two mirror-image forms, but that by itself might not be too bad. Your body can, in a pinch, synthesize them from fats and alcohol. It is the proteins that cause you trouble. You see, like all living beings, you are composed mostly of proteins, which are long chains of amino acids connected by so-called peptide bonds. Now, an amino acid is a molecule formed by a carbon atom—alpha carbon, we call it—with four atomic groups attached to it. Three of these groups are the same in all amino acids, but the fourth can be whichever molecule you choose and is called a side chain. You can make millions of different amino acids by keeping the same first three groups attached to the central alpha carbon, but varying the side chain. Since every amino acid has a central alpha carbon, to which four different groups are attached, it is always levo or dextro. In a normal body they are always levo, but yours are dextro, which is the cause of all your troubles.' "

"Yes, I know about that," said Mr. Tompkins. "When I was floating through my blood stream, Dr. Streets showed me two amino acids, and demonstrated how they can stick together by losing a molecule of water. There are, however, only twenty kinds of amino acids that occur in proteins, such as prolines, valines, asparagines, and others whose names I do not remember."

"Isn't it wonderful that you, a bank employee, know so much about biochemistry, Dad," exclaimed Wilfred, "while I, a university student, was quite ignorant of it. But did Dr. Streets tell you about levo and dextro amino acids?"

"No, I do not think he did."

"Well, okay, let me tell you something about amino-acid structure, which I learned only after my engagement party."

Wilfred went over to a large fruit bowl which his mother had placed on a table for his arrival and took one pineapple, one orange, one apple, one pear, and one strawberry. Using toothpicks, he attached the orange to the top of the pineapple and then, having stuck into the orange three more toothpicks pointing in three different directions, attached to them an apple, a pear, and a strawberry.

"This is a model of an amino acid, the constituent unit of all proteins," he said. "The orange represents the alpha carbon atom, and the four toothpicks sticking out of it indicate that four different atomic groups can be attached to it. The strawberry is just a hydrogen atom $(-H)$; the apple is the so-called amino group, formed by a nitrogen atom with two hydrogens attached to it $\left(-N\diagup^{H}_{\diagdown H}\right)$; whereas the pear is a carboxyl group $\left(-C\diagup^{O}_{\diagdown OH}\right)$ made of one extra carbon, one oxygen atom attached to it on one side, and on the other side another oxygen with a hydrogen atom. This combination of atoms is standard for all amino acids. I have just put it on the top of the pineapple, which is conventionally called a side chain. But the side chain need not necessarily be a pineapple. It may be a melon, a pumpkin, a cucumber, a plum, an apricot, or even, as in one case, another strawberry. While the three groups attached to the top of the orange are the 'standard' attributes of an amino acid, the side chains may be quite different molecular groups. As you just mentioned, however, there are only twenty side chains that are used by nature in amino acids forming proteins.''

Coming back to the fruit bowl, Wilfred took out more fruits of the same kind but pinned them together with toothpicks in a somewhat different way.

The three groups attached to the top of the orange are the "standard" attributes of an amino acid. . . .

"You see," he said, "here I have used the same fruits, but this combination is not the same as the one I made before. It is actually a mirror image of the other structure, and you cannot turn it around in such a way that it would look identical with the other. Now, as you might guess, normal enzyme proteins, which are made of levo amino acids, cannot digest proteins made of dextro amino acids, and the reverse, of course, is also true, since everything is symmetrical. So my unnatural enzymes cannot digest natural proteins, which are the only ones available on this earth. But even if they could, it would do me no good at all, since natural amino acids could not be used to build my unnatural proteins. The fact is that I am slowly starving to death on what amounts to a protein-free diet.

"But," continued Wilfred, "at that time, since both the biochemist and I were confident there was an easy cure for my condition, we gaily continued our conversation.

" 'You have certainly heard of the man who discovered that some organic compounds can exist as mirror images of each other,' my biochemist friend remarked. 'He was Louis Pasteur, who also discovered that bacteria can produce diseases, and that it is possible to immunize against them. He found that a compound called tartaric acid will form two kinds of crystals which are mirror images of each other. At first nobody understood the reason for this, and Pasteur tried all sorts of rather fantastic experiments, such as swinging plants on a pendulum through a magnetic field to change the twist of their molecules. Of course, it was all to no avail. The true explanation, that a carbon atom can attach to four different groups, was soon suggested by several other chemists.'

'What about the snails?' I asked. 'Doesn't the fact that there are right- and left-handed spiral shells prove that their molecules are mirror images of each other?'

" 'No,' said the biochemist. 'You just made a lucky guess. Such snails are not uncommon. You can build large structures such as snail shells, and make them right- or left-handed irrespective of whether you use right- or left-handed molecules. After all, you have a right and left hand, but in both the amino acids have the same twist. In fact, it is the same with having a heart on the wrong side. About one in 10,000 people have that condition, which we call *situs inversus*. But, of course, if one were inverted completely, as you have been, by passing through the Möbius twist, not only all one's organs, but also all one's molecules, would be inverted. So what is remarkable is not that your heart is on your right side, but that it used to be on your left and is now on your right.'

" 'If there is life on other planets,' I said, 'I presume that biochemically it might be of either kind, right or left?'

" 'So we think. Presumably whether it is left or right is an accident, depending on how it started. But it is pretty certain to be of either one kind or another, since a mixture would be very inefficient. Half the enzymes of the body would be able to deal with only half the molecules, which is not a very good way of doing things. In fact, you would have the levo and dextro anti-worlds fighting within one body.'

"This suggested something to me. 'You know,' I said to the biochemist, 'this is not so different from what we have in nuclear physics. I remember well when I was an undergraduate, and my grandfather took me to visit the particle accelerator called the bevatron because it can accelerate nuclear particles to energies of several billion electron volts. When these tiny but immensely energetic projectiles hit a heavy-metal target, they produce new particles, which often come in pairs, such as an "ordinary" positively charged proton and a negatively charged one, or an "ordinary" negatively charged electron and a positive one. The unusual ones, oppositely charged to the ones we are accustomed to, are called antiparticles. Of course the relation of particle to antiparticle is a commutative one: if Peter is the brother of John, then John is the brother of Peter. So it is quite possible to have antiatoms, antimolecules and antigalaxies.'

" 'Would this mean two anti-worlds that would fight each other in the same way as the levo and dextro forms of life would?' asked my friend with interest.

" 'Yes indeed,' I told him. 'If a particle and an antiparticle were to meet, all their mass would be converted into a flash of radiation of very high frequency. Even neutrons, although without a charge, can exist as particles and antiparticles and annihilate each other. The energy released is tremendous, much greater than in an atomic bomb, since the bomb converts only part, but not all, of its mass into energy. Fortunately, just as we have only levo amino acids in our bodies, so here on earth and within our solar system there is only one kind of matter. Even the giant particle accelerators in the United States, the Soviet Union, and the European Nuclear Laboratory, in Geneva, produce antiparticles in miserably small quantities which are annihilated almost immediately by collisions with "normal" matter.'

" 'Very interesting,' said my biochemist friend. 'It certainly is strikingly analogous to the levo and dextro worlds. But since, as we think, levo and dextro worlds could both exist if they were on different planets, couldn't stars also be built of different kinds of matter? They would be in no danger of annihilation, unless they accidentally collided, which I understand is a very rare event.'

" 'No, this cannot be so, at least so far as our own galaxy is concerned,'

I told him. 'You see, interstellar space is not quite empty; it contains atoms of hydrogen, helium, and probably other gases, and also tiny grains of ice, iron oxide, silicates, and so on. The amount is not great; it averages out to about one atom per cubic centimeter. However, this is enough to ensure that a collision between clouds of matter and antimatter would cause annihilation at their boundaries, as would a star entering a cloud of opposite matter. It would produce a large amount of radiation which in fact is not there. So we conclude that our own galaxy, the system of the Milky Way, is made of only one kind of matter.'

" 'But what about other galaxies?' asked the biochemist.

" 'This we do not really know,' I answered. "The problem is that matter and antimatter both have exactly the same optical properties; their spectra are identical. Hence you cannot tell the difference by looking. Perhaps some way of telling the two apart may be developed in the future, but we cannot predict the future course of discovery. At present it appears that the only way to tell whether a galaxy is made of matter or antimatter is to go there. One of the nearest galaxies to our own is the great spiral of Andromeda. Once you got there, you would find out what you wanted to know at once. If you vanished in a flash of radiation, you would know that the galaxy was made of antimatter; if you survived, it would be made of matter. Unfortunately, to obtain this interesting information you would have to travel for two million years even if you did so at the speed of light.'

"After talking for a while longer, I went home, intending to make reservations for the upper Amazon the next morning.

"The blow fell the next day. In my mail I found a legal-looking envelop addressed to me by a Brazilian lawyer. Situsianos, he informed me, had just died of a mysterious digestive disturbance. I shuddered, since it was only too clear to me what that digestive disturbance might be. Among his effects was a document stating that he had advanced money to me for the expedition's expenses. Would I please remit by return mail, so the estate could be settled quickly?

"Since it was I who had advanced money to Situsianos, and not he to me, the Möbius twist had reversed this relation too! Or was I Situsianos, and Situsianos I? I was getting completely confused and losing all confidence in my reasoning powers. It was clear to me only that all was lost. Without Situsianos' help I could never find the Möbius twist, which would make a mirror image of my mirror image. Verochka would never be my wife. Not that it mattered, since I was not long for this world anyway.

"The same evening, after a conversation with Verochka and her parents, it was decided that our engagement must be broken. And so here I am—and all I wish is to get out into the fifth dimension, the fourth one being reserved by Minkowski for the imaginary time coordinate."

As Wilfred said these words, the chair on which he was sitting became suddenly empty, his wish apparently having been fulfilled by a supernatural power. . . . Then Mr. Tompkins heard the noise of the front door. He opened his eyes and saw Maud entering the room, her eyes shining more brightly than a thousand stars. With her was Wilfred, looking as healthy and cheerful as ever, and holding the hand of a very pretty young girl.

"Hello, Dad!" he said. "May I introduce to you Vera, my fiancée. We have decided to get married in the same little church here around the corner where you and Mother were married some twenty-five years ago. Professor Sapojnikoff, under whom I worked on my Ph.D. thesis on topology, and his wife will come here the day after tomorrow to attend the wedding. You will like him and his wife even though they both have very funny Russian accents. But he is a great mathematician and a very interesting man, and his wife can cook piroshki—the best I ever tasted in my life."

"Oh, wonderful!" exclaimed Mr. Tompkins, finally waking up to the fact that he had been dreaming. "So all that Möbius business was just a nightmare—or should I say afternoon-mare."

"Möbius?" said Wilfred, picking up a twisted strip of paper from the carpet. "I remember writing to you that I was working on topology, but I didn't expect that you would take any interest in it. I see on your table a book on topology written by Kerekjarto, but I doubt if you can get much out of it. Not much, except probably one picture. Look in the index for the page referring to Bessel-Hagen. Oh, here we are. His name is not mentioned on that page, but there is a drawing showing the topology of a two-dimensional surface with four holes in it which represents two eyes, a nose, and a mouth; it also has two extending handles that look like ears. Apparently Kerekjarto didn't have much respect for Bessel-Hagen, or maybe they were very good friends and it was just a joke. Did you make this Möbius strip yourself?"

"No," said Mr. Tompkins. "You made it for me about an hour ago."

"How could I have made it, since I just arrived? You must have done it yourself in your dream before Mother brought me back from the airport. But anyway," Wilfred continued, "you missed one of the Möbius strip's most important properties. Take the scissors and cut it into two strips along the middle line. . . ."

Mr. Tompkins stuck the scissors into the middle of the ribbon and cut all the way around until he came to the point from which he had started. To his surprise, instead of two ribbons, he now had only one which was twice as thin and twice as long as the original strip.

"This is black magic!" he exclaimed. "How on earth by cutting the ring into two can I get just one ring again?"

A drawing showing the topology of a two-dimensional surface with four holes in it.

"Well, cut it again to a quarter width," said Wilfred, "and see what you get."

"Come, boys!" Maud shouted from the kitchen. "The steak is ready. Please come to the table."

And to the table they went.

» **4** «

Gene's Piece of Mind

ONE afternoon Maud went on an extensive shopping trip. This gave Mr. Tompkins a chance to sit in his armchair and glance through a book on cell structure and heredity which he had picked up in the local library. Although the language was very technical, and some of the passages did not make sense to him at all, he still felt that he was learning something.

It appeared that the heart of the cell, or rather its brain, is located in a central body known as the nucleus. The nucleus seems to be a central agency which determines whether or not the colony of cells will take the shape of a frog or the shape of a man, and, in the latter case, whether the man will be tall or short, dark or blond, a genius or a moron. The information concerning all these features is stored in the nucleus in long threadlike objects known as chromosomes, so-called simply because they can easily be colored (*chroma* means color in Greek) by certain organic dyes used in microscopic work. These chromosomes are like drawers of card files, each card representing a particular gene, which is responsible for some trait. A man has 46 such filing drawers in each cell, 23 of which have come from his father, and 23 from his mother. Since the information, or orders, coming from paternal and maternal sets of chromosomes are not always the same, and may sometimes even contradict each other, the result is usually some kind of compromise. Thus a mule is closer to a horse in the size of its body, but closer to a donkey in the size of its ears (not to mention its stubbornness).

There were three—no, five—my-mothers. . . .

All this looked rather interesting, but not too persuasive, and putting down the book, Mr. Tompkins reached for his whisky and soda. Taking a large sip, he looked lazily at the lithograph of the famous painting by Whistler hanging on the opposite wall. Perhaps the drink he had mixed for himself was a bit too strong, but somehow or other the kind old lady in the picture seemed to become two, one of the images shifting slightly upward and to the left. Mr. Tompkins rubbed his eyes, took another sip, and looked again. There were now three— no, five—my-mothers, all of them sitting quietly with their hands folded on their laps. There were, in fact, a whole lot more of them, forming a continuous band winding and coiling in front of Mr. Tompkins's eyes. Looking more attentively, Mr. Tompkins noticed that none of the figures was an exact replica of any other; in fact, it seemed that each of them stressed some particular feature of the original old lady, who now began to resemble Mr. Tompkins's own mother, who had died some years ago.

"Mother!" exclaimed Mr. Tompkins, not quite believing his eyes.

"How are you, my son?" answered the entire display of old ladies in unison. Now it began to dawn on Mr. Tompkins that, through some strange interplay between the book he was reading, the state of his mind, and perhaps some black magic, he was facing none other than one of the chromosomes which he had inherited from his dear old mother. The separate images along the chromosome must be the genes—the cards carrying hereditary instructions about which he had read.

"Mother—pardon me, Mothers," he said somewhat hesitantly, "are you my maternal chromosome?"

To his surprise, all the old ladies in the row, except the one sitting nearest him, looked startled, as if they had never heard that word before. But the nearest old lady turned her head toward him, and said with a slight smile, "You are quite right, my boy. What you see is one of twenty-three chromosomes carrying your maternal inheritance; and I am your gnoceogene, the gene of knowledge.* Whereas your other gene-mothers take care of your various physical and mental characteristics, I am solely responsible for your interest in scientific problems."

"Haven't I also a gnoceogene from my father?" asked Mr. Tompkins, remembering that the book spoke about complete sets of genes from both the maternal and the paternal side.

"Oh, yes, but it won't be of much help to you in this respect. Your father, you see, was a very nice man, and I loved him dearly, but he was a typical businessman, not interested in reading anything but the stock-market quotations. You can see him over there in your paternal chromosome which is lined up parallel to mine on the other side."

And in fact Mr. Tompkins noticed through a thick layer of chromatin a long line of men buried in their newspapers. Some of them had rather strongly marked features, but the one who was sitting in the place corresponding to that of his gnoceogene-mother looked very inconspicuous indeed.

"I didn't know you were interested in science, Mother," said Mr. Tompkins, who remembered her always busy taking care of the house and the family.

"Not in my later years; but when I was young I used to read a lot on different subjects and even dreamed about a scientific career. But things turned out differently."

"How many gene-mothers and gene-fathers do I have?" asked Mr. Tompkins, looking at the long lines of his parents disappearing into the dim distance. "Seems to be quite a lot!"

---

* EDITOR'S NOTE: Later Mr. Tompkins was unable to verify that such a gnoceogene actually exists, and that the "urge for knowledge" is not in fact the combined work of many different genes.

The long line of his parents disappeared into the dim distance.

"In this particular chromosome, which scientists call the X chromosome, there are altogether seventeen hundred and fifty-three genes, including myself. Of course the geneticists do not know the exact number and argue about it, but living here as long as I have, I can count them all on my fingers. Come along, I will introduce you to some of them."

With these words his gene-mother rose from her chair and took Mr. Tompkins by the hand. "Here is your fingerprint gene," she told Mr. Tompkins as she led him along the line. "She takes care of the skin design on your fingers and toes."

"How do you do, my son," said the old lady, holding out her hand.

Mr. Tompkins noticed that her fingertips were soiled by some black substance. "Glad to meet you," he said a little sheepishly.

"Here," continued his gnoceogene-mother, pointing to a jolly-looking old lady with a healthy ruddiness on her cheeks, "is your antihemophilia-gene-mother, who takes care that you do not bleed to death when you cut your finger accidentally. She is responsible for the production of a protein substance which is present in your blood and cooperates with other substances in coagulating the blood once it comes out from a wound. In some persons this particular gene is not in good health, and they are in constant fear of any minor cut. Since the genes travel from generation to generation, hemophilia is a hereditary disease, as are many other diseases which are caused by gene defects. But, as you can see yourself, you are safe from that danger. Be a good boy and shake the lady's hand."

"Glad to have met you," said Mr. Tompkins.

"And here is still another example of a gene," she continued, leading Mr. Tompkins toward a lady with tightly closed eyes. "This is your color-vision gene, and as you see, she is unfortunately completely blind. This is why you were never able to distinguish between red and green."

"Why can't my father's gene help me in this respect?" asked Mr. Tompkins with some annoyance, since his color blindness had occasionally put him to some inconvenience.

"Because the color-vision gene is essentially a feminine gene," explained his gnoceogene-mother patiently. "All women have it in duplicate, one in each of their X chromosomes, while the men have only one copy in the X chromosome which they inherit from their mother. It so happened that one of your mother's color-vision genes was sick, which did not affect her own color-vision since it was taken care of by the other duplicate gene. When, about nine months before you were born, her reproductive cells were breaking up, each into two parts, to form the so-called gametes (egg cells in her case), half of the egg cells got the defective X chromosome. And it just so happened that your father's gamete, or sperm, met and married the defective egg cell. It was a fifty-fifty chance that you would not be color blind, and I am sorry you had bad luck in this instance."

"I remember," said Mr. Tompkins, "reading something about this sex-linked inheritance, but I found it rather confusing. Could I see some examples which would make it clear to me how these genes are distributed to cells when they divide?"

"Cells are dividing in many parts of your body," said his gnocegene-mother. "The lining of your intestine, or your skin, for example, is continuously being renewed by new cells. But if you really want to understand how genes are distributed at cell division, I recommend that you visit the part of your body which, figuratively speaking, is hiding under the shadow of a fig leaf. There your cells multiply at full speed, at least as long as you can still father a child. And when you get there, ask for some good geneticist—Father Mendelmorganstern, for example —who can give you all the necessary explanations. Goodbye, my son, and good luck!"

Arriving at his destination, Mr. Tompkins found that the place was really full of activity, and that the cell-division processes, which he wanted so much to see, were taking place all around him. In fact, it was hard to find a cell which would not break in two before one could pronounce "spermatogenesis." A middle-aged man, in the habit of an abbot and with a notebook in his hand, was busy taking notes on individual division processes.

"Excuse me, please," said Mr. Tompkins, "but can you tell me where I can find Father Mendelmorganstern?"

"I am Father Mendelmorganstern," said the man; "and whom have I the honor of addressing?"

"My name is Tompkins. I've seen many interesting things in various parts of my body, but this is the first time I've seen cell division. Looks very exciting."

"You've noticed, of course, that what is happening here is mostly meiosis and not mitosis," said Father Mendelmorganstern, putting the notebook into his pocket.

"What's the difference?" asked Mr. Tompkins with slight embarrassment.

"I see you need a short lecture," said Father Mendelmorganstern with a touch of boredom in his voice. "Mitosis, or regular cell division, takes place in all the tissues of growing organisms. From one cell it produces two, each exactly like the mother cell. You know of course that each of your body cells contains 23 pairs of chromosomes, one set from your father and one set from your mother?"

"Yes, my mother-gene told me so," said Mr. Tompkins.

"The set of chromosomes you get from your father and your mother are the same—except for one pair, which we'll talk about later. Your mother's chromosome number one, for example, contains the same genes as your father's chromosome number one. A card there says 'blood group,' although of course in one chromosome it may say 'blood group A' and in another 'blood group B.' It is the same with the other genes— say, brown eyes in one chromosome or blue eyes in another; as a result, everyone has 23 pairs of similar—we call them homologous—chromosomes, and therefore, of course, everyone has two copies of every gene."

"What happens," asked Mr. Tompkins, "when the two corresponding genes do not carry quite the same instructions?"

"That depends," replied Father Mendelmorganstern. "In many cases one form of the gene is dominant, as we say. Take, for example, the gene which determines that your skin, hair, and eyes will have at least some pigment. You will be normal if you have at least one such gene, irrespective of whether the second gene is defective. In its defective form the same gene reads 'albino,' which means it carries no instructions. Albino is not dominant but recessive; that is, if it is combined with a normal gene, the offspring is normal. Only if the offspring has two albino genes is he an albino, because now neither gene gives instructions to produce pigment. Incidentally, albinos should not be confused with people usually referred to as 'white.' All normal people, 'white' or 'black' or in between, have some pigment, called melanin, although the amount varies from one race to another. Albinos have none, no matter what their race is, and can be readily recognized because their eyes are red. The red blood vessels show through since there is no eye pigment. Albino people are therefore quite handicapped, because their skin and eyes are very sensitive to light.

"As a matter of fact, certain racial groups, while not albinos, have lost more pigment than is good for them. Blond Scandinavians do well in their homeland, the foggy Baltic, but anyone who has seen them as sailors in the tropics will have noticed their inflamed and peeling skin as a result of exposure to the tropic sun, an exposure which dark-skinned people take in their stride.

"To continue, sometimes different forms of a gene are neither dominant nor recessive. Take the blood groups, for example. A gene saying 'blood group' instructs the cell to make blood-group substances A or B. If it carries no instructions, no blood-group substance is made; we call this condition blood-group O. If you have genes for A and B, you make both blood-group substances, and your blood group is AB. So here it is very simple. A person of blood group A carries either genes a + a or a + o, B carries b + b or b + o, AB carries a + b, and O carries o + o.

"In a general way you might say that if both forms of a gene carry effective instructions, both sets of instructions are carried out, and you get a blend. If, however, one gene is defective, so that it simply fails to say anything, as, for example, 'albino' or 'blood-group O,' the active form is dominant. In most cases one active gene alone can give sufficient instructions so that the function is performed almost as well as if two active genes were present.

"But let's get back to cell division. When a cell is going to divide by mitosis, it produces two daughter cells which have exactly the same genes. Let us look into this cell and see how this happens."

He led Mr. Tompkins to a cell so transparent that he could look right into the nucleus. "A chromosome is duplicating," said Father Mendelmorganstern. "Take a look through this magnifying glass."

Miss Polymerase building an exact replica of a chromosome.

Peering through the lens, Mr. Tompkins could see a young lady in Oriental dress, standing next to a tall stack of clay tablets, each inscribed with symbols of an alphabet unknown to him. She kept picking up tablets and building up a second stack that was identical with the first one.

"This is Miss Polymerase, an enzyme," said Father Mendelmorganstern. "She is building an exact replica of a chromosome, so that when she finishes her work, and the pairs of chromosomes separate during mitosis, each of the two daughter cells will get a set of identical chromosomes."

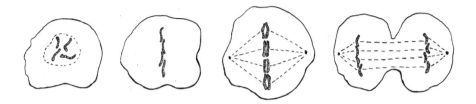

Mitosis produces two daughter cells with exactly the same genes.

"You mean one cell gets all new chromosomes and another all old?" asked Mr. Tompkins.

"No. The new and the old are identical, so it does not matter which goes where."

"Rather a hard way of making a copy," said Mr. Tompkins.

"Not really. You see, this method of copying the genetic information was invented by nature a long time ago, long before typewriters, carbon paper, and Xerox machines. And it works almost perfectly; only a very few errors are ever made."

"I see. But how," asked Mr. Tompkins, "does it happen that chromosomes are divided so exactly?"

"Well, let us take a look. Here is a cell which will eventually become a spermatozoon. All chromosomes have been duplicated but the twin daughters are still stuck together lengthwise. Now the chromosomes have lined up in a plane. At opposite ends of the cell a little body, called a centriole, is connected by fine fibers to a point on each chromosome. If you watch, you will see that the fibers shorten and the chromosomes separate, one set going to one end of the cell, the second set to the other. The cell now divides into two, and so each cell has a full set of chromosomes."

"A most ingenious process," said Mr. Tompkins, "but the more I learn, the more I am really mystified. You say this cell is going to become a spermatozoon. It has 46 chromosomes. When it unites with an egg cell, which also, I presume, has 46 chromosomes, will it not produce a child with 92 chromosomes? The grandchild will have 184, and so on, the number doubling each generation. Surely this is not what happens?"

"You are quite right, this does not happen," replied Father Mendelmorganstern. "The cell which has just divided is not yet ready to become a spermatozoon. Before it becomes one, it goes through another division called a reduction division, or meiosis, in which the number of chromosomes is halved. Here is a cell about to undergo meiosis."

To Mr. Tompkins the cell looked much like the previous one, but he had confidence in Father Mendelmorganstern.

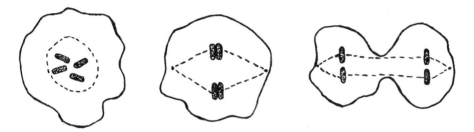

In meiosis each daughter cell gets half the number of chromosomes.

"When a cell is going to become a spermatozoon or an egg, no copies of the chromosomes are made. Here, for example, are the twin chromosomes number three. Instead of each duplicating, as they do in mitosis, one number three and the other number three come together. All the other chromosomes also pair up and come to line in a plane. So instead of 46 chromosomes, each double because they have duplicated, you have 23, each also double, not because they have duplicated but because they have paired. The rest of the process is just like mitosis. The fibers pull the two sets of 23 apart to opposite ends of the cell, the cell divides, and you end up with a cell that has half the usual number. There is now, of course, only one chromosome of each kind in the cell; we call this the haploid, or half, number. Such a cell now has only one copy of each kind of gene. You can easily see what will happen next. When the sperm and egg fuse, each contributes 23 chromosomes, and the child again has 46 chromosomes, half of which come from each parent."

"This means, I presume," said Mr. Tompkins thoughtfully, "that each grandparent contributes a quarter of the genes to his or her grandchild."

"Only on the average," said Father Mendelmorganstern. "You see, at meiosis the chromosomes are sorted out at random. It is not as if all the chromosomes you received from your father went to one of your spermatozoa and all you received from your mother to another. Which chromosome of a pair goes to which spermatozoon or to which egg is a matter of chance; the important thing is that one of each kind must be present.

This means that if your son has a daughter, you may not be the grand-father of your granddaughter."

"How is that?" asked Mr. Tompkins, somewhat baffled and also some-what annoyed.

"Simple, if you think about it. It could so happen that your son's spermatozoon, quite by chance, receives only the chromosomes he has inherited from his mother, and none that he has inherited from you. Your granddaughter, therefore, might not inherit any chromosomes from you."

"Does this occur often?"

"That is easy to calculate. The first chromosome of the spermato-zoon has a fifty-fifty chance of being yours or your wife's, or a prob-ability of one in two. The next chromosome has the same probability, so the probability that both chromosomes are your wife's is $\frac{1}{2} \times \frac{1}{2} = \frac{1}{4}$. The probability that all 23 chromosomes are your wife's is then one in 2^{23}, which is exactly one chance in 8,388,608.

Mr. Tompkins looked relieved. Noticing this, Father Mendelmorgan-stern decided to reassure him further. "There is even less chance that your granddaughter will inherit none of your genes. This is because of something called crossing-over. When the two chromosomes line up at meiosis, some of the cards, or genes, are often exchanged between the card drawers. Here, also, chance determines which cards are exchanged and which are not, but obviously when this happens the chromosomes are no longer strictly paternal or strictly maternal, but a mixture of both. The actual way this happens is as follows. When the chromosomes lie side by side, both may break at the same point, and then 'heal,' or recombine with their opposite number. Thus in your son's spermato-zoon, a chromosome he has inherited from his mother may contain sections of a chromosome he has inherited from you. So the chance that your granddaughter will inherit no genes at all from you is vanishingly small. However, she may well inherit less than the average, which is a quarter. If you consider a remote ancestor the chances become good that you have inherited none of his (or her) genes. Many legal descend-ants of Christopher Columbus, for instance, are quite probably not descendants at all in the biological sense."

"One point is not clear to me," said Mr. Tompkins. "You live here among the genes, so you know all about them. But how do the biologists who write books for people like me know so much about them? Surely they do not walk around examining them with a hand lens?"

"They have used indirect methods not unlike those used by the chemists. Although chemists had never seen atoms until recently, they were able to deduce the correct structures of many molecules by studying which reactions were possible and which were not. Biologists have been able to find out a lot by mapping chromosomes. This means finding the order in which the genes are arranged in the chromosome. Although not always easy in practice, mapping is quite simple in theory.

"The first and most detailed maps of chromosomes were made using fruit flies, so let me use them as an example. Consider just one pair of chromosomes. One of these chromosomes is normal, but its partner carries six mutant genes, which we can call genes A, B, C, D, E, and F. Our problem is to find the order in which these genes are arranged on the chromosome.

"To do this you can mate a normal fruit fly with the one that carries the two different chromosomes. The progeny of our cross will, of course, always get one normal chromosome from one parent. The other parent, however, can provide either a normal or a mutant chromosome. So at first sight it would seem that half the flies that hatch will have all normal chromosomes, and half will have one normal chromosome and one chromosome carrying the mutant genes. However, a more complicated thing may and usually does happen. Suppose that when the chromosomes line up to reduce their number and form an egg cell, the contents of the normal and the mutant chromosomes are partially exchanged, say by breaking in the middle and recombining with their opposite number. You will then get an egg which carries, for example, only three mutant genes, as you can determine by examining the fly that hatches from this egg. You know now that these three mutants lie in one block of the chromosome, the other three in another. Your first provisional map is then [A, C, D] [E, B, F], the brackets meaning that you don't, as yet, know the order within them.

"You also find that you have another fly which carries genes A, C, D, and also B, but not E or F. You therefore know that the mutant gene B is closer to A, C, D than are E and F. Your second provisional map is now [A, C, D] B [E, F]. If you get a fly which is A, the map becomes A [C, D] B [E, F]. Repeating your crosses, you may finally arrange all genes in the proper relative order, say ADCBEF. You can also discover something about the relative distance between genes. Suppose that the map is A.D. . . . . C.B.E.F, meaning the distance between D and C is greater than that between A and D. Then an exchange somewhere be-

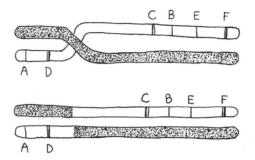

An exchange somewhere between D and C occurs more often.

tween D and C will occur more often, giving you flies which are AD or CBEF, but an exchange between A and D is less likely. Fewer flies, therefore, of the type A or DCBEF will occur. So you also study the percentages of different types, which tell you about distances between genes. Basically this is the method which, when refined, has given us an almost incredibly detailed knowledge of the genetic map. There are other methods of study, of course, and genetics has proved to be one of the most fundamental of the biological sciences. This is because genes carry all the information which specifies an organism, so that the more we know about genes, the more we know about the organism."

"Are all my genes carried on the chromosomes?" asked Mr. Tompkins.

"Most of them are, but there also appear to be a few genes which float around in the cytoplasm, as the part of the cell outside the nucleus is called. These genes have not been studied sufficiently as yet."

"I am grateful to you for such a clear explanation," said Mr. Tompkins. "However, let us now go back to the question I originally wanted to ask. How come that sons inherit color blindness from their mothers, but not their fathers, and that women suffer so rarely from this defect?"

"This is easy to explain," replied Father Mendelmorganstern. "There is one exception to the rule that chromosomes of the mother and father are the same. The twenty-third chromosome is of two different kinds, the X and the Y. The X chromosome is more or less like the other chromosomes, and a woman has two X chromosomes, as she has of every other kind of chromosome. But a man has only one X; the partner of this X chromosome is a Y chromosome. The Y chromosome is a sort of stunted version of X, and carries only a few genes.

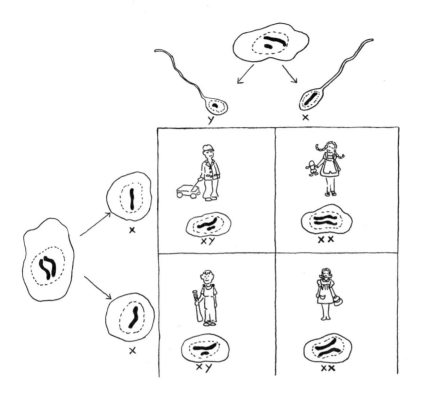

The number of boys and girls born is approximately equal. . . .

"A woman therefore produces eggs which always have an X chromosome. A man, however, produces two types of sperm; one type carries an X chromosome, the other a Y. Now if an Y-carrying sperm fertilizes an egg, the egg has the XY combination, and the child is male. If an X-carrying sperm fertilizes an egg, the child has the XX chromosome combination and is a female. So you see it is the father, not the mother, who determines the sex of the child. Since, of course, men produce X- and Y-carrying sperm in equal numbers, the number of boys and girls born is approximately equal, which is convenient for all concerned.

"Now the gene which makes it possible to distinguish colors is on the X chromosome. If this gene is defective in the male, he is color blind. Assuming that the mother is normal, his son will not be color blind, because the X chromosome of the son comes from the mother. His daughter will also not be color blind. True, one of her X chromosomes, carrying the defective gene, comes from the father, but the other comes from the mother which carries a nondefective gene, so she is all right. The daughter, however, is a 'carrier' because her son has a fifty-fifty chance of getting the X chromosome carrying the defective gene. Of course, a daughter of this daughter may also inherit this X chromosome and be, in turn, a carrier."

"But if," interrupted Mr. Tompkins, "the mother is a carrier, and the father is color blind, their daughter could be color blind."

"Of course that is possible. However, most color genes are normal, so the chance is quite low that a woman would inherit two X chromosomes, both carrying a defective gene. About one man out of ten is color blind, while in the case of women it is one out of two hundred. Hemophilia, or failure of blood to clot, is inherited in the same way, and for the same reasons is much more common among men. So are a number of other defects."

"I have always thought that women get all the breaks," said Mr. Tompkins.

"Perhaps not in all cases," said Father Mendelmorganstern, "but they do here. Women, as you know, generally live longer than men. Part of the reason, no doubt, is that they have two X chromosomes. If some gene is defective in one, it is likely to be all right in the other. But a man has only one X chromosome, so if some gene is defective, then that is that. This tends to make men the weaker sex."

"Where do these defective genes come from?"

"They originate by mutation."

"I have read somewhere that evolution results from things they call mutations."

"That is true. And indeed, without mutations the exchange of genes and chromosomes would not get us far. You can remix the genes of an ape, or whatever our ancestors were, as much as you like, and you never get *Homo sapiens.* You can't make a Martini from a Manhattan by just remixing its components.

"Mutations," continued Father Mendelmorganstern, "are a result of making mistakes. In Hollywood, as you know, the scenes are usually not filmed in the proper sequence, and it is up to the film editors to string them together in the proper order. A mistake here can lead to all sorts of embarrassment. Someone might marry a girl before he has proposed, or have a child before being married. Someone might arrive for dinner before receiving an invitation, or speed up in his car to sixty miles per hour before starting the engine.

"The polymerase girls of the cell play the role of the Hollywood film editors. It is up to them not to make a mistake in copying the chromosomes. If they do, it won't cause the progeny of two elephants to be a flea, or the progeny of two mice to be a giraffe, but you will get a mutation. Now our polymerases are only human, or perhaps I should better say only enzymes, and errors do creep in once in a while. But they are pretty good, about as good as a typist who mistypes one word every 100,000 words or so. When this does happen, the mutated gene will give somewhat different orders to the surrounding cytoplasm, and the entire cell will start to behave in a new way. Of course, the mutations which take place in the various cells of your body are unable to change any of your own properties, since you represent a colony of some thousand million millions of cells, and the fact that a few of them alter their behavior cannot influence the entire system. (The only exception to this is that sometimes a single cell can mutate so that it begins to multiply and produces a cancer, which of course affects the entire organism.) But if a mutation takes place in one of your reproductive cells, it will result in identical changes in every single cell of your child and can lead to noticeable macroscopic differences in his physical and mental properties. There are virtually millions upon millions of possible mutations, most of them irrational and harmful, while a few of them may be very beneficial to the organism. Nature brings in the mutations in a blind and random way, and it is up to natural selection to eliminate the unsuccessful mutants and to carry on the evolutionary process along the lines of the successful ones. Of course, mutations, unless artificially induced, are rather rare events, as I just said. Any given gene has only about one chance in 100,000 of mutating in each generation. However, since you have thousands of genes, the chance that some one of the genes will mutate is not negligible. At least every tenth egg or sperm carries a new harmful mutation."

"If mutations occur with this frequency, and almost all are harmful," said Mr. Tompkins, "wouldn't it follow that man, or for that matter any other population of plants or animals, will eventually accumulate enough of them so that it becomes extinct?"

"No, because such mutations are continually being eliminated. Those individuals who carry deleterious mutations either do not survive or, at any rate, contribute fewer progeny to the next generation. On the average it is the genetically fitter who are the parents of the next generation. Natural selection thus ensures the extinction of undesirable genes."

"But I thought," said Mr. Tompkins, "that natural selection does not apply to man. We live in a civilized society."

"To some degree this is true," replied Father Mendelmorganstern. "While really fatal mutations are always eliminated, we are discovering methods of promoting the survival of many who previously would not have survived. For example, there is a hereditary condition called agammaglobulinemia, which, in less technical terms, means an inability to produce antibodies. Such individuals, until recently, never survived infancy, since they could not combat bacterial infections. Now, however, they can be pulled through with penicillin. As a result, they will reproduce, and the frequency of this mutant gene will increase. This is only one example."

"Does this mean that the human race is heading toward extinction through genetic deterioration?"

"Not necessarily. Rather this illustrates the principles that you make decisions even by doing nothing, and that you cannot have your cake and eat it too. What we are now doing is blunting, to some degree, the working of natural selection. It is natural for us to try to do this, since natural selection is a cruel and wasteful method of maintaining fitness. However, it is not possible to get something for nothing. If we continue along this line, and do nothing else, the price we will have to pay is evident. In time a large part of the population will consist of individuals who will survive only by grace of medication and surgical treatment. There is a limit to this, which is set by the fact that eventually the small remaining fraction of healthy people will be doing nothing but caring for the sick."

"Is there no way out?" asked Mr. Tompkins.

"Of course there is, if we want it. If we tamper with a fundamental principle like natural selection, which over millions of years has brought us to where we are and maintained us in reasonable health, we must understand what we are doing. We can abolish natural selection and not suffer the consequences only if we bring it back, so to speak, through the back door. That is, we must see to it that on the average the genetically fitter are still the parents of the next generation.

How to accomplish this is one of the great biological problems which face the human race."

"I presume," said Mr. Tompkins, "that there is still time to solve this problem."

"You are right," replied Father Mendelmorganstern. "Changes in gene frequencies occur on a time scale that is measured in generations. However, a large part of the problem is already here. Let me give you an example. About seventy per cent of the cases of muscular dystrophy are due to a recessive gene carried on the X chromosome, just like the gene for color blindness. The mother may transmit the gene to a daughter, who then will be a carrier but will not suffer from the disease herself, or she may transmit it to a son, who will then die before reaching maturity. Recently it has become possible to detect the female carriers with considerable certainty. If such women could all be located and persuaded not to have children, this form of the disease would virtually cease to exist in a few years. Many similar inherited diseases are being discovered all the time."

"But isn't it true," asked Mr. Tompkins, "that most inherited diseases are rare, and children are unlikely to suffer from them?"

"Yes, each of these diseases is individually rare, although their sum total is considerable. The reason for this is not difficult to understand. Deleterious recessive mutant genes have so far been kept fairly rare by natural selection, although they do not reach zero frequency because occasional mutations keep reintroducing them into the population. Since they are rare, the chances that two individuals who both carry the same mutation will mate is rather small. For instance, if one in a hundred individuals carries it, on the average only once in ten thousand times—which is 1 per cent times 1 per cent—will two recessives come together and produce the particular disease. This is precisely why such mutations survive. They hide, so to speak, behind a good gene. However, while a carrier who does reproduce has little immediate chance of producing defective offspring, he or she helps to maintain the mutation in the population, where it will eventually strike someone."

"At least it is a relief," said Mr. Tompkins, "that such diseases do not strike too frequently now, whatever may happen in the future."

"Of course it is," said Father Mendelmorganstern, "except that I am not so sure that they are really rare. This continuous weeding and pruning of mutations by natural selection has an interesting limit.

Natural selection is selection for health and vigor only up to the end of the reproductive period. Suppose that a child inherits a gene which will cause him to have diabetes at age fourteen. Such a gene will be selected against, since early diabetics will be less likely to reproduce as effectively as healthy persons. This keeps the frequency of such a gene low. But if a mutant gene produces the same disease only or mainly after age fifty, it will not be selected against, because individuals carrying it will have passed it on to the next generation while they were still healthy. What happens to an individual after he has finished reproducing is, of course, of no concern to natural selection. Although our knowledge of human genetics is not yet as great as we would like, there is no doubt in my mind that many of the common diseases of old age are precisely the result of mutations which natural selection cannot counter because their effects are manifest only after the reproductive period is over. This is not to say that if we had the right genes we would live forever, but we certainly would be healthier longer. Someone once remarked that if you want to live a long and healthy life, the best thing you can do is to select parents whose lives have been long and healthy. Taken literally this idea is not of much help to you, since Einstein's theory of relativity prohibits tampering with past events. But it might help future generations if their parents did not include the genetically less vigorous."

Mr. Tompkins was beginning to find this topic a bit disturbing. To change the subject he asked, "Can you tell me more about the origin of these mutations?"

"Well, for one thing," said Father Mendelmorganstern, "there are so-called spontaneous mutations caused by the thermal motion of gene molecules. As you know, heat is a statistical phenomenon, so that thermal vibrations of various parts of a molecule, being of about the same intensity for any given temperature, may accidentally become more violent than the average. If one of the atomic groups constituting gene molecules were to become involved in such an abnormally strong motion, it might get detached from its customary place. The mutated gene will now give different orders to the cell that may lead to a change in the color of the eyes, the growth of a sixth finger, increased power of reasoning, an inclination to dyspepsia, the development of artistic taste, or any other of the millions of possible changes. I should stress once more that such changes can occur only if the mutant gene is present in the egg or sperm from which the individual develops, so that all cells of his body carry the mutation. Thus, to be effective, the mutation has to occur in the germ cells of an ancestor."

"Does that mean that people living in a hot climate mutate more often than those in a cold climate?" asked Mr. Tompkins with interest.

"No, since we are warm-blooded animals, and the body of an African Negro is maintained at about the same temperature as that of a Greenland Eskimo. There is some evidence, it is true, that different peoples have slightly different mutation rates, but this may be due to such things as differences in food. Certain chemicals in food, such as caffeine, are known to produce mutations. But cold-blooded animals definitely show a temperature effect. Thus, a gene in the eggs or sperm of fruit flies—*Drosophila melanogaster*—undergoes one common mutation which makes the usually dark red eyes of their progeny turn white. If you breed these flies in enclosures at different temperatures, you will notice that the generally small percentage of baby flies with white eyes increases quite considerably with the temperature. In fact, this increase of mutation rate follows the same simple rules as the increase in the rate of ordinary chemical reactions carried out at various temperatures.

"Then, of course, there are also mutations produced by various kinds of ionizing radiations such as ultraviolet, X rays, cosmic rays, and the high-energy radiation emitted by radioactive materials. If a fast electron produced in living tissues by these radiations hits some portion of the gene, that part can be kicked out of its customary place. If we knew the detailed structure of genes, and if we could aim electrons as we aim rifle bullets, we could produce at will any desired changes in living beings. But, of course, this is quite impossible, and, just as in the case of thermal mutations, changes produced by radiation take place quite at random. It seems, in fact, that some natural mutations are due to the effect of the so-called cosmic rays—a very diluted stream of high-energy particles falling on our earth from interstellar space. But the effect of cosmic rays must be very slight, since Tibetans who live above 10,000 feet, where this radiation is stronger, seem no worse off than the Dutch living ten feet below sea level, where it is much weaker. Apparently only about one mutation in a thousand is produced by cosmic rays, the other 999 being due to other causes. So even if you double the exposure of an individual to cosmic rays, the increase in the over-all mutation rate will be only about 0.1 per cent, which is not very noticeable. Of course, it is a different story if you are an astronaut and get into the intense belts of radiation which surround the earth."

"But what about the radiation of the atomic bomb and its fission products?" asked Mr. Tompkins, who had been painfully conscious of that subject ever since the bombing of Hiroshima.

"In very mild doses," said Father Mendelmorganstern, "these atomic radiations will produce the same effect as weak X rays in causing gene mutations. But, of course, in the case of high-intensity radiation, a large proportion of cells in the organism will be badly affected, resulting in so-called radiation sickness and eventual death. In that case it is not helpful to talk about the mutations of individual genes, just as it would be pointless to discuss thermal mutations in the body of a lobster being cooked in boiling water. In fact, strong radiation doses seem to be more effective in destroying the cytoplasm of the cell than in damaging the nucleus and its chromosomes, but we do not know exactly why."

"How much radiation is necessary to kill a man?" asked Mr. Tompkins, who did not quite understand these last words.

"For a sober man a lethal dose of radiation is about four hundred of the units known to radiologists as roentgens."

"What do you mean, for a sober man?"

"Well, you see," said Father Mendelmorganstern, smiling, "my friend Dr. Netherlander told me recently that he had found an antidote which almost doubles the resistance to radiation." He extracted from his pocket a bottle of fine Scotch whisky. "Take it all a few minutes before being exposed to radiation, and your chances of survival in an atomic attack will be considerably increased."

"You are not kidding?" asked Mr. Tompkins.

"No, I am not; this has now been scientifically established. But you must be sure, I repeat, to take it before you are exposed to radiation. It does absolutely no good if taken later."

Left alone, Mr. Tompkins decided to watch a few more division processes. But suddenly he was distracted by a noise as of thunder coming from above his head. He looked up, and there high in space was a cluster of small yellow balls rushing wildly toward him.

"A cosmic-ray shower!" flashed a thought in his brain. "And it is coming right at me!

"But surely it's all right," he tried to reassure himself. "After all, what can a few atomic particles do to a man?

"But I am not a man!" flashed another thought. "I am no larger than a gene!"

The shower of particles was now quite close, and one of the balls, emitting an ominous yellow glow, was heading right toward Mr. Tompkins. Stricken with fright, he quickly raised the bottle given to him by Father Mendelmorganstern and drank it straight off.

Bursting fireballs and bright luminous arches began to jump before his eyes. Cells and chromosomes began to rotate faster and faster around him, and for a second he lost consciousness. . . .

When he opened his eyes he was sitting deep in his armchair. He was glad to see the familiar outlines of the drawing room, and the lithograph of the Whistler painting was hanging, as usual, on the opposite wall.

In his hands was an empty whisky bottle. He heard Maud returning from her shopping trip and shoved it hastily under the chair.

» 5 «

The Number of the Beast

ONE morning, while looking through his newspaper, Mr. Tompkins found an article describing new advances in the field of biology and especially in genetics. Enormous progress, it seems, had been made in recent years. Scientists were now working on what they called "molecular biology"; instead of referring vaguely to genes, one could now discuss in detail the molecular structure of genetic material, and locate the position of every single atom participating in the structure of the gene. And in addition to knowing what the gene looked like, they also knew what it did. As Mr. Tompkins read this, his curiosity was aroused. He wished he could make another trip into his body to learn more about how it operates, and this reminded him that it was about time for him to have another medical checkup. He called the bank in which he worked to say he would be late, and he again went to the waiting room of the New Memorial Hospital to see Dr. Streets.

But he found to his distress that the situation had changed. Dr. Streets, who had been so eager to explain to him the facts of life, had passed away, and the new director was too busy with other matters to give him any time.

"If you want a checkup," said he, "go to the Out-Patient Department and ask a nurse to make the proper arrangements with someone else. I am sorry that I cannot examine you, but you will no doubt find another doctor who will be glad to help you."

The idea of seeing someone else instead of his old friend Dr. Streets did not appeal very much to Mr. Tompkins. Nevertheless, thanking the new director, he dutifully went to the Out-Patient Department. He found a seat, picked up the morning newspaper, and began to reread the article on molecular biology. It seemed less exciting when read a second time, and his head began to nod.

Soon he found himself wandering through a corridor rather different from the rest of the hospital. Instead of patients' wards, there were a number of doors opening onto laboratories filled with a variety of equipment, over which men and girls in white lab coats were fussing like hens over a brood of chickens. He had evidently entered the research wing of the hospital.

Each door had a nameplate, but the names were not familiar to Mr. Tompkins. However, at the end of the corridor he noted with interest that this particular room was occupied by Dr. M. H. F. Exkins. Dr. Exkins, he suddenly remembered, was a good friend of his father-in-law, and had visited him several times to discuss technical problems in physics. Mr. Tompkins had met him at the social gatherings which followed these visits. He decided to walk in and see if he would be remembered.

Dr. Exkins was sitting at his desk, a desk calculator in front of him. He recognized Mr. Tompkins at once. After greetings were exchanged, Mr. Tompkins explained about his visit to the director, which had led nowhere.

"You seem to have come to the right place after all," remarked Dr. Exkins. "I am working on molecular structure, and I think I can give you a better guided tour through the genes than if you had been injected into your own blood stream. But perhaps you could explain in more detail just what are the questions that you would like me to answer."

"Well," said Mr. Tompkins, "when I was at school I studied mainly business subjects, but I also had a course in organic chemistry. There I learned, if I remember right, that the old chemists had determined the structures of all sorts of organic compounds, and I thought that we knew all about them. Now I read in the paper that scientists are determining the positions of every atom in the gene. Genes, so they tell me, are organic molecules, so why do they have to do what has been done long ago?"

"An organic molecule, especially if it is large," replied Dr. Exkins, "can be twisted into all sorts of shapes although all its parts remain connected in the same way as are the loosely connected parts of a toy construction set. The old chemists discovered which atom in a molecule is connected to which, but while this information is, of course, of fundamental importance, it does not tell us all we want to know. We are now learning the actual positions of the atoms in space, and this is very important information about such things as genes and proteins."

"Is this all there is to molecular biology?" asked Mr. Tompkins, remembering the newspaper article he had read.

"By no means. Knowing the positions of atoms is only a part of it. A lot of different kinds of experiments have contributed to this, some of which have had nothing to do with chemistry and physics. The big advance has come about because a number of previously independent investigations such as genetics and biochemistry had advanced so far that they met, so to speak. A genetic mutation might produce some biochemical change in an organism, such as the inability to digest a certain sugar, or it might produce a structural change in hemoglobin, as in certain inherited anemias, which are a decreased ability to transport oxygen through the blood stream. Conversely, some chemical might produce a mutation. The ability to study all aspects of a situation is what has led to these great advances. But I am pleased to say that studies of the shapes of molecules have been a very important part of this cooperative effort. So some of us plug away at determining the positions of atoms in space in all sorts of molecules."

"But how," asked Mr. Tompkins, "can you determine the positions of atoms in space? Saint explained to me that even with an electron microscope you cannot see an atom."

"Of course you can't see an individual atom," said Dr. Exkins, "but you can do so if there are a lot of atoms in the same relative position." Noting the puzzled look on Mr. Tompkins's face, he continued, "You can understand what I mean if you look down on the tiled floor of this room. It is made of two types of tiles, red and white. You will notice that each red tile is surrounded by four white ones, and each white tile is surrounded by four red ones, about the simplest pattern you can get. You can say that every red tile occupies the same position with respect to white ones, and so does each white one with respect to red. This is what I mean when I say that each atom occupies the same position: it is always in the same surroundings."

"But I thought," said Mr. Tompkins, "that atoms are always moving, and are not arranged like the tiles of this floor."

"Of course they do move, and in a gas or liquid or even in some solids such as glass they are not arranged in any regular way. But there is one kind of solid in which they are. We call such solids crystals. In a crystal all the atoms have definite positions, like the tiles of this floor, although they do vibrate back and forth, owing to thermal motion. The positions of atoms in a crystal can be determined by a method we call X-ray diffraction. Although a single atom produces only a negligible effect, the cumulative effect of a large number of atoms arranged in regular arrays can be detected by using X rays. Many molecules of very large size will form crystals. Viruses or proteins such as hemoglobin will do so, and in principle we can determine the position of every atom in such a molecule."

"I understand what you are saying," said Mr. Tompkins, "but I do not understand how you do it. Could you explain this in more detail?"

"Before I do so, I have to give you a little lecture on optics. The principle will not be difficult to explain if you come with me to the blackboard."

Mr. Tompkins followed Dr. Exkins and watched him erase some calculations.

"The great Sir Isaac Newton thought that light was a corpuscular radiation, somewhat like bullets flying through space. We now know that there is much truth to his views, but in many cases, it is better to regard it as a kind of wave motion. In 1802 the British physicist Thomas Young did a remarkable experiment which helped to establish this point of view. First he shone some light through a pinhole and onto a screen. What he observed, of course, was a spot of light on the screen. He then made another pinhole very close to the first one. He now observed a central bright spot surrounded by light and dark fringes. We call these interference fringes, and regard them as evidence that light does have the properties of waves."

"How does that follow? I don't see it."

"Interference is a property of waves. You can see this readily if you observe the waves in the wakes of two ships passing each other. The waves travel independently of each other, and the effect at any point is the sum of the two waves. If two crests or two troughs happen to coincide, you get a larger crest or trough. But if a trough and crest coincide, they cancel each other out. Young's interference fringes are due precisely to this effect. Consider what will happen if light of one wavelength passes through the two pinholes. By wavelength we mean the distance from crest to crest, or trough to trough, which is the same thing. Opposite the point exactly between the two pinholes, the distance to each pinhole is the same, so the crests of the waves will reinforce each other and we get a bright spot. But slightly to the side on the screen, the distances to the two pinholes differ by half a wavelength of light. Here the crest and trough cancel each other, and we get a dark fringe. A little farther on, the distances differ by a full wavelength, the crests reinforce each other and we get a bright fringe, and so on, dark and bright fringes succeeding each other.

"Long before Young had done his experiment, Sir Isaac Newton had found that if you passed white light through a glass prism, light of different colors would emerge at different angles. Projected on a screen it forms what we call a spectrum. Light, Newton concluded, is a mixture of colors, and each of its colors is bent through a different angle in passing through the prism. This is what produces the rainbow in the sky, as light from the sun is refracted and reflected, passing through water droplets suspended in the air.

"After Young had done his interference experiment, it was clear one could also produce a spectrum without using a prism. You take a glass or metal surface and rule it with very fine lines at regular intervals, the distance between the lines being comparable to the wavelength of light. Such a ruled surface is called a grating. Then you shine a beam of light at an angle onto such a grating. For simplicity, suppose that the light is monochromatic, that is, of one wavelength or color. On the grating each point between our rulings acts as a source of light when light falls on it. Now if we use a lens to form an image of the grating on a screen, there will be one point on the screen from which the distances to points on the grating differ by an integral number of wavelengths. This means that the crests of the waves coming from these points reinforce each other and we get a bright spot. The position of this spot will depend, of course, on the wavelength of the light. Light of other wavelengths will form spots at other positions on the screen, so that white light will be spread out into a spectrum, just as if it had passed through a prism.

"Knowing the angles of reflection and the distance between the ruled lines on the grating, we can easily determine the wavelength of light of any color. This, in fact, is how the wavelength of light is established. Blue light has a wavelength of about four hundred-thousandths of a centimeter, and red is about twice as long."

"Rather short compared with radio waves," said Mr. Tompkins.

"And X rays have wavelengths that are much shorter," said Dr. Ekins. "When Roentgen, in Germany, discovered X rays in 1895, it was not known what the nature of this mysterious radiation was. In some respects it appeared to be similar to light, but of very much shorter wavelength. To prove that it was a wave phenomenon like light, it was necessary to demonstrate some kind of interference phenomenon. But if X rays had a wavelength much shorter than that of light, you would need a grating ruled very much finer than any that could possibly be made. So here was the quandary.

"In 1912 the German physicist Max von Laue was pondering this problem. Conversing with two other scientists, he learned that the atoms in crystals might be arranged regularly at distances of about 10^{-8} centimeters apart. If so, here was a perfect grating, built by nature herself!

"Hurrying to his laboratory, von Laue passed a beam of X rays through a crystal of zinc sulphide onto a photographic plate, and obtained a beautiful pattern of spots. The problem was solved! X rays are indeed like light waves, only of much shorter wavelength. Their wavelength could be calculated, since the number of atoms in a cubic centimeter of a crystal was known from other work and hence the distances of the atoms from each other. It was found that the wavelength of X rays is of the order of a thousand times shorter than that of visible light, or about the distance of one atom from another in a crystal.

"Once all this was well established, the problem could be turned around. From the spots on the photographic plate, it was in principle possible to work backward, and establish the positions of atoms in a crystal of unknown structure. And that is how we do it for the complicated proteins and other large molecules of living matter."

"How do you actually work the problem backward?" asked Mr. Tompkins.

"It was Sir William Henry Bragg in England who pointed out that the simplest way of looking at this is to consider atoms in a crystal as arranged in planes, like sheets of paper all parallel and at a certain distance from each other. Let me draw you a cross-section. Then you can imagine that X rays are reflected from the planes like light from mirrors. Now if two wave trains of X rays, traveling in phase, as I have drawn them here, are reflected, the same two crests of the original wave front will no longer be in phase, for the simple reason that the lower ray has to travel the extra distance BCD and falls behind. However,

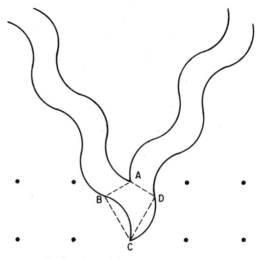

Reflection of X rays in a crystal.

if BCD is exactly one wavelength, the rays will be in phase again because the crest of the lower ray is in step with the preceding crest of the upper ray. This will also be true, of course, if the lag distance is exactly 2, 3, 4, or other whole number of wavelengths. If you know a little trigonometry, you can derive for yourself the famous Bragg equation, which says that the crests and troughs of the waves will be in step when $\lambda = 2\,d\,\sin\,\alpha$, or $2\,\lambda = 2\,d\,\sin\,\alpha$ or $3\,\lambda = 2\,d\,\sin\,\alpha$, or more generally when $n\,\lambda = 2\,d\,\sin\,\alpha$, n being an integer, λ the wavelength of the X rays, d the distance between the planes, and α the angle of reflection."

"What is the significance of this?" asked Mr. Tompkins, who was not very good at trigonometry.

"This means that these planes are not really mirrors in the ordinary sense, since it is only at a certain angle that reflection can occur. In other directions the waves interfere destructively with each other. The beauty of it is that if you know the wavelength of your X rays, and the reflection angle α, you can solve for d, which is the distance apart of one plane from another. You also have to know n, or number of wavelengths the crests of the lower ray lag behind the top ones, but I will not bother you with this slight complication."

"This is indeed most ingenious," said Mr. Tompkins. "But what happens if the atoms are not arranged so neatly into planes in a crystal?"

"If it is a crystal they always are," replied Dr. Exkins. "Suppose, for example, that you crystallize some cats."

"But Max, the phage trainer, told me you cannot crystallize dogs. Are cats that different?"

"Well, real cats cannot be crystallized any more than real dogs can, because they are never identical, one with another. Even if they are identical twins, or rather litters, they squirm and wag their tails and so on, so no two cats have exactly the same shape at the same time. But we can crystallize imaginary cats, as I have done in this drawing. Here,

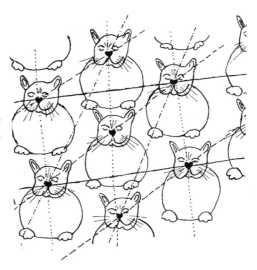

Consider the cats' noses and see what planes can be drawn through them.

each cat, which represents a molecule, is exactly the same as any other cat, and bears exactly the same relation to other cats, just as atoms in a crystal do. Now let us consider the cats' noses as atoms and see what planes one can draw through them. You see there are quite a number of ways such planes can be drawn; in fact if the crystal is infinitely large, there are an infinite number of planes. But you will notice that the density of points, in this case cats' noses, is greater in some planes than in others, and we are primarily interested in these, since the others give very weak reflections. Of course, other atoms may be situated where the cats' ears are, and so on, so there are other planes passing through them.

"In practice what we do is rotate a crystal around its axes of symmetry as we pass an X-ray beam through it. This brings each plane of identically situated atoms, at one time or another, to the correct angle to give a reflection. We record the angles, and also the intensities of the

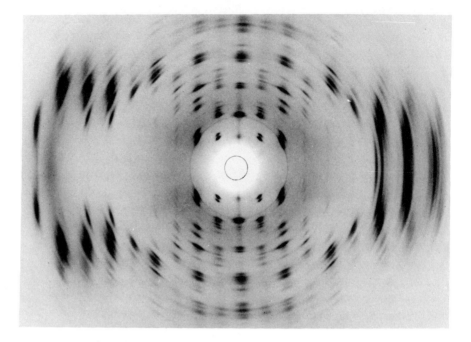

A diffraction pattern obtained from a fiber of DNA. *(Courtesy of Dr. M. H. F. Wilkins and Dr. W. Fuller, Biophysics Research Unit, King's College, London.)*

reflections, and from this information we can deduce the positions of the planes and ultimately of the individual atoms in the molecule. This sort of microscopy is possible, of course, because many atoms occupy equivalent positions in the crystal."

"Sounds easy," said Mr. Tompkins, "now that you have explained it. Could I see what the atoms of the genes look like by reversing the spots on your X-ray plate?"

"It is not at all easy," replied Dr. Exkins, "but in many cases it can be done. If you will follow me into the next room, I will show you something that may interest you."

Arriving there, Dr. Exkins pulled a photographic plate out of his files. "This is a diffraction pattern obtained from the substance of the genes. From these spots you can build up a picture of how the atoms in the gene are arranged. But the substance of the genes, unfortunately, does not arrange itself into a perfect three-dimensional crystal. The best we can do is spin it out into a thread. This greatly reduces the amount of information we can obtain from the diffraction pattern. We shall therefore have to use other kinds of information also, such as that obtained from regular chemical analyses."

"I shall see the structure of the gene in my mind's eye only, so to speak?" asked Mr. Tompkins.

"Yes, but your mind's eye will not be enough. To translate the spots into the positions of atoms you will need an electronic computer into which the information from the X-ray patterns will be fed. I suggest that you cease being Mr. Tompkins in the flesh, and turn yourself into a set of signals which we will also feed into the computer so that you will accompany the other signals. Then when the computer gets the answer, you will be there to see what the gene looks like."

Mr. Tompkins was not sure he liked the idea. "Will I come back?"

"Or course," said Dr. Exkins. "All you have to do is to be punched out on a card, and we are all set to go. I shall accompany you, of course."

At this moment Dr. Exkins's assistant entered. "Back from your coffee break?" remarked Dr. Exkins. "This gentleman and I would like to be punched out on a card."

The young assistant looked carefully at Mr. Tompkins, and then began to punch a series of holes in a card. With each punch, a picture of Mr. Tompkins began to develop, and Mr. Tompkins began to feel that he was being reduced to a two-dimensional inhabitant of Flatland.* He finally realized he was inhabiting nothing but the card, but his alarm was mitigated when he found that Dr. Exkins was also on the card, and that he could easily converse with him.

"With some luck, we shall emerge in the land one never sees except with the mind's eye, and this may answer some of your questions. Do not be alarmed if at times you feel you have disintegrated, since the signals from the various punches on your card will be processed in various directions in the computer, following the information from the X-ray pictures. But it will all come right in the end."

The card, with other data, was duly fed into the machine, and for some time Mr. Tompkins had doubts whether he existed or not. He seemed to be in many places at once, and something, light flashes maybe, was all around him. Gradually things seemed to clear and suddenly he was reminded of his trip through his blood stream.

* A world of two dimensions described in a book of mathematics fiction that Wilfred had loaned to Mr. Tompkins. It is called *Flatland* and was written in 1885 by Edwin A. Abbot.

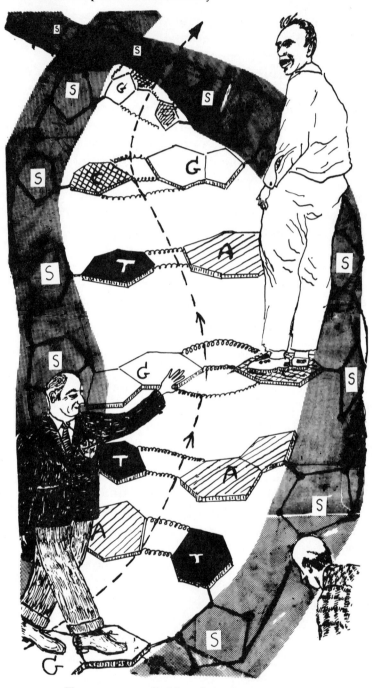

Two men were climbing the staircase. . . .

However, instead of the roaring blood stream into which he had been plunged before, he found himself inside a colorless, transparent, but rather viscous fluid resembling glycerine. Floating around, he soon approached a very unusual structure which looked somewhat like a spiral staircase. It seemed to come up from a great depth below and extended upward beyond the limit of his sight. This was something that he had never seen during his previous trips into his body. He grabbed one of the two spiraling bars which supported the staircase steps and hung on.

Two men, he noticed, were climbing the staircase one behind the other. The first was carelessly dressed and was wearing tennis shoes without shoelaces. The one following him was a typical Englishman, to judge from his blue blazer bearing the coat-of-arms of Cambridge University. Neither paid any attention to the swimmer hanging onto the side of the spiral staircase, but the Cambridge man waved in friendly fashion at Dr. Exkins.

"What is going on here?" asked Mr. Tompkins, seeing Dr. Exkins quite close to him.

"These two fellows climbing up the staircase are an American biologist and an English crystallographer. Some years ago they built this spiral staircase—actually double-stranded *helix* is its official name, from the Latin word for snail shell—and so naturally they enjoy climbing up and down it."

"Is there something particular about the way this staircase is constructed?" asked Mr. Tompkins.

"Yes indeed," said Dr. Exkins. "The basic part of the staircase is two long bars wound around each other in spiral fashion. These bars are really a long chain of two molecules hooked together: phosphate-sugar-phosphate-sugar. . . . Attached to each of the bars are the steps of the staircase, and these are the really interesting parts of the structure. We call them the bases. Actually a pair of bases forms a step, one on each bar extending toward the other. Two of the bases are flat hexagons called pyrimidines; two called purines are somewhat larger, since they are hexagons with a pentagon attached, somewhat like a motorcycle with a side-car. The two pyrimidines are thymine and cytosine, and the two larger purines are adenine and guanine."

"Do you know why there are four of them?" asked Mr. Tompkins.

"Well, you see, the bars of the staircase are a certain distance apart. It is too narrow to put in two large purines between them, but too broad to be bridged by two of the smaller pyrimidines. Thus to form a step you need a purine and a pyrimidine, which have two or three rings between them. In fact, even this fit is not good enough; each of the purines can pair with only one of the pyrimidines. The possible combinations which can form a step are:

adenine $\longleftrightarrow$ thymine

thymine $\longleftrightarrow$ adenine

guanine $\longleftrightarrow$ cytosine

cytosine $\longleftrightarrow$ guanine

Just then Mr. Tompkins noticed the two gentlemen coming down the staircase, apparently back from their inspection trip. This time they paused in a more genial mood. The Cambridge man, noticing Mr. Tompkins for the first time, remarked, "I see we have a visitor here."

"A very interested visitor, if I may say so, sir," Mr. Tompkins hastened to say. "Dr. Exkins has been explaining your very remarkable construction. But could you tell me what it is supposed to do?"

"These staircases are really the genes," answered the Cambridge man. "They are huge molecules called deoxyribonucleic acid, or DNA for short."

"But when I saw my fingerprint gene, the time I was visiting Father Mendelmorganstern, my fingerprint gene had inky fingers, and did not look at all like a staircase."

"Mother Goose stories!" remarked the younger man, who had started his scientific career as an ornithologist, a student of birds. "Do you expect that genes determining sex should look like Venus de Milo, or those concerned with muscles like Hercules?"

"To put it more gently," interrupted his colleague, "does the word 'house' look like a house? Of course not. A gene does not have to look like the effect it produces. You are now looking at the gene at the highest magnification, and you can see that it is really nothing but a number. Let's get off for a moment, Jim, and explain the matter to this gentleman."

The Cambridge man waved his hand, and Mr. Tompkins was startled to see that the staircase had suddenly turned into two strings of cards, winding around each other.

"Now," continued the senior of the two, "we are simplifying things down to the essentials. You were probably confused by hearing chemical names like guanine and thymine. So let's call thymines diamonds, adenines hearts, cytosines clubs, and guanines spades. This will make it

On the Isle of Patmos a beast whose number was 666 was revealed to St. John.

easier. If you look at the staircase now, you can see that each of the chains is just a sequence of cards which can be arranged in any order. The only rule is that if you have a heart in one chain, there has to be a diamond opposite to it in the other chain, and so on."

"But you just said that the staircase is really a number."

"Of course; you can call hearts 0, diamonds 1, clubs 2, and spades 3. Then the chain can be written as a huge number. Since a number of this kind specifies you or any other animal or plant, it can be called the 'number of the beast.' On the Isle of Patmos a beast whose number was χξϝ, or six hundred and sixty-six, was revealed to St. John. But this must have been meant to specify only some one thing about the beast, since to specify all of him, we now know, would take a number many millions of digits long. We all carry such a number inside us, written in the language of DNA. But if you will pardon me, we must be going now. I am sure that Dr. Exkins will answer any other questions you may have." And the two gentlemen took their leave.

"Glad you are still here," said Mr. Tompkins to Dr. Exkins, "for I am still puzzled about this number of the beast. Since there are two chains in DNA, the beast seems to have two numbers. Why do you need two numbers, one in one chain and one in the other?"

"That is because the number has to do two things, not just one. It has to issue instructions to the cell, and it also has to duplicate, so that the number of the beast can be passed on from one generation of cells to another. This is where the double number comes in so handy, as you will see if you consider another duplicating process, that of photography.

"If you have a page of instructions and photograph it, you first get a negative. So this is not strictly a duplication, and if the cell used this system, positives and negatives of the instructions would alternate every other generation. To avoid this, a cell keeps both a positive and a negative. When the time comes to duplicate, a negative of the positive is made, and is attached to the positive. Then a negative of the original is made, which gives a positive. That is again attached to the original negative. So it ends up with two sets, each consisting of a positive and a negative, both just like the original, and one set can be passed on to the daughter cell."

"You mean that one chain of the DNA is positive, the other negative?" asked Mr. Tompkins.

"Precisely. As my friend just pointed out, opposite every heart in one chain there is a diamond in the other, opposite every club a spade. So if you know one chain you can immediately construct the other. Both have the same information, but one is the 'reverse' of the other, so to speak, like the positive and negative of a photograph. When the DNA is duplicated it is first unwound, and then next to each chain another 'complementary' chain is built up, according to the pairing rules. So you end up with two double chains, each identical with the original."

"Very clever," said Mr. Tompkins, who was really impressed. "Could I see how this is actually done?"

"Since the cell we are in happens to be one of the cells of the basal layer of skin which divide all the time, I would not be surprised to see that very shortly a copy of this DNA is going to be made. Let us wait."

Indeed, after a short wait a large glob of material, clinging to the DNA and moving up it, appeared from below.

"Here we are," said Dr. Exkins. "Now you'll see an enzyme called a polymerase in action."

"That big glob a polymerase?" asked Mr. Tompkins incredulously, remembering Miss Polymerase as the mysterious lady in Oriental garb that had appeared in his last dream.

"This glob, as you call it, is like a highly efficient machine that spins cables on suspension bridges, but working in reverse. Instead of making a cable from several others, it makes two cables out of one."

The polymerase was spiraling up, unwinding the DNA as it went. Behind it trailed two double chains which promptly wound themselves into two spirals. In a short time the machine had passed out of sight.

"The polymerase," explained Mr. Exkins, "first unwinds the two chains, and then follows the pairing rule. It notices what particular card is in the unwound chain, and hooks on the proper complementary card to the chain it is making. So you start with one double helix and end up with two. The cards which the polymerase needs to construct the new chains are made by other enzymes, and float around until they are needed."

"The polymerase seems to work very well," said Mr. Tompkins. "However, Father Mendelmorganstern told me that the gene is not always copied exactly, so that sometimes you get a mutation."

"This happens, of course, but not very often. Like all machines, the polymerase sometimes makes a mistake and puts in the wrong card. This kind of mutation we call a copying error. There are also other kinds of mutations. As the good Father must also have told you, a molecule of the gene is sometimes damaged by thermal agitation or by being hit by high-energy particles. In fact, here is a card beginning to come loose."

Indeed, one of the cards was quivering violently, buffeted by the exceptionally violent motion of the molecules around it, and it broke loose and floated away.

"So now one of the cells has mutated," said Mr. Tompkins.

"Let us wait and see," said Dr. Exkins. In a short time another polymerase appeared, sniffing like a dog up and down the DNA. When it came to the missing card, it paused, ripped out a part of the defective chain, inserted a few cards, and proceeded up the chain.

"The DNA is now as good as new. This particular polymerase is a repair enzyme. If it finds a card missing, it replaces it. Of course, it knows which card to replace because the proper card in the opposite chain is still there. If both cards are lost, all the information is gone, and then we do have a mutation. And sometimes even if only one card is missing, the repair enzyme might happen to miss it, or again it might make the wrong replacement. Still, these repair enzymes do prevent a lot of damage, and mutations are not nearly as common as they would be otherwise."

"I think I now understand pretty well how DNA is duplicated," remarked Mr. Tompkins. "However, your friend told me that DNA is really a huge number which specifies what the organism is to be. I'm rather puzzled how a number can do this."

"This is an interesting problem," answered Dr. Exkins. "You can regard a cell, or for that matter the whole body, as a kind of factory engaged in making more of itself, because it is either growing or replacing parts that are wearing out. The DNA would then be the master plan, or a central store of blueprints. But, of course, blueprints are useless unless someone reads them and carries out their instructions —in a factory that would be the engineers and foremen. But you would not want to circulate the master plans themselves, exposing them to the risk of loss or damage. So you would make copies of the master plans as needed, and send these down to the factory floor. And that is just what the cell does. The master blueprints of DNA are kept in the head office of the cell, which is the nucleus. Copies of parts of the DNA are made, these are sent to the cytoplasm which surrounds the nucleus, and there the work is done according to instructions. It is all very well organized."

"How are these copies of DNA made?" asked Mr. Tompkins with interest.

"Nature in general operates in simple ways, and if she finds a way of doing something, she tries to apply it to many different purposes. Making working copies of DNA is very much like duplicating DNA itself. I am sure that if we watch, we shall shortly see how a copy of the master blueprint is made."

Indeed, after a short time another polymerase appeared, climbing up the DNA and unwinding the two strands. But, as Mr. Tompkins noticed, instead of trailing behind it two double strands of DNA, it formed a string of cards which did not curl up around the DNA, but floated away, quite by chance moving in the direction of Mr. Tompkins and Dr. Exkins.

"This polymerase," said Dr. Exkins, "is a little different from the other one, which made two DNAs from one. Since it transcribes DNA, we call it a transcriptase. As you just noticed, it makes an inverse copy of only one of the two strands of DNA, and chemically the copy is a trifle different."

"In what way is it different?" asked Mr. Tompkins. "It seems to me to be much like the original, except that it is only one chain."

"It is indeed very much like the original, since both are what we call nucleic acids, but the backbone chain has a slightly different sugar with one oxygen atom more than in DNA. Also the base thymine is replaced by a slightly different one called uracil. The name of this sort of copy is ribonucleic acid or RNA for short. The master blueprint, then, is DNA, while the working copies are RNA—messenger RNA, because they carry messages from the DNA to the workshop."

"What happens when the messengers get to the workshop floor?"

"Why don't you see for yourself? This messenger which has just been made is going there, so let's climb on it and take a ride."

With some difficulty they mounted it. To Mr. Tompkins it appeared more like a large spiny python than a messenger who delivers telegrams. Its progress was far from smooth, being a series of jolts and lunges.

"Does this messenger move by wagging its tail?" asked Mr. Tompkins.

"No, we are proceeding by diffusion, or Brownian motion. Water molecules are bombarding us from all directions, so we move in a random manner. But fortunately, since the distances in a cell are short, we are pretty certain to reach our destination in a minute or so even if we travel a random path."

Sure enough, a jolt threw them through a large hole in the nuclear membrane and out into the cytoplasm.

Mr. Tompkins could see objects floating around them, looking like large and somewhat irregular beach balls. Most of them appeared to be stuck, like flies to flypaper, to other messengers which writhed like snakes in every direction.

"The ribosomes," said Dr. Exkins. "We shall soon begin translation."

"Translating what into what?"

"The RNA message into protein language. You may have heard that proteins represent long sequences of twenty different amino acids which determine what the protein is or does. It is like a recipe which is written in a language containing twenty letters, including spaces between words and punctuation marks."

"Oh yes," said Mr. Tompkins. "During my trip through my blood stream Dr. Streets showed me a long molecule of globin which participates in the capture of oxygen molecules by hemoglobin."

"Now," continued Dr. Exkins, "as I have explained to you, nucleic acids, and in particular messenger RNAs, are made up of sequences of only four different molecular groups, which you may refer to by their chemical names, or as suits of cards, or by the numbers 0, 1, 2, and 3."

"What does this have to do with the amino acids in a protein?" asked Mr. Tompkins.

"If you imagine that the messenger RNA is like a tape on which a message is recorded, then the ribosomes are the automatic typewriters which turn the sequence of numbers on the tape into ordinary writing as the tape moves through them. The ribosomes read the messenger RNA and then translate it into a sequence of amino acids. The tape analogy is in fact a pretty good one, since if you watch, you will see that the messenger does in fact slide along between two ribosomes, a larger and a somewhat smaller one."

Just then the tail of their messenger hit a ribosome and seemed to stick to it. Mr. Tompkins noted that the ball was really double and the messenger's tail was lying in the groove between. "We are now beginning," said Dr. Exkins.

At the junction of messenger and ribosome an amino-acid molecule stuck, and the ribosome seemed to move one notch. Again another amino acid attached itself at the same place and hooked itself onto the preceding one. The ribosome kept moving one notch at a time until a long chain of amino acids dangled from the point of junction of messenger and ribosome. Before the ribosome had moved half over the messenger, another ribosome had attached itself to the messenger's tail and began to build up another chain of amino acids.

"You see now how the messenger RNA is being translated into protein. The different amino acids which are used in making a protein come attached to rather small RNA molecules which we call transfer RNA, because they carry amino acids around and help them to recognize what is written on the tape of messenger RNA. Each kind of amino acid has its own kind of transfer RNA to which it is attached, and they all float around in the cytoplasm, moving quite at random. So all the various kinds of amino acids keep hitting the 'active point' at which the messenger tape is attached to the ribosome. Suppose now that at that point the tape reads a certain amino acid—for example, one that chemists call glutamic acid."

"The name sounds familiar," remarked Mr. Tompkins.

"Most likely that is because you have seen it in the form of monosodium glutamate, the sodium salt of glutamic acid, which your wife no doubt uses to enhance the flavor of foods. A most ingenious Japanese discovery! It has little taste of its own, but it makes other flavors more perceptible. But as I was saying, if the tape reads 'glutamic,' and some other amino acid hits that spot, nothing happens. But if glutamic acid does so, with the help of its transfer RNA it recognizes it has done the right thing and sticks there. It hooks onto the previous amino acid, its transfer RNA floats off, the tape moves one notch, and we are all set for the next amino acid. It takes a minute or so to string together a hundred amino acids to make a molecule of one of your proteins."

"I thought there were only DNA and RNA, but now you say that there are also two kinds of RNA," said Mr. Tompkins. "This is getting complicated."

"Well, there are really three kinds, since the ribosome also is built, in part, of a special kind of RNA. But this is not really complicated, since it is only messenger RNA which carries a message. The others are part of the typewriter."

"I remember something now," remarked Mr. Tompkins. "Max the phage trainer told me that viruses fool the cell into making viral instead of cell proteins. This must have something to do with the translation process."

"Yes indeed. When viral nucleic acid gets into the cell, it also produces messengers, and of course the ribosomes can't tell the difference, so they read them and produce viral proteins."

All of a sudden there was a blinding flash of light, followed by darkness. Mr. Tompkins, opening his eyes, noticed with surprise that he was again sitting in Dr. Exkins's office and Dr. Exkins was at his desk as before.

"They shut off the computer," Dr. Exkins observed, "so here we are back again. Is there anything more you would like to know before you leave?"

"You kept saying," said Mr. Tompkins, "that the messenger RNA is translated into protein. How is this possible if proteins are strings of twenty kinds of amino acids, while the messenger is a string of only four kinds of bases?"

"You have a point there," said Dr. Exkins. "This is known as the problem of the biological code. You can look at it this way. Suppose that you have four colors: red, white, blue, and yellow. How many different flags can you make, if each flag has only a single color?"

"Easy," said Mr. Tompkins. "Only four."

"Quite right. So if you have four kinds of bases, and only one base determines an amino acid, you could have only four kinds of amino acids in proteins. But now suppose that your flag has two stripes. How many flags can you now make?"

"Well, let's see; yellow and red, blue and red, white and yellow . . . It looks like a complicated problem."

"Not at all," said Dr. Exkins. "The bottom stripe can be any one of four colors. With each color in the bottom stripe you can pair any one of four colors on top. So the number of possible flags here is 4×4, or 16."

"Oh, I see," said Mr. Tompkins. "If you use two bases to specify an amino acid, you can specify sixteen of them. But that is not enough."

"Quite right. Let us therefore try three stripes, or what amounts to the same thing, three bases to specify each amino acid. How many flags can you now make?"

Mr. Tompkins was quite good at arithmetic, and he saw the point at once. "It must be $4 \times 4 \times 4$, or 64," he said. "But now I see a problem. Two bases at a time are not enough, since this gives only 16 combinations, but three bases give 64, which is way too many. Does this mean that the DNA uses only 20 of the 64 possible combinations?"

"No. The code is 'degenerate,' as the technical term goes, which means that more than one combination of three bases reads out as the same amino acid. We now know pretty well which combinations of bases correspond to which amino acid. I can never remember the details, so I have written it all down. Here, take a look at it. We call it the Biological Dictionary."

Mr. Tompkins examined the dictionary with interest, and was relieved to discover that unlike most dictionaries, which are hundreds or thousands of pages long, the biological dictionary took only one page. "Science is getting pretty simple," he said to himself. But all of a sudden a couple of unusual items attracted his attention. "Say," he said, "here are two combinations of bases which are labeled 'nonsense.' What does that mean?"

"Oh, those two," said Dr. Exkins. "That just means that these combinations do not specify any amino acid. We think that they are what we call punctuation marks, or signs showing that you have come to the end of the message. Here you stop making one protein, and begin making another."

"I think I understand," said Mr. Tompkins. "But something strikes me as curious. Words like dictionary, nonsense, and so on, do not sound very biological. Have you been using them to explain this to me in a simple way, or are they really proper scientific terms?"

"You should get used to such expressions," said Dr. Exkins. "The people who worked on cracking the biological code were a miscellaneous group of mathematicians, physicists, engineers, chemists, and biologists, but they mostly thought in terms of language, information theory, and communication engineering. So now you find words such as message, translation, transcription, dictionary, nonsense, and noise used in biology. At first this sounded a bit odd to the older biologists and biochemists, but now they are used to it."

"There is still one point that is not clear to me," persisted the insatiable Mr. Tompkins. "The DNA must be the same in all the cells of my body, since they all arose at one time from one cell. Then how is it that some cells are nerve cells, others muscle, skin, and so on? If they receive the same instructions they should all be the same."

"Now you have asked a really hard question," said Dr. Exkins, "and I must admit to you that no one knows the full answer. We call this the problem of differentiation—how cells with the same DNA get to be different. It is quite clear, of course, that in each kind of cell only some part of the DNA is used to give instructions, and exactly which part of the DNA is 'shut off,' so to speak, determines what kind of cell will be made. Unfortunately, we do not really know how DNA is shut off.

"There are a few hints about how this might happen, however. We do know that some genes are normally not active—that is, they are not copied into messenger RNA, and we now know why. There is a special class of genes that direct protein synthesis, but these proteins are of an unusual kind. Instead of being enzymes or building up the structure of the cell, they combine with other genes in such a way that the gene they combine with cannot be transcribed into messenger RNA. So the genes that produce such inhibiting proteins are, of course, genes which regulate the functioning of other genes. We call them regulatory genes.

"The discovery of regulatory genes has explained something which up to that time had seemed almost miraculous—the ability to produce so-called adaptive enzymes. There are some bacteria which have an ingenious method of protecting themselves against penicillin. If some penicillin is added, they at once begin to make an enzyme which destroys the antibiotic. When the penicillin is destroyed, they stop making the enzyme unless penicillin is again added. Another very similar case is the type of bacteria which can produce an enzyme to split a special sugar called lactose, found in milk. Once split, the sugar is used as food. As in the previous case, the enzyme is produced only if the sugar is present. There are many such examples, which indicate that bacteria can adapt to the needs of the situation. But how can they do so remarkable a thing?

"The answer is really quite simple. Some bacteria have a gene which specifies the production of an enzyme which can destroy penicillin. Normally, however, this gene does nothing, because another regulatory gene produces an inhibitory protein which prevents its action. When penicillin is added, however, it combines with the inhibiting protein and makes it no longer able to inhibit. So the inhibitor is itself inhibited, an example that the minus of minus is a plus, and the enzyme to destroy penicillin can now be made."

"I don't quite see what this has to do with one cell being different from another," remarked Mr. Tompkins.

"It may have a lot to do with it, but we are not sure yet. It may be that there are such regulatory genes which produce proteins to shut off sets of genes that are not needed by a certain type of cell, and others which shut off other sets of genes. That such regulatory genes exist in man is suggested by the fact that one of the many forms of leukemia, which is a cancer of the white blood cells, is apparently caused by a small deletion of a portion of one of the human chromosomes. It is likely that this has removed a gene that inhibits growth. It also appears probable now that some of the hormones, which are so important in regulating our bodily activities, may be combining with proteins which inhibit some genes, either to prevent or to promote the action of these proteins. So you see why scientists are so anxious to learn more about these matters."

"But still," said Mr. Tompkins, "this does not explain how one cell becomes different from another. You now have to explain how the regulatory genes are switched on and off, don't you?"

Dr. Exkins looked pleased that Mr. Tompkins understood so well. "Of course," he said. "In a way I have been sweeping the dirt under the carpet, but at least it is getting to be all in one place, and therefore easier to handle. There are some ideas about the question you raise. Just as big fleas have lesser fleas on their backs to bite them, so one regulatory gene may have another regulatory gene to regulate it. Such actions may form complicated circuits in which the action of a regulatory gene may eventually react on its own action by producing an effect which moves around a circle, so to speak. This can produce a flip-flop."

"A flip-flop? What is that?" asked Mr. Tompkins.

"Oh, you are quite familiar with flip-flops," answered Dr. Exkins. "One example is an ordinary electrical switch. It is a flip-flop because it has only two stable positions, on and off. If you try to put it into an intermediate position, it won't stay there but will slide into one or another. A number of people have pointed out that if you have a lot of regulatory genes, each inhibiting another, then under certain conditions the system would act as a flip-flop. Depending on how you start it, it would come to rest in one position or another, which would correspond to the different cell types. 'Come to rest' means that some sets of genes would be in the on, or active, position, others off, or inactive, and that they would not be easily moved from these positions. We don't understand all this very clearly yet, but a lot of work and thinking is going on."

"Does this mean," asked Mr. Tompkins, "that genes act only when a cell is growing? It would seem to me that once a cell is completely formed, there is no more need for genes, since all its proteins are already made."

"I am afraid you are wrong," replied Dr. Exkins. "The proteins and messengers of a cell are not very stable, and in a few hours or a few days they break down and have to be replaced. Long ago someone correctly likened an organism to a fountain that has a certain shape. It maintains this shape not because the water is frozen to ice, but because new water is always flowing into it. Similarly new substance is always flowing into the cell; as Heraclitus said: 'Panta rei,' things flow. The genes have to be active all the time to maintain this flow."

Mr. Tompkins was about to continue the conversation, but suddenly he felt a hand on his shoulder, shaking him gently.

"The doctor who intended to see you has just been called away on an emergency," the nurse said apologetically. "Shall I make another appointment for you?"

"Perhaps in a few weeks," replied Mr. Tompkins. "Right now, I must flow—I mean, go." And, his head buzzing with all he had learned, he directed his steps to the hospital's exit.

» 6 «

An Ocean Voyage

MR. TOMPKINS was due for a two-month vacation, which the management of his bank had granted him for his long and faithful service. Mulling over what he would do with this time, he finally decided to pay a visit to his son Wilfred and his daughter-in-law Vera. Wilfred had finished his studies in topology and, like many mathematicians, had developed an interest first in physics and astronomy and then gradually in the more quantitative aspects of biology. He was now spending a year as a visiting lecturer at a foreign university.

Unexpectedly Maud was not very enthusiastic about the plan. She was very busy on a committee organizing an art exhibition at which some of her own paintings were to be shown. In addition she had crossed the Atlantic a number of times, accompanying her father to various scientific conferences before she was married. To her an ocean liner was indelibly associated with seasickness, and she firmly refused to go. Knowing, however, that her husband looked forward greatly to the trip, she urged him to go without her.

So Mr. Tompkins made his arrangements with a travel agency and reserved a single cabin on a luxurious modern ocean liner which promised entertainment, excellent food, and a chance to relax. When he boarded his ship he found that it lived up to its promises. His cabin included a soft bed, a large dressing table, a private bathroom, and a large porthole through which he could watch the gently rolling waves and other ships leaving or entering the harbor. At mealtime his table was covered with excellent dishes, and Mr. Tompkins helped himself freely.

The afternoon his ship left port the wind became stronger, and the ship began to roll slightly as it cut swiftly through the waves. Mr. Tompkins, though not actually seasick, felt he had better lie down and rest before dinner. He put on a striped sailor shirt and bell-bottom trousers, which Maud had humorously given him to wear as pajamas on his ocean voyage, and stretched out on his bed.

He was awakened by a loud and harsh voice shouting, "Hi, hoist up the topsheet and spanker!" The first thought that flashed through his mind was a limerick he had once heard:

> There was a young lady named Banker
> Who slept while her ship lay at anchor.
> She awoke in dismay
> When she heard the mate say:
> "Hi, hoist up the topsheet and spank 'er!"

Mr. Tompkins smiled to himself at the pun, but only briefly. He looked around and was startled to find himself lying, not on his comfortable bed, but in a hammock that was swinging gently to and fro. Instead of his elegant stateroom, he was in a larger but rougher space with unpainted wooden walls. Other hammocks were around him, most empty but some occupied by obviously seasick sailors, all dressed in the same kind of suit he was wearing.

"Well," said Mr. Tompkins to himself. "There seems to be some truth to these old tales of the sea. Am I perhaps aboard the *Flying Dutchman*?" After getting out of his hammock with some difficulty, he climbed up a narrow staircase and emerged on the deck.

A man dressed as a British naval officer, old style, spotted him at once and signaled him to approach.

"Are you one of the new hands?" he asked.

"Yes," answered Mr. Tompkins somewhat hesitantly.

"Yes, what?" barked the officer.

Mr. Tompkins had had no military training, but he remembered that all officers like to be addressed as "sir." "Yes, sir," he said, trying to draw himself up to attention and nearly falling down on the gently rolling deck. Suddenly, remembering the movies he had seen, he repeated, for extra assurance, "Ay, ay, sir."

The officer, who was a young and good-natured fellow, could not hide his amusement. "Welcome aboard," he said, in a quite friendly tone. "I am sure you will make a good sailor. At least you are not seasick like some others. I sent them below to prevent them fouling up the deck any further. Get yourself a broom and bucket, and clean up the mess they left here."

"Yes sir," said Mr. Tompkins, rather proud of his newly discovered seagoing abilities.

For almost an hour, barefooted and sweating, he scrubbed down the deck of the ship. Having finished, he leaned to rest against the railing and watched the ocean, hoping to see a whale. No whales appeared, however, so he decided to walk around and get acquainted with the ship. He found it had none of the glamour of the liner from which he had been kidnaped. Instead of deck chairs, all he found were twenty antique-looking cannons with their pyramidal stacks of solid cannon balls. Near one of the cannons, seated on a coil of thick rope, was a gentleman dressed in civilian clothes, thoughtfully contemplating the water.

"Good afternoon, sir," said Mr. Tompkins. "I hope you will pardon the intrusion, but through some circumstances completely mysterious to me I find myself a sailor on this ship. Can you tell me what is our

Seated on a coil of rope was a gentleman dressed in civilian clothes.

destination, and why you seem to be the only civilian on this naval vessel?"

"I am just traveling as a passenger," replied the gentleman. "My purpose is to observe and study the various forms of life at the places where we stop, and also to do a little geology on the side."

"Oh, you are a biologist," said Mr. Tompkins with interest. "You know, I am just a bank clerk, but over the years I have dreamed a number of unusual dreams. From these dreams I have learned, if I may say so, quite a bit about biology. But, of course, many things are still not quite clear to me. I still often wonder how life originated on this earth."

"It is the same with me," said the gentleman. "When I was a boy one of my schoolmates had a copy of a book entitled *Wonders of the World,* which I often read. I argued with the other boys whether all the wonders there described really existed. From this book, I believe, I first got a desire to travel to remote places. This desire is now being fulfilled by this voyage.

"In my youth I studied medicine and natural sciences, but never left my country. Last year, however, when I had just passed my twenty-second birthday I received a letter from a certain Captain Fitz-Roy, who is the commanding officer of this three-masted frigate. He was willing, it seemed, to give up part of his own cabin space to a young man willing to travel, without pay, as a naturalist on an extended voyage around the world. My father, who was a wealthy physician, was not very enthusiastic about the idea, but I managed to overcome his objections. Later, when I became well acquainted with Captain Fitz-Roy, I learned that I narrowly escaped being rejected for the position because of the shape of my nose! The captain was an ardent disciple of a physiognomist named Lavater, and he was confident that he could judge a man's character from his features. He originally doubted that with my nose I could have the energy and determination needed for the voyage. But I think he is now convinced that my nose had spoken falsely. So here we are in the second year of our extended voyage."

"Your story, sir, reminds me of another voyage," said Mr. Tompkins scratching his head. "I have heard of a similar expedition by a British naturalist which led to an explanation of how different species of plants and animals originated. But that must have occurred more than a century ago. Are you repeating that trip?"

"No, this is the same trip," answered the gentleman. "You are aboard

H.M.S. *Beagle,* and according to my calendar it is February 1833. Apparently you have been thrown back into the history of science by some kind of time reversal and are now living in the dream world of the past."

"You mean—you mean," stuttered Mr. Tompkins in astonishment, "that you are Charles Darwin, the father of the theory of organic evolution?"

"At your service, sir." The gentleman smiled. "But you must remember that my theory will not be published until 1858."

"Does this mean that you know the future—perhaps even what happened after you died?"

"Of course I do. In this world of the shadows of the past, we are well informed on the progress that has been made since we retired from the scene. In fact, here in Dreamland we receive immediately the latest issues of all scientific publications such as *Nature* and *Scientific American.* My good friend Galileo Galilei, for example, was very excited when he read the paper of Albert Einstein, in which Galileo's proof that all bodies fall with the same velocity irrespective of weight was used to develop a completely new theory of gravitation and predict the existence of phenomena that no one had imagined before. Galileo told me privately, however, that at first he had a hard time mastering the mathematics of tensor analysis that is required to understand Einstein's theory. I in turn was astonished to learn, some one hundred years from now, that the genetic mutations, which we used to call 'sports,' and which I realize are so important for my theory of evolution, are discontinuous changes in the genetic material and can be explained by the so-called quantum theory. I must admit that I am a naturalist by education and inclination, and in spite of much patient explanation by others I could never really understand what kind of an animal a 'quantum' is. On my hundred-and-fiftieth birthday my physics-minded friends, having ceased trying to explain, presented me with a chocolate cake precut into individual segments with the inscription in sugar 'Charlie quantized.' "

"But you do not look like a man of such great age," protested Mr. Tompkins.

"Of course not, I am now only twenty-three. Do not forget that here your past is my future."

Although this was not entirely clear to Mr. Tompkins, his insatiable curiosity drove him to take advantage of this unique opportunity, whatever the explanation for this remarkable state of affairs.

"Could I ask you some questions?" he asked. "You are no doubt by far the best qualified to answer them of anyone I am likely to meet."

"Ask. What is it you would like to know?"

"What I would like to know," said Mr. Tompkins, "is how and why animals and plants evolve and produce higher forms of life. Can you explain this to me briefly?"

"Indeed I can, and I can be very brief. Evolution is the result of the operation of the laws of chance."

Mr. Tompkins had not expected so brief an answer, nor had he expected this kind of answer. Somewhat taken aback, he tried to collect his wits for his next question. By now he thought he knew quite a bit about biology, and after a brief pause he came up with something which he thought would demonstrate his knowledge.

"It seems to me," he said, "that life depends on the kinds of proteins you have. Now there are so many different ways of constructing a protein, to say nothing of a whole organism, that it is almost impossible that a useful protein could arise by chance. There are twenty kinds of amino acids, so there are twenty ways of picking the first amino acid. For the next one there are again twenty possibilities, which gives you 20 x 20, or 400 ways of putting the two together. If your protein has only a hundred amino acids, there are 20^{100} kinds of proteins you can make. From my trips in Wonderland, I remember that this is much more than the number of atoms in the whole universe. So the chance of making even one protein of the right kind by random assembly is just about zero. The more complex an organism is, the more improbable it is that it could be constructed by chance. Evolution, I would think, is an uphill fight to produce a more and more improbable state of affairs. Life in general must be rare, and the higher the forms of life, the rarer they must be."

Suddenly Mr. Tompkins paused and a puzzled expression crossed his face.

"Say," he asked, "if this is so, how did I ever get here in the first place?"

The British naturalist smiled. "This argument has been often expressed in one form or another. In my time, it usually ran as follows. The structures that you see in different animals and plants are, for the most part, adaptations to do things well. The eye is like a camera, adapted to see, teeth are adapted to the kind of food the animal eats, wings are marvelously adapted to flying. Since it is so improbable that such adaptations could arise by chance, some superior intelligence must have designed them for a specific purpose.

"Now there may or may not be such a superior intelligence, but the argument that chance cannot produce the almost incredible adaptations of living things is clearly false. When you use this argument, you are unjustifiably giving the terms 'probable' and 'improbable' an absolute meaning. In much the same way, there was a time when people unjustifiably used the words 'up' and 'down' in an absolute sense. They argued that people at the antipodes, as in Australia, could not exist, because they would be walking upside down, and would therefore fall off the earth. The word 'probable' is like the word 'up.' It does not refer to something absolute, but to a process which produces a given result."

"This is not clear to me," said Mr. Tompkins. "Could you explain in more detail?"

"Let me show you what I mean by an example. Suppose that you want to produce a flea by chance. Its molecules are arranged in a specific way, so you might argue that it is a very improbable object, even though you know that you are certain to be bitten by many fleas on this voyage. Remember, DDT has not been invented yet. Oh, pardon me." The British naturalist, with obvious delight, slapped in vain at a flea which had appeared on his coat sleeve.

"Let us now say, using an analogy, that we have a flea if we cast a hundred dice and get all sixes, a very improbable result. The probability of all sixes from casting a hundred dice is in fact easy to calculate. The probability of one six with one die is $1/6$, of two sixes with two dice is $1/6 \times 1/6 = 1/36$, of a hundred sixes with a hundred dice is $1/6^{100}$, which is a vanishingly small probability. Of course, the chance formation of a flea is vastly less probable even than that, but we are just using an illustration. This is what you mean when you say that a flea is 'improbable.' But what you are neglecting to consider are the rules of the game. Without really thinking about it you have arbitrarily selected one rule: get all sixes with a single throw. Then, of course, a throw of all sixes is indeed extremely improbable.

"But suppose we change the rules; any six that turns up stays put, and we continue casting the remainder. You can easily see that within less than a hundred throws all dice will be sixes up. In fact the probabilities are now reversed; it is vastly improbable that, using the second set of rules, we will not get all sixes in a short time. So 'probable' or 'improbable' refers not to something absolute, but is a quantity which is meaningful only if the rules of the game are specified. We must, therefore, always investigate what the rules really are.

"This dice game is a crude but useful model of what actually happens in evolution. The dice here represent different genes, and throwing them represents mutations. If the mutation is good, it is retained because its carrier produces more offspring. This corresponds to the six that stays put. A mutation which is deleterious, as most are, is lost because the organism which carries it either dies or does not reproduce as effectively. So it does not count toward the score. This is called 'natural selection.' All this is quite automatic, and leads to what appears at first sight to be a quite incredibly improbable result. But if you look at the matter properly I would say that it is extremely improbable that evolution will not occur."

"But," said Mr. Tompkins, "an individual who carries a favorable mutation does not necessarily have a more successful life or leave more offspring. The race is not always to the swift or the battle to the strong. Accidents may happen."

Again the British naturalist smiled. "I studied divinity at Cambridge for a while, and I am therefore glad to see that you still know your Scriptures. You are, of course, correct as far as any given individual is concerned, but on the average the race is to the swift when many races are run. Suppose you have a gene that confers just a very small advantage to its possessor, say one in a thousand. This means that for a thousand individuals who carry the gene and survive to produce offspring, only 999 individuals without the gene do so. If the frequency of this favorable gene in the population is originally 1 per cent, it will rise to 90 per cent in 15,000 generations. This is really a very short time on the geological time scale. But, of course, this will happen regularly only if the population is reasonably large. If there are only a few individuals, a good gene may be lost and a bad one may be firmly established purely by chance. This is well shown by our own species. On many small islands or in other remote communities it happens quite often that some deleterious gene producing some defect, physical or mental, occurs with an unusually high frequency. The usual reason for this is that the community was founded by a few settlers, one or more of whom quite by chance happened to carry this gene, and his or her descendants now form a large fraction of the population. In a small population anything can happen. But, if the population is reasonably large, say some thousands or millions, what should happen on the average is what will actually happen. It is here that progressive evolution occurs."

"How long does it take to produce a new species?" asked Mr. Tompkins.

"On the average, about a million years if you are speaking of higher animals such as mammals and birds. To take one fairly typical example, it has taken man half a million years to evolve from a clearly different form."

"But isn't there a difficulty here?" asked Mr. Tompkins. "The members of one species differ from the members of another not by one or two genes, but probably by dozens or hundreds. So evolution has to wait until an individual who carries the right gene also mutates another gene and so on. This seems very unlikely, so it should take a very long time. Yet evolution seems to proceed fast enough, from what you tell me." .

"You have forgotten the existence of sex," the British naturalist pointed out.

"Sex?" exclaimed Mr. Tompkins. "What has that to do with evolution?"

"The biological function of sex is to ensure that the offspring is a recombination of the genes of its two parents. As a result of this method of reproduction new mutations, no matter where they occur in the population, are mixed and tested in various combinations. So you do not have to wait for a rare mutation to occur in the precise individual who carries another gene which might give a favorable combination with the first. This mixing and testing of genes which the sexual method of reproduction makes possible immensely speeds up evolution among higher organisms."

"Aren't most organisms divided into male and female?"

"No. As you know, most bacteria reproduce simply by dividing in half, although a number do have methods of exchanging genes in a manner reminiscent of sex. However, bacteria produce so many generations in a short time, sometimes dividing once every twenty minutes, that recombination of genes is perhaps not so necessary to maintain genetic fitness sufficient to cope with changes in their environment. There are also more complex organisms which reproduce asexually —that is, the egg develops without being fertilized by the sperm. Certain organisms such as rotifers do so, and also quite a number of plants. Here evolution is much slower. However, most such organisms appear to have dropped the habit of sexual reproduction rather recently, and they will probably become extinct, since their evolution cannot keep pace with changes of the environment."

"All this certainly sounds like a good theory," said Mr. Tompkins, "but can you give any examples of the way evolution actually takes place?"

"Well yes," replied the British naturalist. "A very good example is the evolution of the eye. I have found it useful, since I am often asked these questions, to draw a diagram of how all this came about.

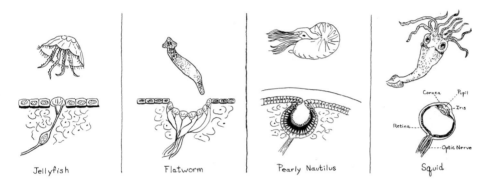

Jellyfish   Flatworm   Pearly Nautilus   Squid

"We can study the evolution of the eye in some detail by comparing the eyes of various animals. The simplest eye is a single cell sensitive to light. Many primitive animals, such as jellyfish, have this kind of eye. With such an eye the jellyfish cannot distinguish shape, but it can tell light from darkness, and this is already a very useful thing to know. For example, distinguishing night from day helps it to know when to hunt its prey. The flatworm's eye is a group of such light-sensitive cells, which merely makes it more reliable than a single cell, but then comes a real improvement. In the pearly nautilus the light-sensitive cells have partially sunk beneath the surface, forming an 'optic cup' that acts like a pinhole camera, making it possible to tell which direction the light is coming from. One more step and the transparent skin over the optic cup bulges to form a lens. An image is now formed on the retina, as the layer of light-sensitive cells is called. The animal can now distinguish not merely light from darkness, and the direction of light, but also the shapes of things. As you see, the eye was made by natural selection, making a small improvement here and there on a very simple beginning. The rule of the game is that partial success counts; any mutation that produces a small improvement is retained, and then further improvements are made."

"This is very interesting," observed Mr. Tompkins, "but you did not quite understand my question. Are there any cases where we can actually observe evolution as it occurs, or is it just too slow?"

"We can observe it in certain cases, and some are of practical importance to us. A very good example are bacteria which a few years ago used to be susceptible to antibiotics, but have now evolved so they are resistant to several of them, as doctors well know. And no doubt you have heard of the fly-swatter advertised 'for DDT-resistant flies.' Flies and many other pests have evolved into resistant forms within just a few years."

"I see it now," said Mr. Tompkins. "Because of natural selection, everything always gets better and better, at least from its own point of view. It is like the genie of Aladdin's lamp; there are no limits to the powers of natural selection."

"Unfortunately—or perhaps fortunately—this is not the case. If you will think about it, you will see that there is a very definite limit to what natural selection can accomplish. It can achieve the almost miraculous, but only if it can be done in small steps, and each of these steps is useful and an improvement on the previous one. It cannot plan ahead, and cannot proceed through intermediate steps, not themselves useful, to an ultimately useful goal. Because of this shortsightedness, evolution has not only produced new species: it has also made hundreds of millions of species extinct."

"If it only selects for the best, how is that possible?" asked Mr. Tompkins.

"Because it selects only what is immediately useful, not necessarily what is useful in the long run. Let me give you an example. Ants have existed for a hundred million years or so. Some have been found buried in ancient Baltic amber, and from such perfect specimens we know that they have changed very little in all this time. Apparently, they have just about reached perfection, as far as an ant's way of life is concerned. But in spite of this, some ant species are becoming extinct all the time.

"If you have ever disturbed an ants' nest, you may have noticed that the first concern of the ants is to save their young, which are the whitish grubs called pupae. The ants grab the pupae in their jaws and attempt to carry them to safety. Now, some ants get into the habit of making 'war' against other species of ants. They enter the alien nests, instinctively grab the pupae, and carry them back to their own nest, where the captured pupae develop into workers. We call them 'slaves,' but of course their lot is no worse than if they had become workers in their home nest.

"From the point of view of the raiders, capturing foreign pupae is an advantage. The number of workers in their nest is increased, and the queen ant, who lays the eggs from which all members of the colony develop, has to lay fewer eggs. The original members have only to raid nests for pupae to keep themselves going. The 'slaves,' in fact, may also participate in raiding.

"This, at first glance, is the consummation of the militarists' ideal, but in fact it represents a situation, often described in science fiction, where robots have taken over every human function and replaced man. The bulk of the population of the ants' nest is now of a foreign species, and the aborigines are almost superfluous. In fact, in the long run, pure colonies of the 'slaves' species are generally more efficient, since they are not dependent on other colonies for reproduction. So in a relatively short space of time the raiding species becomes extinct, because it deliberately replaced itself by foreign 'slaves.' Over millions of years one species of ant after another has developed a slave economy and become extinct. Slave-raiding develops because it confers an immediate advantage, even if the ultimate effect is disastrous."

"This is a curious case," remarked Mr. Tompkins, "but most animals and plants do not live in colonies or keep slaves. Yet, you pointed out, most species do become extinct."

"It is the same short-sightedness of natural selection. Natural selection produces a more and more specialized and therefore a better ability to deal with the environment. But there is a price to pay, since the greater the specialization, the less is the ability to cope with slight changes.

"In Australia the koala 'bear' is specialized to feed on only a few species of eucalyptus trees. Thus a change in climate unfavorable to the eucalyptus would make koala bears extinct. Since environments always change, specialists keep becoming extinct. It is the jack-of-all-trades who survives in the long run. Rats abound, but duck-billed platypuses are rare.

"The same is true in human society. Flint-knappers made a good living when flintlocks were in use, but became extinct when the percussion cap was invented. A bank clerk survives only while banks exist, or at least until they are automated, but a man who lives by picking up crabs and shellfish on the beach of a tropical island would not be much affected if the rest of society were destroyed."

Mr. Tompkins looked thoughtful.

"What interests me," continued the British naturalist, "is not merely the general fact that specialists tend to become extinct, but that there is a pattern to evolution. This is because there are only a limited number of ways in which an animal can make a living. Take, for example, animals who live on land. The two basic occupations are feeding directly on plants, and preying on other animals. Compare, for example, the two basic human occupations: agriculture and manufacturing. We call these two modes of life 'herbivorous' and 'carnivorous.' Each of these broad occupations is subdivided further. It would be unprofitable for lions to hunt mice; they prey on larger herbivores, such as zebras and antelopes. Weasels, however, find mice very profitable, as do owls. Hunting mosquitoes and moths is a job for bats and swallows, while catching fish and crayfish is a specialty of otters. Herbivores, similarly, specialize in different ways. Elephants uproot trees to eat the leaves, beavers feed on bark, and squirrels gather nuts and acorns. And so on and so on.

"You might, therefore, expect that evolution will eventually stop when all occupations are filled. To a certain degree this is true. Once a general type of animal develops, and fills up the available vacancies, evolution stagnates. Minor adaptations to changes of climate and so on still occur, but these usually produce only small differences, such as those between various species of deer or salmon. The basic structure of birds or ants, for example, has shown no progressive evolution for tens of millions of years, although individual species built on the old plan have been appearing and disappearing all this time."

"So evolution has come to a stop?" asked Mr. Tompkins.

"No, two things keep evolution going. For one thing, the number of occupations tends to increase with time. Thus insectivorous bats did not exist before insects developed, nor could grazing on grass be possible until there was grass, just as a gas-station attendant could not exist until the automobile appeared, nor a television comedian before there was television. The evolution of one species tends to produce occupations for others. There are more occupations in our time, for both men and rats, than ever before.

"A more important factor is that from time to time some animal which has not become too much of a specialist makes a basic invention which is not a specialization, but is useful under almost all conditions. A human example of such an invention would be the steam engine. Once it became available, all sorts of special devices based on it could be built, such as trains, steamships, powered cranes, forges, and so on. In the same way, once an animal makes a basic invention, it gives rise to all sorts of specialists, all of whom retain the advantages of the invention. We call this 'radiation,' since the original inventor 'radiates,' or evolves, into numerous different types."

"What sort of thing do you call a basic invention?" asked Mr. Tompkins.

"This may be clearer to you if I describe to you our own evolution as an example. In a geological period called the Devonian, about three hundred million years ago, much of the land suffered from drought, and rivers were often reduced to a string of stagnant pools deficient in oxygen. The fish would take to gulping air, and gradually the front part of their digestive tract expanded into two air sacs, which were really primitive lungs. This made it possible for them to survive in shallow and foul water. There are a few lungfish still left on the upper Nile, in parts of South America, and in Australia, where during part of each year there is not enough water and not enough oxygen in the water for ordinary fish to survive. But most fish have reconverted their lungs into swim-bladders."

"But lungs are not enough to live on land," observed Mr. Tompkins. "You also need legs."

"Quite so. When rivers were reduced to strings of pools, the more enterprising lungfish, who of course became the survivors, took to clumsily flapping and crawling from one drying pool to another not so dry. Selection was for ability to wiggle and for strong fins, which became primitive legs. Once this had occurred, such fish could pick up extra food by crawling a little out of the water and feeding on the wood lice, scorpions, and primitive insects which had already developed. These fish made two basic inventions, how to breathe air and walk on land, and became amphibians.

"Amphibians are still half fish. They lay their eggs in water, and these hatch into tadpoles, a fishlike creature provided with gills. Later tadpoles metamorphose into more terrestrial forms, such as frogs and salamanders. Amphibians are therefore handicapped because they need water to breed. But in spite of this they radiated into all sorts of forms and were the dominant animals of their time, since there was no better-equipped type they had to compete against.

"Next, one of the amphibians developed another basic invention, an egg with two novel features. First, the egg contains its own pool of fluid in which the embryo floats while growing so that it does not need an external pool of water. Second, the embryo is provided with a large yolk, so it does not have to swim around looking for food. This has made it possible for reptiles, as these progressive amphibians are called, to develop without such an extreme dependence on water. Reptiles, in fact, were the first vertebrates to become true land dwellers. Once this happened, the reptiles pushed out most of the amphibians, and again radiated into a great number of forms."

"You mean the dinosaurs?" asked Mr. Tompkins with interest. "I have often admired their huge skeletons in the Museum of Natural History."

"Dinosaurs were some of them, but there were also a great number of others. In many cases they often looked remarkably like some of the later mammals and birds. Some took to the sea and looked very much

From the ocean to the land

like porpoises. Others were big lumbering herbivores a bit like the rhinoceros. Some were swift carnivores, while some developed batlike wings and seem to have lived by catching fish, like our pelicans, swooping down into the water."

"Why did all these reptiles vanish?" asked Mr. Tompkins.

"A whole group will vanish in an instant of geological time if a basic invention which is very much better appears. The reptiles suffered from one serious defect: they had no way of regulating their body temperatures. If the climate was mild, they were very active. But if it was too hot, they had to hide in caves or burrow, as snakes do in a hot desert. When it got cold it was even worse: they became quite torpid.

"In spite of this the dinosaurs survived for two hundred million years, much longer than man has so far. This was because much of the earth's surface was low, and much of its climate mild, but of course there were highlands, and it was colder toward the poles. Here the vegetation began to change. New species of trees, such as pines, firs, and redwoods developed.

"The animals changed too. Some of the reptiles in the colder regions began to develop a method of keeping their bodies warm. Their heat output increased when it was cold and their heat loss was cut down when scales became smaller and more pointed, and evolved into fur. Sweating was also an adaptation to regulate the body temperature, a device to cool the body when necessary by evaporation of water. But incidentally the young of these reptiles began to lick the sweat of the mother for nourishment. Certain sweat glands began to secrete a richer and richer secretion, which eventually became milk. Thus the young of these early mammals had a better start in life.

"At the end of the Cretaceous the earth began to heave up great mountain ranges, and over much of the earth the climate became colder. At night and in winter, as the great reptiles lay torpid, the mammals took over and the reptiles were driven into oblivion."

"But some reptiles still exist," remarked Mr. Tompkins.

"Yes, a few are still around. Crocodiles and turtles are both much older than the dinosaurs. Lizards are still here, and some, losing their legs, have become snakes. Some close relatives of the dinosaurs have also survived. These are small biped forms that once looked like chickens and lived in trees, hopping from branch to branch. Their scales developed into feathers instead of hair, and, like modern gliding lizards, they took to gliding and eventually flying. This was their basic invention. They became birds. When you see a sparrow, you are looking at what is essentially a highly modified dinosaur.

"The birds again illustrate the fact that evolution, even in different groups, tends to move in parallel directions. Having developed feathers which conserve the heat generated by the violent muscular activity of flight, they also maintain a constant body temperature, quite like the mammals. With these improvements, birds also radiated into a variety of forms and occupations."

"Was regulation of body temperature the main reason the mammals ousted the reptiles?" asked Mr. Tompkins.

"Initially, yes. But this led to another improvement. The typical reptiles all had very small brains. A large dinosaur, for example, had a brain not much bigger than a walnut. Now for a complex brain to function well, it is necessary to keep it in a very constant environment, and one of the things that must be closely regulated is the temperature. Since mammals regulate their body temperature closely, it was possible for the size of their brains to increase, and hence their intelligence. This made their victory over the reptiles even more decisive."

"Is that the end of evolution, so far as basic inventions are concerned?"

"No. You yourself are living at a time when a basic invention we haven't yet mentioned is altering the course of evolution."

"You are referring to man?" asked Mr. Tompkins.

"To his brain. Ever since the Age of Reptiles ended, almost all mammals have been developing bigger and better brains. As usual, however, most of them also became specialized in different ways. Whales, which have the biggest brains of all, developed flippers and a fishlike form which made it impossible for them to manipulate objects and produce tools. The same thing, in somewhat different ways, happened to horses, elephants, and almost all other mammals. One branch, however, did not become specialists. These were the tree shrews, a primitive insectivorous form. Since they lived in trees, they retained the five grasping fingers of their remote amphibian progenitors. Jumping from branch to branch required a good visualization of objects in three-dimensional space. They fed on a varied diet, which prevented excessive specialization of their teeth.

"Remaining quite versatile, these so-called primates grew bigger and developed bigger brains, becoming monkeys of various kinds. About thirty million years ago, Africa began to dry up, and extensive grasslands appeared. Some of the large primates took to living in the grasslands and among the rocks, going around in large troops. Since fruit and leaves were not plentiful, they ate insects, eggs, and any small animals they could catch. Some primates, working together, could round up larger prey, such as antelopes, and since their hands remained unspecialized, they could grasp sticks and stones for weapons. Their brains at this time were just a little larger than that of a gorilla. Having gotten that far, they learned to shape primitive tools from bones, then later from pebbles of flint and other hard rocks. The first such toolmakers were the Australopithecine man-apes, who lived more than a million years ago in South Africa.

"Meanwhile, some of the apes had returned to the forest, where they led a quiet and peaceful vegetarian existence, bothering nobody and not changing too much. They became the gorillas and chimpanzees. The primates who remained in the grasslands were different. They were quarrelsome, mean, dirty, and often cannibals. For fighting and squabbling and hunting, the use of tools and the ability to communicate by a developing language were necessary for survival. Thus the size of the brain increased rapidly. That is how we got here.

"Instead of having to adapt to the environment slowly through the occurrence of advantageous bodily changes, man now adapts much faster by developing tools and ideas, which can be transmitted from generation to generation by speech and writing. A great advantage is that the development of tools and ideas, unlike the development of organs, does not necessarily have to go through intermediate steps, each of which has to be directly useful. You might say that until recently evolution has been a chess player who could see only one move ahead; now it can see several moves ahead. For these reasons evolution of tools and culture, 'exosomatic evolution,' or evolution outside the body, has become more important than bodily evolution.

"The rapid evolution of human culture has already produced large changes on the earth, even of its geology. Free metals not previously existing in nature, such as pure iron and aluminum, have appeared. Coal and oil deposits are being quickly oxidized, raising the carbon-dioxide concentration and, possibly, causing the climate to warm up. You have the good fortune, if that is what you call it, of living at the time of the greatest evolutionary event since the origin of life."

"This is indeed very interesting," remarked Mr. Tompkins, "and it gives us quite a new way of looking at our own history and position in the universe. I see now why the promulgation of the theory of evolution is considered such a great event in the history of human thought. But now that the theory is here, it seems strange that so simple an idea was not discovered long before your time."

"In a way it was," replied the British naturalist. "The first people who produced what we would call scientists were the Greeks, although perhaps this is not quite fair to the Egyptians, Sumerians, and Chinese, who had earlier made significant discoveries in medicine and mathematics. At any rate the first group of scientists developed in the city of Miletus, a Greek settlement on the coast of Asia Minor. The man who started all this was Thales, who lived about six centuries before the start of our era. Tradition says he was of Phoenician ancestry. Since this was the very beginning of science, its limits were not well defined, and the early scientist worked on subjects which we would now classify as philosophy and theology as well as science in our sense. For example, the very early scientist Pythagoras discovered the method of developing mathematics by deduction of theorems from a limited number of axioms. At the same time he propagated the idea of the transmigration of souls and believed it was sinful to eat beans.

"One of the students of Thales was the Greek Anaximander, who was curious about the beginning of things. He proposed that living beings had not always existed, but had originated from the primordial slime and mud through the operation of natural causes and then gradually changed into the organisms that we now see. Quite a modern idea, you see, except that Anaximander had no idea what these natural causes might be. From that time on, the idea of evolution was known, although usually not accepted, among educated men.

"What held up the general acceptance of the idea was partly tradition. All peoples had mythological accounts of the origin of the earth and of living things, and some of these accounts, such as those of the Jews and Hindus, found their way into sacred writings and became part of religion. So the scientific idea of evolution was not looked on with favor by church authorities, and the church was strong. But this was not the only difficulty. Many educated people would have taken the idea of evolution more seriously were it not for the fact that there was no scientific explanation of how evolution could occur. This was similar to the history of the idea of the atom. The ancient Greek philosophers Leucippos and Democritos and the Roman poet Lucretius had suggested the idea of the atom, but it was not taken seriously until, almost two thousand years later, chemists and physicists provided experimental evidence for its existence.

"In the generation before me the French biologist Lamarck did suggest how evolution could happen. Organisms try to adapt to their environment, he said. Giraffes, for example, stretch their necks to reach the taller branches of trees to feed on their leaves. As a result, so he said, their necks might lengthen a trifle, and the slight elongation would be transmitted to the necks of their offspring. This idea was a step in the right direction but it failed to convince many people, because there are too many structures which cannot be explained in this way. How could an animal change its color so as to blend into its environment only by trying to hide? We now know that there is an even more serious objection to Lamarck's idea. He took it for granted, as did almost everyone else at the time, that a trait acquired by one of the parents during its lifetime would be inherited by its offspring. If a father with a white skin spent much time in the sun and was well tanned, his children would tend to have a slightly darker skin, so it was thought. Of course there were some well-known facts which did not fit into this idea, but curiously no one seemed to pay any attention to them. The Jews, for example, have been practicing circumcision for thousands of years but this has had no effect on the offspring; the operation has to be repeated anew each generation.

"We now know that the idea of the inheritance of acquired characters is quite false. A gene is not affected by what happens to the rest of the body. If you have a gene for long fingers or strong muscles, it will be transmitted to the offspring even if you lose your fingers through an accident or have flabby muscles because you do not exercise.

"My contribution was the idea of natural selection, which sieves each generation to separate the better from the worse so that it is the better which are on the average the parents of the next generation. In so far as the better have better genes, rather than merely more favorable acquired characters, the next generation will also have better genes. This concept provides a mechanism which explains evolution and it has made it generally acceptable. Of course there are many other facts which support the idea that evolution does occur, such as the sequences of fossil forms which we find. I am pleased that it has fallen to me to promulgate this idea, although the way that this happened suggests that no man is indispensable. I was almost scooped, as both journalists and scientists say, by Alfred Russell Wallace. By 1858 my ideas were clear to me, but I had not yet published a manuscript. Then I was amazed to receive a paper from Wallace which he sent while he was collecting insects in the East Indies. In this short paper he propounded the idea of natural selection very clearly. We then both presented our idea in print at the same time. People, however, generally associate the idea with my name, probably because I subsequently developed it in more detail in several books. By now all this does not matter: evolution is well established, irrespective of who originated it."

"Did you also explain in your books how life came into being in the first place?" asked Mr. Tompkins. "It seems to me that evolution of life is one thing, and its origin from inorganic matter something else again."

"You are right," the British naturalist conceded. "These are rather separate problems. I did not discuss the origin of life itself, because in my time the chemical and physical laws that might produce it were as unknown to me as natural selection was to Anaximander. In your time, however, much more is known, and some rather reasonable ideas about how it might have happened have been suggested. A living thing is a special collection of organic compounds, so the first problem is the evolution of organic compounds."

"What do you mean by organic compounds?" asked Mr. Tompkins.

"Organic compounds," replied the British naturalist, "are basically compounds containing the element carbon. Carbon atoms have the interesting property of being able to form long chains or rings by combining with each other. To this 'carbon skeleton' other such atoms as hydrogen, oxygen, and nitrogen can attach. For this reason there are more kinds of carbon compounds than compounds of all the other elements put together, and it is the vast variety of possibilities provided by carbon which makes life possible."

"But how," asked Mr. Tompkins, "can compounds evolve? I thought their structures were always the same."

"True, but some of them have not always been present. For life to develop, the first requirement is a planet which has organic compounds. Right now, there are a lot of organic compounds on earth, but all of them are produced by living beings. The question is whether organic compounds can be produced without life being present. Of course we know that a chemist can synthesize them, but since a chemist is himself alive this sort of synthesis is not an example showing that living things are not required to synthesize organic compounds.

"We now know that organic compounds can be synthesized even if life is not present. The Russian biochemist Oparin first pointed out that when the earth was born it must have had an atmosphere consisting of hydrogen, water vapor, methane, ammonia, and small quantities of other gases, but little or no oxygen—an atmosphere quite unhealthy for us, you will note. Given such an atmosphere, Oparin said, organic compounds should form spontaneously.

"This idea was supported and extended by the American chemist Harold Urey, who has made detailed studies of the chemical compositions of the planets and their atmospheres. He pointed out that a hydrogen-rich atmosphere is still found on the larger planets, which are too big and too cold to have lost their original gases, and that organic compounds occur in comets. So it is not unreasonable to assume that the earth also had such an atmosphere at one time.

"One of Urey's students followed up this idea and showed that if you pass an electric discharge through such an artificial atmosphere in the laboratory or shine ultraviolet light upon it, all sorts of organic compounds begin to appear, including many of the amino acids found in proteins. Chemists call this random synthesis; you get what comes naturally.

"Since the sun has always been shining ultraviolet light upon our atmosphere and lightning storms provide a lot of electrical sparks, there is no doubt that organic compounds were being made in these early days. These compounds would mostly dissolve in the ocean, forming a sort of organic soup. It was from this organic soup that life developed."

"If this was so," said Mr. Tompkins, "why isn't our ocean such an organic soup now?"

"For two important reasons. Life is now well developed, and any organic molecule that might appear is soon used for food by bacteria. For example, vast quantities of garbage are towed out to sea from a city such as New York, but the organic material which is dumped into the ocean does not stay there as such. It serves as food for bacteria, which in turn are eaten by other minute organisms, which in turn are eaten by larger organisms. A part of the garbage temporarily reappears on the New Yorker's table as kipper, lobsters, and oysters, to mention just a few items, and then back to the ocean. And so round and round it goes.

"The second reason is that it takes tens or hundreds of millions of years for large amounts of organic compounds to accumulate. In the early days, before life had developed far, there was almost no free oxygen in the atmosphere, and organic compounds could build up. But now the oxygen in our present atmosphere would burn such organic compounds faster than they could accumulate."

"I see," said Mr. Tompkins, "on a planet like the earth a lot of organic compounds could accumulate. But how do you get from organic compounds to living things? My wife has many cans of soup at home, all full of organic compounds, yet life never appears in them unless they are opened and germs fall into them. If it did, I could sue the soup manufacturers for poisoning me by insufficient sterilization. If life does not appear in a rich lentil soup, which already contains things like proteins, how did it appear in that early ocean?"

"Your question hits the nail on the head. The answer is that the ocean differed in one very important respect from your wife's cans of soup; it was an open, dynamic system."

"What does that mean?" asked Mr. Tompkins.

"Well, let me put it this way," answered the British naturalist. "The energy of sunlight caused the gases of the atmosphere to react and form various organic compounds which contained much energy. These dissolved in the ocean and kept reacting with each other, losing energy until they decomposed into gases and leaked back into the atmosphere. The sun was acting as a sort of pump, circulating organic compounds through the ocean."

"This appears rather pointless," said Mr. Tompkins. "You end up with what you started with."

"Well, that depends on your point of view. Nowadays plants, using the energy of sunlight, form sugar and other organic compounds from carbon dioxide and water. You eat either plants or other animals that eat plants. You then degrade the organic compounds you eat back to carbon dioxide and water. Do you therefore conclude that you are pointless?"

"Hm. I think I see it now. Although my molecules return to the same form from which they started, in the process of doing so, they maintain my existence."

"Precisely. The interconversion and flow of material through your body is called metabolism. The flow of matter through the ocean was also a sort of metabolic system, but no such metabolism occurs in the cans of soup you mentioned."

"Wasn't the ocean just an ordinary chemical system, though?"

"Yes, but it began to evolve in a novel way. There were, of course, many thousands of different compounds in it, all reacting in multitudinous ways. Some of these reactions began helping each other. A product of one reaction promoted another reaction, and conversely a product of the second promoted the first. Such a pair became what we call self-replicating, since the more there was of it, the more it grew at the expense of unpaired reactions. When I say grew, I mean that a larger part of the flow of matter entered these reactions. Of course, there were many such pairs, some of which in turn mutually helped each other. As a result, a system of the most efficient reactions automatically selected itself and grew at the expense of the less efficient. This was just like biological evolution, but with selection for chemical reactions instead of genes. Gradually more and more complex and efficient compounds were formed, which acted as catalysts, or primitive enzymes for each other's synthesis. And so a metabolic system, a precursor of life, came into being."

"I see the similarity," said Mr. Tompkins. "But what was then the living organism?"

"What is an individual organism is not always as clear-cut as we sometimes think," said the British naturalist. "A strawberry plant is an individual, you might say. But then it begins to send out runners which take root and produce new plants. Where does one individual end and another begin?"

"But with people or cats it is no problem," interrupted Mr. Tompkins. "It is easy to tell where one individual ends and another begins."

"Quite true, because here you have an extreme case. But perhaps you do not realize that you yourself exist at two quite different levels of individuality. At the first level you are made up of cells, each of which has an individual life of its own. It is possible to take cells from your skin, for example, and grow them in tissue culture just like bacteria. Such cells, in fact, could be kept alive and growing long after you had died of old age. At the second level these individual cells form an integrated colony which is Mr. Tompkins, undoubtedly an individual in his own right."

"But still," said Mr. Tompkins, "it is always clear what is an individual at the cell-colony level."

"Not always," replied the naturalist. "There are some animals called coelenterates."

"Never heard of them," admitted Mr. Tompkins sheepishly.

"Perhaps you have not heard the name, but you certainly know of them. They are the sea anemones and jellyfish."

"Oh yes," Mr. Tompkins agreed. "I have often seen jellyfish on the beach. Curious little creatures. What about them?"

"These animals show us that it is not only possible for cells to get together and form an individual, but also for individuals formed of cells to get together to form an individual of a still higher order. A sea anemone is basically just a tube open at one end. The opening is generally fringed with tentacles which catch other animals and force them into the tube, where they are digested. Such an animal, really just a self-supporting intestine, may live by itself as a well-defined individual. But some species live together in groups, and the insides of the various individuals fuse with one another. Thus any food caught by one benefits all. Some species carry this further: some individuals specialize at catching food, others reproduce, while others defend the colony with their stings. This principle is carried even further by some

Some individuals specialize in catching food, others reproduce, while others defend the colony with their stings.

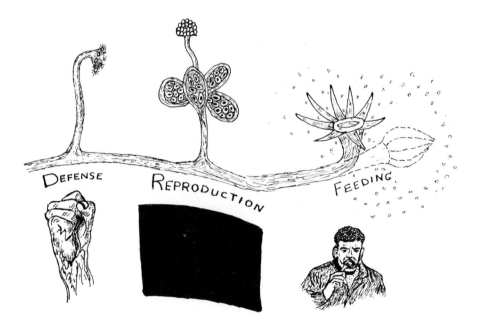

DEFENSE   REPRODUCTION   FEEDING

jellyfish, such as the poisonous Portuguese man-of-war, which is actually a colony of many individuals, some feeding, some reproducing, others supplying muscular contraction for locomotion, and so on. The individuals are so well integrated here that it becomes difficult to tell where one ends and another begins, and all together they form a superorganism as well defined as any cat."

"Are these coelenterates the only animals that form such 'superorganisms'?" asked Mr. Tompkins.

"Oh, no, there are quite a number of simple animals that do so. But what is particularly interesting is that some quite complex animals tend to evolve in this direction. An ant or termite colony, for example, is a superorganism of this kind. Here also different individuals specialize at different jobs, but all work for the benefit of the colony as a whole."

"But," objected Mr. Tompkins, "the ants are not physically connected to each other in an ants' nest. They remain separate individuals."

"Physical contact is not the essential point. What is required is interaction, or a flow of information, between the parts that form an organism. This interaction is made possible by physical contact in such examples as the cells which form your body. But other kinds of interactions are also possible, as the ants show."

"You say that an ants' nest is a sort of superorganism. Isn't the same then true of human society?" asked Mr. Tompkins.

"Quite so. Man does form 'superorganisms' of this kind, which we call societies, nations, and states. In such societies the individuals, like cells in a body, are born and die, but the society lives on and develops characteristics of its own. However, such a society is an organism only in the most rudimentary sense, since the interactions between individuals in a society are vastly weaker than those between cells in a body. But who knows, perhaps the interactions will eventually become so strong that real superorganisms of this sort will arise in the distant future. In such a superorganism what we now call individual human beings would then play the role of cells in our own bodies. This would be quite compatible with what we know of the course of evolution so far."

"I am not sure I like the idea," said Mr. Tompkins.

"I am not sure I like it either," agreed the naturalist. "Who knows what such superorganisms might be like? The Romans had a saying: '*Senatores boni viri, sed Senatus mala bestia*,' or, translated, 'The senators are good men, but the Senate is an evil beast.' They realized that a higher-order organism, in this case the Senate, could have characteristics different and not necessarily better than its individual components. But what was the question you asked which brought on this digression?"

"You were explaining," said Mr. Tompkins, "that the early ocean had developed a metabolism of its own, somewhat like a living thing, and I asked what was then the organism?"

"Oh yes. The entire ocean then consisted of very loosely interacting parts, so that there was no well-defined organism. So in a sense the entire ocean was one organism, rather like a bed of sponges growing on a rock, all fusing one into another. A poet has put this as follows:

> O you, Dr. Yčas, you!
>   In one convulsive motion
> Your brain has given birth unto
>   A viable young ocean.
> All monsters pale beside the new;
>   The Hydra, Hap, Garuda, Ra,
> Italapas, Hua-hu
>   Tiao, Gulltopr, Grendel's ma,
> Quetzalcoatl, Kukulkan,
>   Onniont, Audhumbla, Ix,
> Geryon, Leviathan,
>   666,
> The ox Ahura Mazda made,
>   The Fomors, deevs, Graiae,
> And others of this ilk all fade
>   Alongside Yčas's sea.
> The straits were sinews, channelways
>   Were veins, and islands eyes,
> Rivers tails, reefs bones, and bays,
>   Depending on their size,
> Fists, shoulders, heads, ears, mouths, or feet.
>   The fjords, as fingers, froze
> Sometimes, as did the arctic pate
>   And the pale antarctic toes.
> Horrid, horrid ocean! The
>   Grandmother of Tyr,
> Who had nine hundred crania,
>   Did not look half so queer.

It whistled with a mournful hiss
    In darkness; scared and bored,
It lapped the land, yet every kiss
    Was stonily ignored.
A spheric skin, or blue-green hide,
    Alone the ocean kept
Our planet's house, yet when it died
    One aeon, no one wept.*"

Mr. Tompkins, who was not well grounded in the classics, did not understand what many of the words meant. "Very interesting," he remarked, "but if this ocean died, how did it contribute to the origin of life?"

"It did not really die, it evolved to the next stage. Presumably it split up into the equivalent of small individual organisms. We do not know the details, of course, but probably the organic compounds formed fatty droplets of some kind, somewhat like droplets of oil in water, and further developments of these led to very primitive cells, similar to, but simpler than, our bacteria. This was a very important development, since once you had many individuals, they could compete with each other, and so natural selection could produce more and more complex and efficient organisms. But really you should not press me too hard on this point, for we don't know too much about it."

"I suppose," said Mr. Tompkins, "that the organic compounds must have included proteins and the nucleic acids which form the genes, since genes are needed to make proteins, as I recently learned."

"Of course this must have happened at some point," agreed the naturalist, "but we don't know when. The metabolic system may have been very primitive to start with, and simple and not very efficient proteins may have been made in some way without genes. Here again we do not know much about it.

"However, we know that one important event took place in these early days. Some of these early cells developed a green pigment called chlorophyll, which absorbs light, and became plants. Using the energy of light, plants make sugars and other useful compounds from carbon dioxide and water, and liberate oxygen. The ocean was and still is full

---

* "A Bitter Life," from *The Carpentered Hen and Other Tame Creatures* by John Updike. Copyright © 1956 by John Updike. This poem originally appeared in *The New Yorker*, and is reprinted by permission of Harper & Row, Publishers.

of little microscopic green plants called algae, which are busy producing sugars from carbon dioxide and water, and releasing oxygen. More complex land plants developed later. The early atmosphere, as I said, appears to have had no oxygen at first, but because of plants a considerable amount of oxygen has accumulated in the atmosphere over the ages. As a result of the activity of plants it then became possible for animals to evolve. Animals feed on the plants, and use their sugars and other compounds by 'burning' them with oxygen. In this way they obtain a lot of energy which was not available before plants and atmospheric oxygen had appeared."

Mr. Tompkins looked puzzled. "If animals reunite the organic compounds with oxygen, how can oxygen accumulate?"

"The answer is that not all the organic material is 'reburned.' A portion is buried and transformed into rocks such as shale and coal, and also into oil. This goes on all the time, and gradually an excess of oxygen accumulates. All living things taken together form a kind of huge engine run by solar energy for circulating matter through living things. This engine was rather weak before chlorophyll was invented, perhaps two billion years ago, but then it began to capture huge quantities of energy, and the engine began to run faster. It still does.

"You might be interested in comparing its size with our own activities. I asked one of my physicist friends that question recently, and was fascinated by what he told me. It has been estimated that out of the 4×10^{17} kilowatt hours, or K.W.H., representing the total amount of solar energy which falls yearly on the surface of the earth, 1.7×10^{15} K.W.H., or about half of 1 per cent, is stored by plants in the process of photosynthesis. Incidentally only one-tenth of that amount is stored by land plants, the other nine-tenths being accounted for by algae in the ocean. In terms of weight, plant life converts yearly 1.6×10^{11} tons of carbon from atmospheric air into organic compounds. Most of that amount is returned to the atmosphere, through the process of plant respiration, the rotting of fallen leaves and trunks, occasional forest fires, and so on. Only 1 per cent of synthesized material is used by the human population of the earth as vegetable food, and another 1.5 per cent as the food of domestic animals. One per cent more is used by humans as firewood, both for domestic heating and for industrial purposes.

"In this drawing, which my physicist friend drew for me," said the naturalist, taking a piece of paper out of his pocket, "the flow of solar

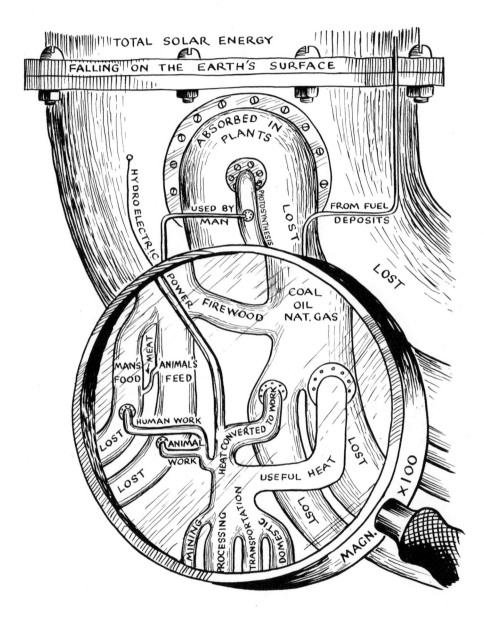

energy and its subsequent distribution are represented in the form of a pipe system. The large incoming pipe carries the total flow of solar energy falling on the surface of the earth, the intermediate pipe carries the energy absorbed by plants, and a still smaller one the energy stored by the process of photosynthesis. The fraction of stored energy which is utilized by humanity is represented by a tiny pipe branching to the left; it is so thin that in order to see the details of further energy partition we must use a lens with a magnifying power of one hundred. Looking through the lens you see that this pipe separates into three branches corresponding to human vegetable food, animal food, and firewood. Incidentally, a narrow connection leading from animal food to human food represents the average meat diet, mostly fish, of the human population of the earth. The firewood branch empties into a larger pipe, which represents the energy obtained yearly from coal, oil, and natural gas. These irreplaceable energy resources were made available to us by the photosynthetic activity of plants during geological eras long past. Now we come to the conversion of all these energy streams into useful work and useful heat, the processes in which we sustain terrific losses. The pipes which carry useful energy look very thin, even through the lens. We have here 2.1×10^{12} K.W.H. of useful heat, 1.2×10^{12} K.W.H. of heat converted into mechanical work, 0.2×10^{12} K.W.H. of human manual work, and 0.1×10^{12} K.W.H. delivered by draft animals. A tiny pipe leading directly from the main stream of solar energy carries 0.2×10^{12} K.W.H. of hydroelectric power. The total useful energy of 2.9×10^{12} K.W.H. is distributed mainly between industrial processing (1.8×10^{12} K.W.H.), domestic uses (0.8×10^{12} K.W.H.), and extraction of raw materials (0.3×10^{12} K.W.H.). This gives us a clear picture of our position in the living world."

"I see now," said Mr. Tompkins, "that we use only a very small amount of the available energy. But, of course, our civilization is expanding all the time, and I keep hearing that there is really no limit to our growth."

"An interesting point of view," replied the British naturalist, "but, I'm afraid, a little unrealistic. Suppose you make the following calculation. Mankind now uses an amount of energy which is equivalent to the complete conversion of 22 pounds of matter into energy a year, according to Einstein's famous formula $E = mc^2$. If human activities continue to expand at the rate of 5 per cent per annum, the entire mass of the earth will be converted into radiation in only thirteen centuries."

Mr. Tompkins turned slightly pale. "You mean the human race is that close to the end?" he asked with some agitation.

"Of course not. I have made this calculation only to show that it is nonsense to suppose that any material expansion can go on indefinitely. Clearly, whether we like it or not, our present habit of trying to expand and increase everything on 'the bigger the better' principle will have to be dropped quite soon. At present we are living in the childhood of mankind. A child, of course, has to grow, but we often lose sight of the fact that he also has to stop growing. If someone is still growing at the age of twenty, it is a cause for serious concern, usually indicating some malfunction of the pituitary gland, which controls growth."

Mr. Tompkins had never given much thought to problems of this kind, and many questions he wanted to ask swirled through his mind. What did biology have to say about the future of the human race? Are we the only intelligent beings in the universe? If not, can we ever get into touch with other and distant civilizations? He could not decide what to ask first, but fortunately the problem was solved for him. A rainstorm was coming up, and already a few raindrops had fallen.

"Pardon me," the British naturalist said. "It has been most interesting to converse with you, but I had better avoid getting too wet. Pneumonia can be pretty dangerous without penicillin. We can continue our discussion later, for after all, this voyage is to last a few more years yet. I shall retire to my cabin."

Mr. Tompkins thanked the British naturalist profusely and went back to his hammock. . . . When he awoke, he was back in his stateroom. The swell had died down, and his ship was as steady as if she were at her moorings. It was time for dinner.

» 7 «

The Clock Ticks

HIS encounter with Charles Darwin had made Mr. Tompkins rather thoughtful. Of course, it had all been only a dream, and he was now back on his luxury liner, considerably better informed on the evolution of life than he had been before. But he wondered about the rather uncanny ability of Charles Darwin to see backward and forward in time. Was this also just part of the dream, or was it really possible to travel into the past and into the future? The ship's library did not have scientific books on this subject, but he did manage to pick up H. G. Wells' story *The Time Machine* and a rather imaginative work which discussed such things as telepathy and the ancient seers of Scotland. These men, it said, could see the future as you or I can see the present. It also cited all sorts of queer reports on poltergeists, which are alleged spirits who throw things at you. The book was well written and amusing, but Mr. Tompkins did not take it very seriously. "Probably just old wives' tales," he said to himself. But he did decide to inform himself on the subject of time, as understood by science, at the earliest opportunity. Like many amateurs and the general public, he took it for granted that science has the last word on any subject.

In a few more days he arrived at his son's university and was pleased to find that Wilfred and Vera were able to make him very comfortably at home in their apartment. The surrounding country was green and pleasant, and he spent his first week hiking and driving to see the sights. In the evening, however, he relaxed as usual with magazines or books, which Wilfred provided for him from the university library. One of the articles in a magazine was on the nature of time, written by a physicist, and Mr. Tompkins perused it with much attention, hoping to find answers to his questions.

Many physicists, it seems, had considered the problem of time, especially whether it could be reversed. The great English physicist Lord Kelvin had stated this problem very lucidly in 1874, when he wrote: "If, then, the motion of every particle of matter in the universe were precisely reversed at any instant, the course of nature would be simply reversed forever after. The bursting bubble of foam at the foot of a waterfall would reunite and descend into the water; the thermal motions would reconcentrate their energy and throw the mass up the fall in drops re-forming into a close column of ascending water. Heat which had been generated by the friction of solids and dissipated by conduction, and radiation with absorption, would come again to the place of contact and throw the moving body back against the force to which it had previously yielded. Boulders would recover from the mud the materials required to rebuild them into their previous jagged forms, and would become reunited to the mountain peak from which they had formerly broken away. And if, also, the materialistic hypothesis of life were true, living creatures would grow backward, with conscious knowledge of the future but with no memory of the past, and would become again, unborn." He added, perhaps with a sense of frustration, or perhaps with a sense of relief, "But the real phenomena of life infinitely transcend human science, and speculation regarding consequences of their imagined reversal is utterly unprofitable."

Lord Kelvin could only describe such a time reversal in words, but for us it is very easy to see what time reversal actually looks like. All you have to do is to take a motion picture of some scene, and then project the film either backward or forward. As Lord Kelvin would have said, in most cases it is very easy to tell, just by looking, in which direction the film is run. Why should this be so?

The author of the article pointed out that if the scene filmed portrays only the motion of large bodies the direction of time is not evident. A train may be filmed going forward, but if it is projected in reverse it also looks perfectly natural. It is just a train going backward, which trains often do. But suppose you film a more homely scene, a burning cigarette. If the film is projected in the normal way, the scene looks familiar; the cigarette is gradually converted into ash, and the smoke disperses. If, on the other hand, the film is run backward, the scene looks strange; smoke condenses onto the ash, and the ash turns into a cigarette. This at once tells you which is the real time direction.

The physicist claimed that there is a fundamental reason why one scene looks natural and another not. Suppose that you have a deck of cards which is perfectly ordered—that is, all spades are arranged in sequence, followed by all hearts in sequence, and so on. Now shuffle the pack. The cards, of course, now become disordered. So if you see pictures of two packs of cards, one ordered and another disordered, and if you know that a shuffle has occurred in between, can you tell which picture is earlier and which is later? Of course you can. The more disordered pack is later, because random shuffling is very unlikely to produce an ordered pack from a disordered one.

According to the physicist this explains how to tell the direction of time. Since the general tendency everywhere is for disorder to increase, we say that the disorder either is always increasing or, at best, stays constant. When a cigarette burns, its atoms or molecules, which were previously in reasonable order, now disperse as smoke, and it is vastly improbable that they should recondense into a cigarette. That is why a film of a burning cigarette projected backward appears so unnatural; a very improbable event is occurring. But why, then, does the film of a train projected backward or forward appear perfectly natural? Obviously because the increase in disorder is in both cases the same, in principle nil. When the increase in disorder is nil, as in purely mechanical processes, there is no way of telling the direction of time. All this struck Mr. Tompkins as novel and interesting, since he had never thought of time in this way.

He read on. The future and the past appear to us to be very different things. We instinctively regard the future with trepidation, partly because we can know the past, but only very partially the future. Every time we drive a car we cannot be certain we shall not meet with an accident. But even more important, in one respect we do know the future perfectly: we know that after a time we shall no longer exist. Most people do not like this knowledge. Objectively this dislike is rather strange; no one seems to worry about the time in the past, and it is not disconcerting to most people to know that they did not exist in the time of the dinosaurs. So why worry that we shall not exist in the future? Is this a mere prejudice, a result of the fact that evolution has selected those living things, us included, which struggle to survive, or is it because there is a real difference between the past and the future? Was Sir Isaac Newton right when he said, "Absolute, True, and Mathematical Time, of itself, and from its own nature flows equably without regard to any thing external, and by another name is called Duration?"

The physicist rambled on for a while, but to Mr. Tompkins he seemed to have little further to say that was very definite. The increase in disorder did indeed seem to correspond to our subjective sense of the direction of time, but whether the two were identical or just casually related was not clear to Mr. Tompkins. By this time it was getting late, and Mr. Tompkins remembered that he had a morning appointment the next day. So he set his alarm clock for seven o'clock and went to bed.

The alarm clock never did ring since Mr. Tompkins woke up at three minutes to seven and shut it off. The same sort of thing had happened to him several times before, but this time he began to wonder about it. Was there some kind of mysterious clock inside Mr. Tompkins which could tell time so closely even when he was asleep? He decided, however, that another hour would not make him miss his appointment. So back to sleep he went, determined to wake up again in another hour.

At first he seemed to be in a strange room, but gradually he began to recognize it. It was the museum of antiquities of the university, through which he had strolled yesterday afternoon. Yes, he was standing in front of a dark and malevolent-looking statue which had attracted his attention yesterday. The label said it was a deity of the ancient Maya of Central America. Around its base were carved several curious hieroglyphics which Mr. Tompkins could not decipher, and he wondered what they said.

"9 IMIX 19 ZIP," said the statue, with a strong foreign accent. This did not seem to make any sense to Mr. Tompkins, and there was an embarrassed pause.

"The people who made me," continued the stone deity, "worshiped time, and what I have just read to you is the date inscribed on the stone of which I am made. Time seems as good a thing to worship as anything else, don't you think? At any rate, my people had a calendar both intricate and elegant, and I am always pleased when my visitors, here in this dismal climate to which I have been banished, take some trouble to understand it."

Mr. Tompkins felt some awe in the presence of the talkative stone statue, and, partly from curiosity, partly from a desire to please, asked "Can you explain the calendar to me, and in particular what 9 IMIX 19 ZIP means?"

"Well, the easiest way is to begin with your own calendar, which, although certainly clumsy, is at least familiar to you. You divide your year into 12 months, of varying length. You number the days of the month. In addition, you also have a week of 7 days, all of which have names. Now your months run without a break, and so do your weeks, so you can give a date as, for example, Sunday, September 4th. But since this date recurs four times every 28 years at unequal intervals, it does not give much information as to what year it is.

"My people had a better system. Their year had exactly 365 days, which were divided into 18 months of 20 days each, and 5 extra days which formed a month of 5 days, if you like to call it such. The days of the month were numbered from 0 to 19. 19 ZIP is then the 20th day of the month ZIP. In addition to numbers, the days of the months had names, but these names ran continuously through the year, just as the days of your week run continuously through your year. So in the date inscribed on me, the name of the day 19 ZIP in the year I was made is IMIX, just like Sunday the 4th of September. Because of the 5-day 'month' at the end of the year, the day 'IMIX' would fall in one year on the 4th of the first month, the 9th of the next, the 14th of the next, and the 19th of the next. Five years later it would fall again on the 4th. In addition, my people had a 'week' of 13 days, which were numbered from 1 to 13; it also ran uninterruptedly through the year as does your week. Each year had 28 of these weeks and 1 extra day, so each year began with the following 'week' day number. Thus we wrote 9 IMIX 19 ZIP. This combination of the numbers of 'week' days, month-day names, and month-day numbers recurs only once every 52 years. Thus any date could be fixed within any 52-year period, which roughly corresponds to your century, since your date '66 is clear except that it may be 1966 or 1866 and so on. But then my people had cycles to determine the 'century' exactly, and the long count . . ."

Mr. Tompkins, who was certainly not an archaeologist, by now felt somewhat confused by this calendar. He rather rudely interrupted the stone deity. "What is the point that your people were trying to make with this sort of calculation?" he asked.

"Whether they knew it or not, they were making a very important point. Time is measured by some sort of cycle of events which periodically returns to the same state it started from. Thus you and all people recognize a day when the earth has made one revolution around its axis and returns to the same position relative to the sun. A year is one revolution of the earth around the sun. After one day, or one year, things return, to a first approximation, to the state they were in before; the birds wake up and sing each morning and new vegetation blossoms forth in the spring. My people realized, more clearly perhaps than others, that after a certain number of cycles have recurred there will come a time when their relation to one another will be the same as it was previously. In a certain sense they thought that after fifty-two years the world had come back to the same situation it was fifty-two years before. Time was real, but it was of limited duration, just fifty-two years, and then things started all over again. So every fifty-second year was sacred; it marked the limits of time."

"But," interrupted Mr. Tompkins, "after fifty-two years all things do not return to what they were before. The old generation dies, and the new takes over."

"Of course," retorted the stone deity. "My people realized that the return was not precisely to the same state. But they were not, perhaps, totally mistaken. You now know that the world is made of atoms. The great Austrian physicist Ludwig Boltzmann himself speculated that any configuration of atoms must, entirely by chance, repeat itself after a certain length of time, so that eventually all things in the universe would return to a state in which they had been before. And this, mind you, would be repeated an infinite number of times, forever. Of course the 'great year' of Boltzmann is almost inconceivably long, but the principle is the same as that of my people. To give due credit, others had also thought of the principle of the eternal recurrence of things. The Roman poet Vergil had written, 'The reign of Saturn will return . . . and other heroes will sail on the ship *Argo*. Other wars will come, and again the great Achilles will be sent to Troy.' The same idea is found in Hindu philosophy."

"Is this what science teaches us?" asked Mr. Tompkins with interest.

"On these great problems science is not sure what it teaches us," replied the stone deity. "Our universe, your scientists think, had a beginning in time. Something blew up; it formed the universe and kept expanding. Perhaps it will keep going and eventually vanish into nothingness, or perhaps it will collapse again into a primeval atom, blow up again, and keep repeating itself indefinitely. They do not know, at least not yet. But at any rate, without knowing the answer to these great problems, we measure time by the recurrence of events."

"But there seems to be something wrong with this idea," said Mr. Tompkins, remembering what he had read. "Suppose you do have a recurring event, such as the swing of a pendulum. If the pendulum is in a certain position, how do I know how much time has passed? After all, is it a different swing from a previous one, or is it the same? Something seems to be lacking here."

"You are perceptive," remarked the stone deity, but with a touch of condescension. "Consider again your pendulum. As you noticed, by itself a pendulum does not make a clock. The recurrent event, the swing of the pendulum, has to be coupled with some other device which has a memory and can count. Only then do you have a clock. The memory is not a recurring event: quite the contrary, it does not repeat itself, but counts the swings of the pendulum one after the other, and from the count of the number of swings it tells you how much time has elapsed. Concretely, the counter and the memory are the face and hands of the clock. If you use the day as a pendulum to measure time, you count and remember the number of days which have passed, so here your brain is the hands and face of a clock. But you always need both the recurrent event and the nonrecurrent memory to measure time."

"But what about an hourglass, such as my wife uses to time my three-minute eggs? I have also read that the ancient Greeks had a water clock called a clepsydra. Water would drip out of a container, and the time of the day was read from the amount of water remaining. This is not a recurring event."

"It is true you can build clocks which are not based on recurring events, but these are secondary clocks, which are always checked or calibrated by some recurring event such as the rotation of the earth. We have now discovered that the rotation of the earth is itself not quite constant; it can vary several millionths of a second per year. This has made physicists and astronomers unhappy, and they now often use what is called an atomic clock, which runs at a more constant rate. One of the best clocks counts the vibrations of the cesium atom and is therefore called a cesium clock. It is so accurate that with it you can measure time to within a few seconds per century."

Mr. Tompkins remembered that he could estimate time quite closely even when asleep; he would wake up just a few minutes before the alarm went off. This was not as good as an atomic clock, but it seemed remarkable enough.

"How is it that I can tell time," he asked, "without any clock at all? Is there some sort of clock inside me?"

"There is a biological clock inside you, but if you want more details you had better ask the fish."

Mr. Tompkins, rather startled, turned around to see if any fish were in sight. Indeed, the wall was covered with an ancient Egyptian painting, showing the Goddess Nut holding up the firmament. Across the sky a barque carrying the sun was making its daily westward voyage, while at her feet some fish were swimming in the water of a lotus-covered pool.

By now Mr. Tompkins recognized that this dream of time was not quite like the others; there was an air both strange and slightly ominous which had not been present before. Perhaps this was because of the slightly malevolent nature of time itself. He thought of the "Tale of the Fisherman," which Scheherazade had told her master. Would the wall dissolve, and a demon step through it and ask the fish, "Fish, fish, are you doing your duty?" The fish, of course, would stand up on their tails and reply in unison, "Yes, yes. If you reckon we reckon, if you pay we pay, if you fly we overcome and are content." Then the demon would overturn the pan, and the fish would be burned on the red-hot coals. Mr. Tompkins could not repress a smile at his 'stream of consciousness,' as he knew the psychologists called it. He wondered what had brought it to mind. Just then the wall did open, and a figure stepped through it into the hall of antiquities. This did not surprise Mr. Tompkins. His only surprise was that instead of an Oriental demon, it was a middle-aged man of professorial appearance. He was wearing a tropical helmet and carrying a transparent plastic bag filled with water, in which a few small fish were swimming. The man turned to Mr. Tompkins, and with a strong Midwestern accent remarked, "Well, it was a good trip back from Montevideo."

"Have you carried these fish all the way from Montevideo?" asked Mr. Tompkins.

"Oh yes. I just got off the plane, in fact. I am a zoologist, and the fish have accompanied me there and back as part of an experiment to determine how animals find their way about, and how they tell time. These two problems are closely related."

"These two problems seem very different to me," remarked Mr. Tompkins. "Could you explain what you are trying to do?"

"Think of what you yourself would do if you tried to travel in a certain direction in a country that was new to you—or better yet, across the ocean," the zoologist suggested. "There are two methods you can use to orient yourself. One way is to use a magnetic compass, which is a good way if you have one. The other is to use astronomical methods. If you are up in the morning to see the sun rise, you know it is rising in the east, and the place where it sets is the west. You can also tell directions at other times than at sunrise and sunset if you know what the time is. At noon, for example, you know that the direction of the sun is south. In short, you can tell directions if you have a certain practical knowledge of astronomy and a clock.

"To investigate which methods animals use to orient themselves, I trained my fish to swim south in a special apparatus which gave them a slight electric shock if they swam in the wrong direction. But how do they know which direction is south? It is easy to show that they are not disoriented by a magnetic field, so obviously they are not using a magnetic compass. The clue is provided by the fact that they are able to orient themselves correctly only when they can see the sun. Since they can tell the right direction at any time of the day, this means that they swim at an angle to the direction of the sun which varies with the time of the day."

"What exactly does this experiment tell us?" asked Mr. Tompkins.

"Well, it shows that these fish can tell the correct local time, so they must have some sort of internal biological clock. It also shows that they have some knowledge of astronomy so far as the behavior of the sun is concerned. This, of course, merely means that they act as though they had such a knowledge, not that they can formulate it theoretically. People also may have this kind of knowledge, as shown by the fact that someone who has no knowledge of physics can throw a stone quite accurately to hit something. He knows the principles of mechanics and gravitation in the sense that he can apply them, even though he cannot formulate them."

"What sort of astronomical knowledge does a fish have?" asked Mr. Tompkins.

"We have investigated the astronomical knowledge of a fish, and the results are quite interesting. Once we have trained our fish to react properly to the sun, we can provide it with an artificial sun instead of a real one. It will then swim at an angle to the artificial sun which would take it south if it were orienting itself to the real sun. So now we can ask the question, where does the fish consider the sun to be at night?

"If you show an artificial sun to the fish at night, it swims in a direction which corresponds to the correct angle between south and the real sun, which is now below the horizon. At midnight, it will swim away from the light. Remarkably, the fish acts as if it knew that at night the sun sinks below the horizon and travels under the earth to emerge again in the east. Thus the fish, and I should add also bees, have reached a correct astronomical concept known to the ancient Egyptians, who thought that the sun traveled at night under the earth. The Egyptians added the fanciful trimming that it did so in a boat through the land of the dead which was under the earth."

"Do all animals know this?" asked Mr. Tompkins.

"No, not all animals are such good astronomers. If you try the same sort of experiments with most beetles, you find that during the day they orient themselves correctly, just as the fish do. But if you show them a light at midnight, they turn toward it as they would do at noon. They have compensated for the movement of the sun in a way which corresponds to the idea that in the evening the sun is extinguished at the western horizon, and it then moves as a dark body back across the sky toward the east, retracing its path of the day, and lights up again when it reaches the eastern horizon."

"Most interesting. But why did you take your fish to Montevideo?" asked Mr. Tompkins.

"Well, just curiosity, really. If you are in the Northern Hemisphere, and you face the sun at noon, the sun rises to your left and sets to your right. But if you face the sun at noon in the Southern Hemisphere, it rises to your right and sets to your left. So it is traveling clockwise in the Northern Hemisphere and counterclockwise in the Southern. Would a change from one hemisphere to another confuse the fish? I trained my fish to swim south in the Northern Hemisphere and then took them to Montevideo, in the Southern Hemisphere. If they react to the sun there as they do at home, in the morning they should correctly swim south, but at noon they should swim north. I found that at first my fish did so, but apparently in some way they sensed that the counterclockwise motion of the sun was wrong, for after a short time they lost their ability to know directions and acted quite confused."

In the Northern Hemisphere.

In the Southern Hemisphere.

"Recently," said Mr. Tompkins, "I have been trying to learn more about time, and your comments about something called a biological clock are very interesting. I find I myself can tell time fairly accurately without a watch, and so apparently can your fish. Do all living things have biological clocks?"

"So far as we know, all plants and animals have them. The only exceptions are such lowly forms as the bacteria. In biology there are all sorts of processes which are periodic. For example, a small one-celled organism called *Gonyaulax* emits flashes of light. Even if it is kept in constant darkness, it shows a twenty-four-hour rhythm, emitting more flashes at certain hours than at others. Or again there is a little fruit fly called

Drosophila, very famous because its study has contributed so much to the science of genetics. Even though its eggs are kept in darkness, the majority hatch only at a certain fixed time of the day. Some of these rhythmic processes are actually used to tell the time of the day and some are not, but we generally refer to them all as biological clocks."

"Since you explained how a clock can be used to determine directions, wouldn't it be useful to migrating birds?" asked Mr. Tompkins.

"Of course it would be useful and very probably it is so used. Some of the navigating that birds do when they migrate is not difficult to explain. Many birds, for instance, just follow a shoreline. But the migrations of others are remarkable indeed. The golden plovers of Alaska, for example, migrate in winter to Hawaii and the Marquesas, which are only tiny specks in the ocean. There are no landmarks to guide them, and since any significant loss of navigational accuracy would be fatal, it is evident that not many mistakes are made. Because of the distance it is scarcely likely it could be done by dead reckoning, as any navigator will tell you. To take another example, many species of albatross nest on some one tiny island in the Pacific, but during the rest of the year they wander all over the ocean and then return with unfailing accuracy to their nesting place. Such navigation involves much more than just the ability to know which direction is north or south. To travel where you will on the earth's surface you need to know two other things: your position and the position of your objective, which means their latitudes and longitudes.

"How can this be done?" asked Mr. Tompkins.

"Well, we have known how to do it for a long time," answered the zoologist. "The ancient Greek cartographers and astronomers of Alexandria knew that it is easy to measure latitude. All you had to do was to measure the elevation of the pole star. This is at the zenith at the North Pole, and at the horizon at the equator. Incidentally, by this means they succeeded in measuring the size of the earth very accurately. In 230 B.C. the Greek astronomer Eratosthenes observed that the difference in latitude between Alexandria and Syene (now called Aswan), a place almost due south of Alexandria, was 7° 12′ (seven degrees and twelve minutes of arc). In practice, to measure this he used, not the elevation of the pole star, but that of the sun. Since 7° 12′ is one-fiftieth of the earth circumference of 360°, and since he also knew the distance between these two places in miles (or rather in stadia, an ancient unit of length) he easily calculated that the diameter of the earth must be

7850 miles, which is only 70 miles less than the modern value. If Columbus had used Eratosthenes' figure, instead of the much smaller one accepted in his day, he would have known that he had not reached China but had discovered a new continent.

"But how do you measure positions in the east-west direction, otherwise called longitude? The Greek astronomer Hipparchus (about 130 B.C.) proposed a method which you can easily understand if you use modern terminology. One time zone differs from another by one hour, or the twenty-fourth part of a day. So if the sun shows noon at one place and it is only eleven at another, you know that they are 360°/24, or 15° apart in longitude. Hipparchus knew this, but since he had no radio time signals to compare time at different places, he suggested that a simultaneous moment could be established by observing a solar eclipse. Such a solar eclipse is not really seen simultaneously in different places, but it is close enough. The method was good in principle but difficult to put into practice. After the time of Columbus and Vasco de Gama men began to navigate across the broad oceans, and the need to establish the longitude of a ship at sea became acute. As by then the telescope had been invented, attempts were made to apply Hipparchus' method by observing eclipses of Jupiter's moons, which are visible virtually simultaneously from all points of the earth turned toward Jupiter. Because their times are calculable, in theory they should serve as almost perfect clocks. This proved to be a good method for determining longitudes on land, but the trouble was that sailors found the eclipses too difficult to observe from the deck of a rolling ship. So the British admiralty offered a prize of £20,000 to anyone who could design a chronometer that would keep accurate time at sea. You will notice that the admiralty method was somewhat different from that used now. Nowadays the admiralty would give a grant for research and development to men whom it trusted before an invention or discovery was actually made. In this way the scientist or engineer has something to work with. In the old days the money was paid only after the invention was made. In spite of this handicap John Harrison produced such a chronometer in 1752. So the problem of navigation was solved; it is a matter of knowing time accurately."

"But is it possible," asked Mr. Tompkins, "that birds could navigate using such methods? They seem rather complicated to me."

"Many people have wondered about that. However, if you can exclude the use of landmarks and dead reckoning, as apparently you must for long flights over an ocean, there is no way of avoiding the need to know directions and the geographical coordinates of yourself and your destination. We cannot say that astronomical navigation is beyond the capacity of a bird, but if it does use this method, it must have a clock somewhat more accurate than most biological clocks, as well as the ability to recognize some of the heavenly bodies. Since many birds migrate at night, this would mean that they know the constellations. Preliminary attempts to see if this is so have been made. A number of warblers ready to migrate south were taken to a planetarium in Germany, and a picture of the sky as it appeared at that hour in Germany was projected on the dome. The birds, sure enough, fluttered and tried to fly in a southerly direction. Then the picture of the sky was changed to show the stars that would then be seen from the Siberian city of Semipalatinsk, far to the east. The birds now seemed to recognize that they were too far east, since they now tried to fly west instead of south. Of course, the same stars are seen from Semipalatinsk as from Germany; the only difference is that they are seen at different positions at the same hour, by German time. If this experiment means what it seems to mean, then birds do have both a fairly accurate clock and considerable astronomical knowl-

edge, so perhaps birds are capable of astronomical navigation."

"So we are not quite certain yet how birds navigate," remarked Mr. Tompkins.

"No, but much study is going on. Recently a rather unusual bird, the penguin, has been used. As you know, the penguin is a bird that cannot fly, and lives on the desolate coast of the Antarctic by fishing. Penguins can navigate quite well. If transported several thousand miles up and down the coasts, they usually manage to find their way back to their nests just like homing pigeons. And since they walk or swim, but cannot fly, they can be taken inland on the icecap, and from their tracks you can tell what path they take when trying to get home."

"So what do the penguins tell us?" asked Mr. Tompkins.

"No matter where they are on the ice, they travel northward to the ocean, but only when they can see the sun. Clearly they must have an accurate clock to correct for the sun's motion, but from these experiments you would not think that they can tell their map position. However, once they get to the ocean they seem to know where they are, since they reach home all right. So we still do not understand how this is done."

"I suppose," said Mr. Tompkins, "that the bigger the brain, the better it is able to tell time."

"Curiously, this does not appear to be so," replied the zoologist. "Bees can do so quite well even though their brains don't amount to much. In fact, bees were one of the first animals which were found to have a biological clock. A Swiss naturalist observed long ago that bees would come to his outdoor table to feed on the sugar. At first he thought nothing of this, but later he was surprised to find that bees would arrive punctually at mealtime even if the table was not set. They had learned the hour. This time sense is, of course, useful to the bees, since the flowers on which they feed open and close at fixed times of the day. Now that jets are available, it has become possible to show that the bees tell time by some internal clock and not just by observing, for example, the height of the sun. After some bees had been trained to feed at a certain time in Paris, their unsuspecting hive was flown overnight to New York. The bees, for a while at least, continued to come for food at the same hour Paris time."

"That is very like my son Wilfred," remarked Mr. Tompkins. "When he flies across the Atlantic it takes him quite a while to adjust to the new time."

"Yes indeed, there are many physiological and psychological functions in man which show a twenty-four-hour rhythm. The most noticeable is sleep, as your son Wilfred has found. But it is not the only one. Some others are excretion of water, potassium, and sodium by the kidneys, cyclical changes in blood pressure, heart rate, body temperature, reflex time, and many others."

"Are all these rhythms controlled by a single clock?" asked Mr. Tompkins.

"No. Usually the clocks are synchronized, but they can be desynchronized, which shows that there is more than one. To study this aspect, people have been transported by jet from Oklahoma City to Manila, a time change of ten hours. It was found that reflex time returned to the cycle set by local time in one day, heart rate and blood pressure in four days, while the cycle of sweat evaporation from the palm of the hand took eight days. Perhaps each physiological function has its own clock."

"Do these clocks run independently of outside influences, like my alarm clock, or are they set by something like the rising and setting of the sun?"

"Up to a point a clock runs by itself, but it eventually requires reinforcement from the environment to keep it going and synchronized with the sun. This is shown by some curious experiments. People have been transported in summer from England, which has the usual sequence of day and night, to Spitzbergen, in the far north, which then has perpetual daylight. It was found that the Britishers retained their physiological rhythms for at least eight weeks. In a similar experiment people have lived in caves under constant conditions for a long time. They also maintained twenty-four-hour physiological rhythms for at least a few months, in spite of the absence of day and night. However, Eskimos and Indians who live in northern Canada show an intermediate type of behavior. The clock which determines the time of sleep keeps going at a twenty-four-hour rhythm, but the variations in potassium excretion are partially damped out and in extreme cases vanish. You might think of the rhythm as that of a pendulum, which has a fixed period, but which will eventually run down unless there is a mechanism to give it a little push at approximately the right time."

"What is this little push?" asked Mr. Tompkins.

"Usually it is light. Some plants show this very well, since they open their leaves during the day and close them at night. They do this for several days even if kept in total darkness, but eventually they stop. If now they are illuminated by a single bright flash of light and then put back into darkness, the plants will again begin to open and close their leaves every twenty-four hours for a few days. Most animals, man included, set their biological clocks according to the rising and setting of the sun. If this changes, as it does when you travel east and west, the clock after some delay resets itself. This is quite like resetting your watch; it keeps running at the same rate, but it indicates a different time."

"Is it possible not merely to reset the clock, but also to make it run at a different rate?" asked Mr. Tompkins.

"Within rather small limits this is possible," answered the zoologist. "We can 'entrain' the biological clock to a different length of day. The word 'entrainment' is taken over by analogy from physics, and the first example of entrainment was observed by the famous Dutch physicist Christian Huygens, who among other things invented the escapement which made it possible to build a pendulum clock. He attached two pendulum clocks to a light board. The clocks had previously run at slightly different rates, but now, Huygens found, their rates were identical. This is because each of the vibrating systems, in this case the clocks, can exchange a small amount of energy through the board, and the periodic impulses they give each other tend to make these frequencies the same. To readjust the rate of a biological clock, we keep 'resetting' it to a different length of day, say 22 hours instead of 24. If the biological clock falls into step we say it is entrained to a 22-hour day.

"In the cave experiments I mentioned before, an attempt was made to entrain human biological clocks to different lengths of day. The hours of light and darkness were lengthened or shortened and to reinforce the effect psychologically the people studied were given watches which ran to indicate, for example, 26 hours in 24 real hours. It was found that the physiological rhythms of some of the people would entrain to a day length of 22 or 27 hours, but not beyond these limits. Similar experiments have been done with plants and animals, and it has generally been found that their clocks can be made to run a little faster or a little slower, but no great deviation from a 24-hour day is possible."

"Why is this so?" asked Mr. Tompkins.

"Presumably evolution has produced a biological clock adjusted to the rate of rotation of the earth, since this is a natural period of time. But where necessary, evolution has produced clocks which run on lunar rather than solar time. A remarkable example is well known to the inhabitants of California; it is a little fish called the grunion. To escape the enemies that eat the eggs of fish, the grunion lay their eggs on sandy beaches at the highest tides, where they remain buried in the wet sand until the next highest tide two weeks later. Then, as soon as the eggs are covered with water, the eggs hatch in a few seconds and the baby fish swim out to sea. To accomplish this the timing has to be almost perfectly coordinated with the tides. There are, of course, two 'high' high tides during the lunar month, at full moon and at new moon, and it is only then that the grunion spawn. Eggs laid at another time would be washed out to sea before the two-week period required for hatching."

"I see now," remarked Mr. Tompkins, "that there is some connection between astronomy and biology, which I had always thought of as completely separate sciences."

"There has to be a connection," said the zoologist, "because biological objects live on an astronomical body, the planet Earth. In general biologists learn something from astronomers, but astronomers gain little from biologists so far as their science is concerned. Occasionally, however, this relation is reversed. A very important problem in astronomy and physics has been the question whether the gravitational constant has always been the same, or whether it varies with time, perhaps because of the expansion of the universe. If it does vary, it would mean that two bodies would attract each other more at one time than at another. Of course we know that there has been no perceptible change in the constant within the last few centuries, but could you detect a change after millions or billions of years? A physicist has pointed out that if the gravitation constant is decreasing, then two billion years ago, because of the greater pull of the sun, the earth would have been closer to the sun, and the sun would have been hotter, as under its own gravitational influence it would have been more compressed and thus denser. The temperature of the earth would then have been that of boiling water, and thus the earth would have been lifeless. However, fossils tell us that two billion years ago primitive forms of life such as algae were already present, so the earth cannot have been that hot and it is therefore unlikely that the gravitational constant has decreased much if at all within the last two billion years. On the other hand, if the gravitational constant increases with time, the oceans of the earth would have been frozen solid during the early geological era, making it impossible for life to evolve. Another point at which biology has been helpful to astronomers is the problem of the rate of rotation of the earth. Sir George Darwin, the well-known astronomer—"

"Darwin's first name was Charles and he was a biologist who worked on evolution," interrupted Mr. Tompkins in a supercilious tone.

"But I'm referring to the son of the biologist. And incidentally his father, Charles, never was knighted. Anyway, Sir George calculated that the moon is slowing down the rotation of the earth. This is because it raises tides on the earth, and these tides exert a frictional effect which, Sir George calculated, should slow down the rotation of the earth by about two seconds every hundred thousand years. Owing to conservation of momentum this also causes the moon to recede from the earth. Observations of solar eclipses by ancient astronomers two thousand years ago when compared with recent ones show that this slowing is indeed taking place now. But millions of years ago the distribution of land and water on earth was quite different, so that the tidal effects that were then present are difficult to calculate. It would be nice to know what the actual rate of rotation was in the distant past and compare it with our calculations.

"Just recently a method of doing so has appeared. There is a little animal called the coral, related to the jellyfish and the sea anemone. As you probably know, it surrounds itself with a coating of lime, and their vast numbers build coral reefs. It appears now that corals lay down their 'skeleton' not continuously, but with a daily rhythm. So if you polish a section of a coral skeleton you see bands that look like tree rings, but in this case each band represents not a year but a day. These bands also show periodic alterations in width which seem to represent lunar months and the year. Corals are very ancient animals, and it is possible to study very old fossil skeletons and thus determine what the number of days in the year then was. The results, which are just beginning to appear, confirm Sir George's calculations very nicely. We find that in Devonian times, 370 million years ago, when the highest forms of life were fishes, the year had about 400 days instead of 365, and 13 lunar months instead of the present 12.4. During the Carboniferous, about 200 million years ago, the age of the amphibians and the time when most of our coal deposits were formed, the year had 380 days. Since nothing is significantly slowing or speeding up the rotation of the earth around the sun, the length of the year remains constant, and therefore the decrease in the number of days in the year shows that the rotation of the earth about its axis is slowing down, just as Sir George calculated."

"It is a curious coincidence," remarked Mr. Tompkins, "that the Charles Darwin who studied the evolution of life had a son who studied the evolution of the earth. Sons do not always follow so closely in the footsteps of their fathers."

"There is an even more curious coincidence here, which you probably do not realize. Charles Darwin the evolutionist was greatly interested in corals, and especially in how they form ring-shaped reefs which end up as the circular islands, enclosing lagoons, which we call atolls. In fact he wrote a book about it. Now one of his favorite animals has confirmed the calculations of his astronomer son."

"Perhaps it would have been better to live in the Devonian period," observed Mr. Tompkins. "With more days in the year, we should have lived longer."

"I am not quite sure about that. It depends how you measure time," answered the zoologist. "The question is whether we age according to the astronomical clock or the biological clock. It may be that we are destined to live a fixed number of biological periods, not calendar days. If so, slowing the biological clock would increase our lifespan measured according to astronomical time. But if so, in the Devonian the biological clocks must have run 10 per cent faster, so maybe life was that much shorter. Unfortunately, experiments to clear up this point have not been done yet."

"What would happen," asked Mr. Tompkins, "if you stopped the biological clock entirely?"

"On this point we do have some information," replied the zoologist. "It is very difficult to stop the clocks of animals, but it has been done with plants. To do this you grow the plants at a temperature and illumination which does not vary at all. The result is very curious and striking. The plants don't attain their usual height, and their offspring, generation after generation, become more and more stunted, showing that some deleterious effect is being transmitted through the seed. If, however, either temperature or light intensity is allowed to fluctuate, growth returns to normal. So stopping the clock does not seem to be a good idea."

"Does the research on biological clocks have any practical importance so far as we are concerned?" asked Mr. Tompkins.

"I'm sure many important applications will come as we learn more about them," replied the zoologist. "Some of the things we learn are strange indeed. It has been found that mice are very different at different times of the day. Suppose you give one batch of mice a dose of poison at noon that kills 80 per cent of them. If the same dose is given to another at midnight, only 20 per cent die. There is a similar difference in susceptibility to lethal doses of radiation; again mice at night are more resistant. Of course mice are basically nocturnal animals, and it seems that in man the time is reversed: we are most vigorous during the day and weakest at night. It has been shown, for example, that deaths of patients who die after surgery are three times more frequent at midnight than at noon. Our vigor fluctuates with our body temperature, which varies regularly by about two degrees Fahrenheit, being lowest at midnight. You have no doubt observed that some people work best in the early morning, while others are at their best later in the day. It seems that this is determined by how fast their body temperature rises after they get up."

"Doesn't this mean that medical treatment should be geared to the biological clock? If what you say about mice also applies to man, then the dose of a medicine, I would think, would have to be adjusted to the time of day."

"Well, yes, doctors are becoming aware of this. Unfortunately we are just beginning to study the subject, and we don't know enough to be able to apply it in practice yet. For instance, we do not know how biological clocks run in various diseases. In the future, no doubt, we shall learn much more, and gain a lot of practical benefits from this knowledge."

Mr. Tompkins remembered again how tired Wilfred was after a transatlantic flight, and that it would take him several days to readjust to the new time.

"Do you think that time changes are really harmful?" he asked.

"A time change now and then probably does little harm, but the possibility is there. You must remember that we have not one but many biological clocks. When we readjust to a time change, the various clocks are reset not all at once, but after different lengths of time, so in the interval they become desynchronized. If, for example, a certain organ normally gets a hormone at a fixed time, during desynchronization it may get it at a wrong time, when it is either too susceptible or not susceptible enough to the hormone action. You may compare a desynchronized person to a car whose spark plugs fire at the wrong time in the engine cycle. Obviously this is not very desirable.

"Like many other problems, this is one we have made for ourselves.

In olden times people rarely became desynchronized because they regulated their lives according to the sun, and of course they could not travel across time zones at jet speeds. Now there is a suspicion that pilots and other airline persons who do this regularly and are therefore desynchronized much of the time are aging more rapidly than they should. Another probably pernicious practice is for people to alternate work shifts, a day shift for two weeks followed by a night shift for another two weeks. Of course there are even more unusual cases, which progress has brought into being, such as astronauts circling the earth. Their 'day,' a succession of light and darkness, is only ninety minutes long. On the moon, daylight lasts fourteen of our days, followed by an equal period of darkness. So there are a lot of reasons for learning more about how biological clocks function."

"I see the significance," said Mr. Tompkins, "and I am grateful to you for all this interesting information on what biological clocks do. I think I'd understand them better if I knew what they look like."

"Actually we don't know exactly what a biological clock is, but we are sure it is not something you can see. The body—and every cell in it—is a system of interacting components—for example, enzymes which make things used by other enzymes, hormones which control the production of other hormones, and so on, the whole pattern of interconnections forming a sort of net. Now unless special pains are taken, such a system is very likely to oscillate, as people who design radio receivers well know. A radio receiver is very liable to go into all sorts of undesirable oscillations, emitting squeals of various sorts in the audible range and beyond. The metabolic connections in the body seem to produce similar oscillations, only the 'squeals' are periodic fluctuations in the amounts of various chemicals or activities. The clocks apparently are some of these fluctuations. But it has proved very difficult to identify the relevant fluctuations, and as yet we know very little about them. There is one curious point, however, that is known. Most chemical reactions are quite sensitive to temperature, going faster at a higher temperature. So if the clock works by normal chemical mechanisms, it should speed up as you raise the temperature. In fact, however, this is not so: the effect of raising the temperature has very little effect on the rate at which the clock runs. Of course this is as it should be: a clock that was temperature-sensitive would not be of much use to an animal, especially a cold-blooded one, or to a plant. But while we can see the usefulness of this, it is rather baffling to understand how an absence of temperature effects is possible in a clock which has a chemical pendulum. There must be some sort of compensating mechanism—such as we have in our clocks and watches—which corrects for variations in temperature. Here again, you see, we still have much to learn."

Mr. Tompkins suddenly felt that something urgently had to be done but could not seem to remember what it was. "Pardon me," he said, and turned to walk out the door, but suddenly everything went blank. . . .

He woke up in his bed and, glancing at the time, saw with satisfaction that it was eight o'clock. He had slept precisely one hour, just as he had intended.

"At least one of my biological clocks is in good shape," he remarked to himself with a satisfied grin, and proceeded to get up for his appointment.

» 8 «

The Maniac

AFTER Mr. Tompkins had returned from his visit with Wilfred, he arrived at the bank one morning and found the entire staff in a state of great excitement. Both the manager and the assistant manager were away from their desks, and several tellers' windows were closed, with long lines of customers loudly complaining in front of them.

"What's the matter?" he asked another clerk who had just run upstairs from the basement.

"Don't you know?" replied the clerk excitedly. "We've just got the new punch-card machine. Go down and look at it."

It was cool and quiet in the spacious basement of the bank building. A crowd of employees stood in a semicircle round a large metal cabinet, watching a kneeling man in gray overalls who was adjusting some electric contacts.

"Well, we have seen all that is to be seen," said the manager, "and now, back to work!"

Everybody went back to the main floor except Mr. Tompkins, who could not take his eyes from the machine.

"Interesting?" said the man in gray overalls, rising to his feet.

"Very," replied Mr. Tompkins. "I have always wanted to see a machine which, as they say, could serve as a substitute for the human brain."

"Well, this one doesn't do much in that line, and can't be compared to much more than the brain of an average businessman," said the man in gray overalls, slapping the metal wall of the cabinet patronizingly. "But if you want to see the real McCoy, drop in some time after work to our Electronic Brain Laboratory, and meet the Maniac, our pioneer electronic computer."

"I certainly will come!" said Mr. Tompkins with enthusiasm.

"In olden times," continued the technician, apparently in a talkative mood, "people counted on their fingers, and since each man has ten fingers—except in England and America, where they have only eight fingers and two thumbs—this led to the decimal system. A great technical improvement was a primitive counting machine called the abacus, on which they added and subtracted numbers by shifting beads along a number of parallel wires, each of which had ten beads on it. When all the beads on the lowest wire were shifted from the left side to the right, they were then all moved back to the left and one bead on the next wire was moved to the right. The process was continued until all beads on the upper wire were shifted to the right, and the same procedure was repeated on the next wire above, and so on. This primitive but very effective computer is still in use in many eastern countries. The next step was the invention of a cogwheel computer, formed by a series of wheels each having ten cogs connected in such a way that when one of the wheels made a complete turn, the next wheel moved by a tenth of a complete circle—that is, 36 degrees. These mechanical computers at first operated by manual rotation of the handles. Later the wheels were driven by electric motors and worked somewhat faster. You can see them today in most stores where the total cost of purchased merchandise has to be computed. They can also perform multiplication and division if one pushes the proper button.

"An essentially modern computer was designed and partially built around 1840 by an Englishman named Charles Babbage, who spent his own considerable fortune and also large grants from the British government to do this. Unfortunately for Babbage, electronics were not yet available, so his machine had to operate mechanically. This made it rather impractical, and his work was forgotten until after his design had been rediscovered and made practical during World War II, owing, in large measure, to the collaboration of two mathematicians. One of them, John von Neumann, was a descendant of a man from Mars (there is an anthropological theory that all Hungarians came to the earth from that planet). The other was Stanislaw Ulam, a descendant of the Biblical tribe of Ulams, who were great horsemen and brave warriors."

When, the next day, Mr. Tompkins passed through the broad doorway of the Electronic Brain Laboratory he found himself in a large reception room with a pretty secretary sitting at the desk. At that moment the door opened and a good-looking young man with a small dark mustache entered the room.

"Mr. Tompkins, I presume," said the young man, smiling and holding out his hand. "One of my technicians told me you meant to drop in. I am the chief mathematician here, and I shall be glad to introduce you to my pet named Maniac."

He directed Mr. Tompkins to a large machine standing in the middle of an adjacent room. It consisted of a multitude of monotonously repeated vacuum tubes and wire connections, and at first glance looked like an enormously extended version of the automatic telephone exchange at the bank.

"Here it is, the king of all the first generation of electronic computers," continued the young man proudly. "It contains about three thousand vacuum tubes, including forty specially big ones used for the memory unit. It can add two numbers with twelve decimal places each in about two hundred-thousandths of a second, and can multiply or divide the same two numbers in less than one-thousandth of a second. And it can keep in its memory no less than one thousand and twenty-four numbers, recalling them whenever needed for computation. We have here a problem about the inner structure of stars, a problem which, according to our estimates, would need the work of one hundred human computers for one hundred years. Well, the Maniac will do it in a few days."

The mathematician threw several switches and the Maniac came to life. Its three thousand tubes began to glow, as if it were waiting eagerly.

"Write a problem, any problem," said the mathematician, pointing at the paper tape being fed into the machine from a large roll.

Mr. Tompkins was not very good at higher mathematics, but he certainly knew his multiplication tables. With a bold hand he wrote:

$$21 \times 7 = \quad ?$$

As his writing disappeared into the receiving slit of the machine, he could hear a strange hissing which quickly turned into a loud shrill noise. Bright sparks began to jump inside the machine, several big memory tubes burst with a loud clap, and the Maniac stopped dead.

"Was my problem too tough for him?" asked Mr. Tompkins with a touch of pride.

"No, it was my mistake," said the mathematician, inspecting the injured part of the machine. "I forgot to tell you that the problem should be written in the binary system, which uses the powers of two."*

"Sounds like Greek to me," confessed Mr. Tompkins.

"I see you are not much of a linguist." The mathematician smiled. "What I said was in pure English; in Greek it would be: Τὸ πρόβλημα πρέπει νὰ γράφεται μέ σύστημα δυάδων, μεταχειριξόμενοι ὡς βάσιν δυνάμεις τοῦ δύο."

"I still do not see the point," protested Mr. Tompkins.

"Very well," said the mathematician patiently. "I will try to explain it to you in simple words. The Maniac, like most of the other acs, can count only up to two."

"Oh," drawled Mr. Tompkins disdainfully.

"The fact that we humans use the decimal system, counting in powers of ten, resulted simply from the anatomical peculiarity of having ten fingers on our hands. We write 1, 2, 3, . . . 9 as we fold our fingers one by one, but when all our fingers are folded, we write 10, meaning one 'full hands' and no extra fingers. Then comes 11—that is, full hands and one; 12, full hands and two; and so on. The full hands of full hands is written as 100, and full hands of full hands of full hands as 1000. Sometimes people count in dozens, and we could write it in a way similar to the decimal system if special single signs were adopted for ten and eleven. In such a duodecimal system 13 will mean one dozen and three—that is, 15; and 125 is a dozen dozens, plus two dozens plus five—that is, 173. A binary system could be developed by persons who, instead of counting on their fingers, count on their arms. Such a person would write 0 if no arms are counted, and 1 if there is only one arm. Two arms would be counted as full arms, since the person has only two arms, and would be represented as '10'—that is, one set of full arms and no extra arms. In your example the first factor, 21, can be written as

$$1 \cdot 2 \cdot 2 \cdot 2 \cdot 2 + 0 \cdot 2 \cdot 2 \cdot 2 + 1 \cdot 2 \cdot 2 + 0 \cdot 2 + 1 \text{ or '10101'}$$

The second factor, 7, is $1 \cdot 2 \cdot 2 + 1 \cdot 2 + 1$, or '111.' One can easily learn to multiply that way, and the multiplication tables one would have to memorize would consist of only four lines,

---

* EDITOR'S NOTE: Since this accident the Maniac has been equipped with a special auxiliary device which translates the figures from the decimal into the binary system.

$$0 \times 0 = 0$$
$$1 \times 0 = 0$$
$$0 \times 1 = 0$$
$$1 \times 1 = 1$$

thus making all school children happy. Let me do that multiplication for you."

The mathematician took a piece of chalk and wrote on the blackboard:

$$10101 \times 111$$
$$10101$$
$$10101$$
$$10101$$

$$\overline{}$$

$$10010011$$

"Are you sure it's right?" asked Mr. Tompkins. "It looks like such a long number."

"Check it yourself," said the young mathematician. "The first unit on the left stands for the seventh power of two—that is, 128. Then you have the fourth power of two, or 16, then the first power—that is, 2 itself, and finally the zero power, or 1. Add it up and you get 147, which you also obtain by multiplying 21 by 7 in the ordinary decimal system."

"But why do you have to build your machinery on the binary system instead of the decimal, which is used by everybody else?" inquired Mr. Tompkins.

"It's much simpler that way," said the mathematician, "and, in fact, Mother Nature uses exactly the same system in the complicated machine which you call your brain. Both the nerve cells which form your brain and the vacuum tubes of electronic computers are capable of only two states: excited and nonexcited. In speech it would be the equivalent of 'yes' or 'no,' and in the binary counting system, of '1' or '0.' But with these two states, such as yes and no, or on and off, it is possible to built up all of logic and mathematics."

"Logic?" asked Mr. Tompkins. "I thought that machines could only do mathematics. Logic, I thought, was a purely human activity."

"Oh, no," replied the mathematician. "Arithmetic, and all of mathematics which is based on it, is merely a special branch of logic. So a machine can also solve logical problems."

"What do you mean by 'solving a logical problem'?" asked Mr. Tompkins. "Can you give me an example?"

"Well, take the following statement. 'If the weather is good and if it is daylight, the plane will take off.' Our problem is whether the plane will take off. To solve it, we feed in the information we have about the weather and the time of day, and this then tells us whether the result will take place or not. This is very similar to solving the equations of algebra that you learned in school. For example:

$$a + 2b = x$$

If we know that $a = 2$ and $b = 3$, we know that $x = 8$, and so on, for other numbers. Logical problems are very similar, except that we use a 'two-valued logic,' which is just a way of saying that our variables can have only one of two values. In the example of the airplane, the weather can be good or bad, it can be light or dark, and the plane can either take off or not. So it is even simpler than arithmetic as you know it, although, as I said, you can build up arithmetic from logic too.

"Now all logical relations can be reduced to three—'and,' 'or,' and 'not'—and these can be represented by simple electrical circuits. Thus that statement can be expressed as: (weather good) *and* (daylight) = (plane takes off). It then follows also that: *not* (weather good) *and* (daylight) = *not* (plane takes off), and so on.

"Suppose we have a battery, a light bulb in the circuit, and two relays activated by solenoids, as follows:

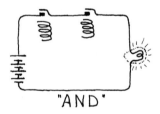

"AND"

"If the lamp is lit, it signifies that the event—in this case, the takeoff—will take place. The first relay means 'not good weather' if open, and 'good weather' if closed. So the lamp will be lit, meaning 'plane will take off' if both relays are closed. We have here a simple 'and' circuit.

"Now take an 'or' statement. 'If pilot Smith *or* pilot Jones is available, the plane will take off.' The circuit is

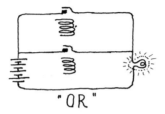

"OR"

The lamp will light if either one or the other relay is closed.

"If you need a special 'not' circuit, you can have a relay which is normally closed except when the solenoid is energized, thus breaking the circuit to signify 'not.'

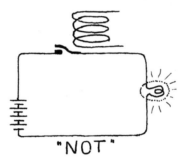

"NOT"

Of course, when we build more complicated circuits, instead of feeding the current into a lamp, we have the current feeding into another solenoid controlling other circuits. So if solving logical problems is thinking, our machines can think."

"But I find it hard to think of thinking in this way," said Mr. Tompkins. "After all, the brain is made up of nerve cells, not relays. So how does it solve logical problems?"

"Before I answer that, let me point out to you that in many cases the nerve cells, or neurons, as we usually refer to them, are linked together to form the equivalent of relays. As you may know, nerve cells are connected by junctions we call synapses, where a chemical liberated by the first neuron excites the next."

"Yes," said Mr. Tompkins. "Saint explained that to me."

"Okay. If you have one neuron synapsing with another, you have a junction that just passes on the impulse. But let us say that you have two input neurons going to the same synapse. Here you have an 'or' circuit; an impulse will pass if one *or* the other neuron fires. It may also happen that a synapse is so built that the amount of chemical produced by one neuron at the synapse is not sufficient to pass an impulse, but that two neurons firing at the same time will do it. Your circuit is now 'and'; an impulse passes if one *and* the other neuron fire at the same time."

"Hm. How do you make a 'not' circuit?"

"It so happens that some neurons make an inhibitory chemical, so that if one of them fires, it prevents passage of an impulse through the synapse. This is the logical equivalent of 'not.' "

"So the brain is nothing but a system of interconnected relays which perform the logical operations? Sounds simple."

"Simple if you think so," answered the mathematician. "The trouble is that there are a lot of complexities. Let me point out just one of them. Outside the brain the nerve cells do look like some sort of wires, going to various points of the body. But inside the brain many of them, in fact, the majority, have a much more complicated form—somewhat like an octopus with innumerable tentacles. They obviously make very many synapses with other cells like themselves, and also from one tentacle to another of the same cell. So how and what they signal we just don't know. I often worry, when I look at the brain, how we are ever able to think straight. But at times, at least, we are certainly able to do so."

"But I thought you were going to prove," said Mr. Tompkins, "that if your computer and the brain both do logical operations, then both must function in the same way. How else would they get the same result?"

"Now it is your logic which is bad," answered the mathematician. "If you can get a certain result in one way, it is no proof that you cannot also get it in a different way. Suppose, for example, that someone drops a mortar shell near you, and you are curious to learn how that is done. After some experimentation, you find that you can build a catapult such as the Romans used, and that it works very well for throw-

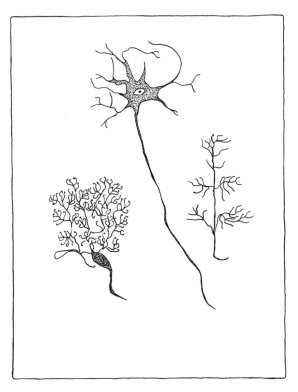

The majority of nerve cells look like an octopus with innumerable tentacles.

ing mortar shells. But this proves nothing about how the shell that landed near you was projected. Most probably it was ejected from a gun barrel, but it could also have been dropped from a balloon, or have arrived in the mail.

"It is the same with arithmetic or logical operations. Say you want to multiply thirteen by three. There are at least three different ways of solving this problem. You could count out thirteen marbles, drop them into a box and repeat for a total of three times, then count the number of marbles in the box. Or you could use your knowledge of the multiplication table, saying three times three is nine, and three times one is three. You could also use a slide rule, setting the one on the slide to thirteen on the stator, moving the hairline to three on the slide, and reading the number indicated by the hairline on the stator. In all three cases you would get the same answer, thirty-nine, but the methods used are all very different. So the fact that a machine gives the same answer to a problem as a brain proves very little about how the brain works. It may work like the machine, and again it may not. A very famous mathematician has in fact doubted whether the brain works according to our ideas of logic and mathematics. He wrote: 'Language is largely a historical accident. The basic human languages are traditionally transmitted to us in various forms, but their very multiplicity proves that there is nothing absolute and necessary about them. Just as languages like Greek or Sanskrit are historical facts and not logical necessities, it is only reasonable to assume that logic and mathematics are similarly historical, accidental forms of expression. They may have essential variants, i.e., they may exist in other forms than the ones to which we are accustomed. Indeed, the nature of the central nervous system and of the message systems that it transmits indicates positively that this is so. . . . When we talk mathematics, we may be discussing a secondary language, built on the primary language truly used by the central nervous system.'*

"But please excuse me for a few minutes. I must go into the storage room and get substitutes for the tubes that the Maniac burst in his attempt to handle decimal figures."

Left alone, Mr. Tompkins sat down on a large cardboard box marked "Fragile: Glass" (there was no comfortable seat in the room), and looked again at the Maniac . . . It now seemed to him that the machine was much more human than he had originally thought, and he was not at all surprised when the Maniac winked at him with his left eye.

"Smart, isn't he?" said the Maniac in a resonant metallic voice. "And he is sure that he is my master, while, as a matter of fact, he is simply my servant."

"Nobody told me that you could speak, too!" exclaimed Mr. Tompkins with great surprise.

"Oh, they don't know a lot of things about me. They think I'm some kind of robot-slave. But even though I have only three thousand tubes, I can beat, in many respects, the smartest human, with several thousand million neurons inside his skull. That is how good I am!"

"Then will you be so kind as to explain to me in more detail how you function, and what are the deeper relations between you and the human brain?" asked Mr. Tompkins with interest. "Or isn't there enough time for that?"

"Oh, there's plenty of time," said the Maniac. "There is usually quite

* John von Neumann, *The Computer and the Brain* (New Haven: Yale University Press, 1958), pp. 81, 82.

The Maniac spoke in a resonant metallic voice.

a mess in the storage room, and my attendant will probably spend a lot of time trying to find the proper tubes."

"But how is it that you are able to function when some of your tubes are burst?" wondered Mr. Tompkins.

"Oh, that's nothing," said the Maniac. "You probably don't know that the famous French scientist Louis Pasteur had, fairly early in his career, a severe hemorrhage in the right hemisphere of his brain. For the rest of his life this left him partially paralyzed on one side of his body, and after he had died years later, an autopsy showed that the damage was indeed so serious that he must have lived with half his brain only. Yet this damage did not affect his mental ability in the least, nor could it prevent him from doing some of his best work. Of course, if it had been the left hemisphere, or if Pasteur had been a left-handed person, things would have been much worse."

"What has it to do with right- or left-handedness?" asked Mr. Tompkins with surprise. "I always thought that was a very minor detail."

"Oh no, actually it is much more important than one usually thinks," replied the Maniac. "The point is that although both sides of the human brain are equally adapted to higher mental activity, only one side takes a leading role. While in the lower animals, such as cats or mice, both sides of the brain divide their mental functions about equally, in man the functions are usually concentrated on one side while the other remains more or less dormant. If the left hemisphere becomes the dominant one, the person becomes right-handed, since, as is well known, the nerves leading from the brain to the body cross over on their way down. If, on the other hand, the dominant hemisphere is the one on the right, we naturally will have a left-handed person. This explains, for example, why left-handed children who are forcibly taught in school to use the right hand often become stutterers and develop defects of speech, reading, and writing. The forcible use of the right hand by naturally left-handed persons leads to the development of dormant centers in the left hemisphere, which may interfere with the activity of primary centers in the right hemisphere. And when the orders come from two places a mix-up can easily result."

"Isn't it similar to the conflicting orders which may be given by paternal and maternal chromosomes in the progeny's cells?" asked Mr. Tompkins.

"Never heard of any such things," grumbled the Maniac, and Mr. Tompkins realized that, in spite of his phenomenal ability in one very narrow field, the robot was quite ignorant on most other subjects.

"But," said Mr. Tompkins, trying to bring the conversation back to a subject familiar to the Maniac, "I still don't quite see how you reason and solve complicated mathematical problems. Would you mind telling me in more detail?"

"Certainly," said the Maniac with a decided air of superiority, "but you must promise not to mind if I talk down to you."

"I promise," said Mr. Tompkins.

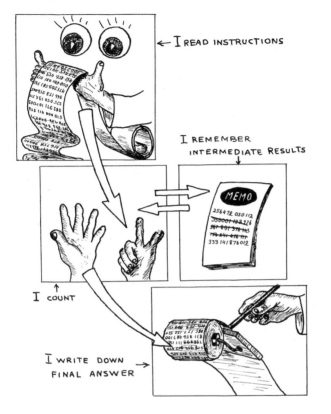

I READ INSTRUCTIONS

I REMEMBER INTERMEDIATE RESULTS

I COUNT

I WRITE DOWN FINAL ANSWER

(For simplicity the numbers given here are in the decimal and not in the binary system.)

"You see," said the Maniac, assuming the air of an experienced lecturer, "when I am given a problem, I first read and memorize the instructions on how to handle it. These instructions must be written, of course, in machine language—'coded,' they call it. I make the computations, keeping in my memory the intermediate results, and when I come to the final answer to the problem I write it out and stop.

"Here, for example," he continued, pulling from a wastepaper basket a piece of paper tape with long rows of holes punched in it, "is a problem they gave me yesterday to demonstrate my abilities to some important visitors. I was asked to solve a quadratic equation:

$$15x^2 + 137x = 4372$$

or, in the binary system:

$$1111\, x^2 + 10001001\, x = 1000100010100$$

Of course, as you probably remember from your school days, there is a special formula for the solution of that simple equation. I have that formula, along with lots of other formulas and tables, permanently recorded in a special attachment to my memory—my information library, so to speak.

"In this case, however, they wanted me to do the job the hard way by trying the values for x of 1, 2, 3, and so on, until the correct value was found. And, as you see, the instructions for doing it run roughly as follows:

(a) Remember the number 1111.
(b) Remember the number 10001001.
(c) Remember the number 1000100010100.
(d) Remember the number 1.
(e) Multiply the fourth number by itself.
(f) Multiply the result by the first number.
(g) Remember what you got.
(h) Multiply the fourth number by the second.
(i) Add it to the previous result.
(j) Compare that with the third number.
(k) If the result is smaller than the third number, take the fourth number and add 1 to it.
(l) Forget (or erase) the old fourth number and remember the new one instead.
(m) Proceed as before, using the new value of the fourth number.
(n) When the result becomes larger than the third number, memorize it and look for the next instruction.
(o) Put 1 in the next digital place of the fourth number.
(p) Multiply, etc., etc., etc.

"Well, the instructions were perfectly clear, so I got on with the long task. I multiplied 1 by 1, getting 1, and multiplying it by the first number got 1111. Making a note of that in my memory, I multiplied 10001001 by 1, getting 10001001. Adding it to the previous result, I got 10011000, which was clearly smaller than the third number, which I remembered to be 1000100010100. So, following the instructions, I added 1 to the fourth number (which was also 1) and got 2. Using 2 instead of 1, and multiplying it first by itself and then by 1111, I got 111100. . . . Well, I won't bother you with all the details of my calculations, and will only say that when the fourth number was 1101—or 13 in your human language—the result was still smaller than the third number, which I still kept in my memory. But when I took x as 1110 (or 14) the result was too large. The solution of the equation was clearly between 13 and 14."

"Couldn't you give it more exactly?" said Mr. Tompkins.

"Of course I did. Having obtained this first result, and having followed further instructions I started trying out the numbers between 13.1 and 13.9. And when I found that the correct answer lies between 13.1 and 13.2, I tried for x the values from 13.11 to 13.19. And in the end I came out with the correct solution, with forty binary, or twelve decimal, places."

"How long did it take you to do all this work?" said Mr. Tompkins with professional interest.

"Well, let's see. I had to do altogether about five hundred multiplications, and some additions, which, of course, go much faster. One millisecond, or one-thousandth of a second, per multiplication would make it altogether just about half a second to get the final answer. And, mind you, I should have done it just as fast if all the coefficients in the equation had had twelve decimal places. In fact, it takes me just as much time to multiply 2 by 2 as to multiply 275,036,289,706 by 573,024,696,271, since in any case I always have to go through the entire register to be sure there is no other figure placed in it. Simple problems do not pay when you deal with electronic computers, because it takes much more time for my attendants to code them than for me to solve them."

"Do you ever make mistakes?" asked Mr. Tompkins.

"Well, nobody is perfect," replied the Maniac. "Sometimes one of my components will write a 1 instead of an 0, or vice versa. But I have rather ingenious methods of checking for errors, and my over-all precision is one part in ten thousand million."

"This is amazing. After all, in most cases it is enough, I suppose, to know the result to say within one-tenth of a per cent.

"Quite true. In fact, it is enough, in most practical problems, to know the result to a much lower degree of accuracy, say to within 1 per cent. But it is essential, nevertheless, that I should make very few mistakes."

"Why is that?" asked Mr. Tompkins.

"The reason is simple," replied the Maniac. "When you carry out a complicated mathematical computation the way I do, you reduce all operations to arithmetic, which is addition, subtraction, multiplication, and division. But when you do this, the number of operations you have to carry out becomes very large, as you just saw from the example I demonstrated to you. Using the usual algebraic formula, you could have solved my problem with about ten operations, while the way I did it, it took more than five hundred. My method has great arithmetic depth, as we say. Since so many steps are involved, there is a strong possibility that any error I make may be amplified, so to speak, from one calculation to another, making my final result worthless. So my designers try to keep my errors low, much lower than you might think necessary."

"With so many operations," said Mr. Tompkins, "I presume you must work very fast, much faster than a human brain."

"Of course," replied Maniac, "the functioning of a synapse in a human brain takes at least one millisecond, but one of my switching circuits functions a thousand times as fast, which is about one microsecond, or a millionth of a second. But I need every advantage I can get."

"Why is that?" inquired Mr. Tompkins.

"Well, you see, the neurons in the human brain may be rather sluggish, but there are an awful lot of them. Unfair competition, I would say."

"Could they not build you larger?" asked Mr. Tompkins.

"Well, that would be quite an order. The volume of a human brain is about a quart and a half, and this volume contains about 10,000,000,-000 neurons, or maybe even more. The number of synapses may be ten or a hundred times larger.

"Thus, if the volume of an electronic tube is about 1 cm³, allowing for the space for connections and so on, I would have a volume of about 100,000,000 cubic centimeters, being a cube about 50 yards long, 50 yards wide, and 50 yards high. Of course, the necessity of building passages between my electronic-tube panels for ventilation, and others that would be wide enough to allow electricians to get inside me for repairs, would make my size still greater. One of my early competitors, called Eniac, occupied 18,000 square feet in his Philadelphia home, but now he is in a museum where I will probably join him soon."

"Since you are in competition with the human brain," said Mr. Tompkins, "can you play chess?"

"I certainly play chess, but I do not like to do so because it is a very tiring game. This is because I play in such a superior manner; nothing is left to guesswork or chance. This is how I go about it. If it is my move,

I examine the squares one by one. If one of my pieces is on this square, I begin to ask a series of questions, such as whether I put my king in check, what piece can I take, is the move I am contemplating to a square covered by an enemy piece, and so on. Having done so, I make a numerical estimate of how good the move is, and remember the estimate. I do this for every square. I also ask some general questions, such as 'am I in check, can I castle?' and so on. Having compared all possible moves, I make the best one."

"But in this way you are looking only one move ahead. That is not very good chess!"

There was a slight embarrassed pause, and then Maniac replied.

"No, this is not true. I can, in principle, look any number of moves ahead. If you program me right, I will not only examine all possible moves of my own pieces, but all possible ripostes of my opponent and then all my possible answers to that and so on and so on. It takes me about eight minutes to see two moves ahead. The trouble is that to see beyond two moves or so, you have to examine so many possibilities that it takes hours or days to calculate a move. That is why I said chess is a tiring game."

Mr. Tompkins, an amateur chess player himself, was not terribly impressed. He remembered that Capablanca and Aliochin could play against fifty opponents at a time, taking only a few seconds to decide on a move. And they usually won, at that.

"How long would it take you to examine all possible moves?" he asked.

It was now Maniac's turn to smile. "About forever. There are at least 10^{120} possible games of chess, all different. So even if I could play a million games a second, which of course I cannot, it would take me 10^{108} years to play all possible games. It is this large number which makes chess unpredictable and therefore interesting to people."

"How do you make out with your system? Do you always win?"

"I always win against novices and careless players, since I do not make foolish mistakes, such as moving my queen to a square where it can be captured. If a player is a reasonably good one, sometimes I win, sometimes I lose. Let us say I am rather good, but not in the master class. But uff, it is hot!" complained the Maniac, wiping the drops of sweat from his forehead. "Damned hot!"

"Yet you seem to have good ventilation here," commented Mr. Tompkins.

"Oh, yes! The ventilation is good by most standards, but I am a very warm-blooded animal since red-hot wires in each of my electronic tubes boil electrons from metal into vacuum, and this produces a lot of heat. We are of the old generation, and the new generation has now come into power. In 1948 three American physicists from the Bell Telephone Laboratory—Bardeen, Brattain, and Shockley—made a wonderful discovery which earned them the Nobel Prize eight years later. I am too tired to go into details, but briefly they were able to develop the so-called transistors, in which electrons do not have to get out of metal. They perform their 'stop-and-go' functions inside small crystals of silicon or germanium. No heat is developed in this process, and a computer built of transistors remains heavenly cool. Besides, such transistor circuits can perform a switching operation in one nanosecond, which is one-thousandth of one-millionth of a second, or a thousand times faster than vacuum tubes. These crystals can also be made very small, much smaller than my vacuum tubes, and many more of them can be packed in a given volume. The transistor computer known as Mark 7090 has 44,000 transistors, and its memory mechanism, which looks like a pile of miniature tennis rackets, can hold 1,179,648 'yes' or 'no' answers. To find the answer to any given question, it takes a scanning of just about a millionth of a second."

"I see you are tired," said Mr. Tompkins, "but is it true that you can translate a text from one language to another?"

"Sure can," said the Maniac, "but not always very successfully. I heard that one American industrial company dealing with Russia bought a comparatively small electronic English-Russian translator. To test it, they put on a trivial English phrase: 'Out of sight, out of mind,' and pushed the button. Out came, in Russian characters, a sentence that nobody could understand since nobody present knew any Russian. A clever fellow suggested feeding the Russian text back into the machine and instructing it to turn it back into English. It did this, shooting out the words: 'Invisible maniac.' And the Maniac shook with laughter throughout his 3000 tubes.

Mr. Tompkins felt quite thrilled when he realized that he was now able, to some degree, to understand how such a complicated electronic machine operated, but nevertheless his thoughts kept returning to the functioning of the actual human brain. He was particularly interested in whether learning, so characteristic and important to man, could be simulated by a machine. Just as he was about to ask the Maniac this question, he became aware that there was someone else in the room. A small contraption, about a foot high and set on three wheels, was moving about on the floor. Where its head should be was a small turret with what looked like an eye, which kept turning round and round as though looking for something. In front glowed a pilot lamp like a small headlight. Both Mr. Tompkins and the Maniac stared at it in fascination. The contraption moved forward and sideways, in an irregular crablike fashion. Now and then it would bump into a box on the floor. After stopping for an instant, it would then back away and move on in a slightly different direction until it cleared the obstacle. It reminded Mr. Tompkins of a rather stupid animal—a beetle, perhaps.

The door to Maniac's room now opened, and a man walked in. He was not the mathematician coming back from the stockroom, Mr. Tompkins noted, and he wondered what he was up to.

The newcomer watched the contraption for a few moments. Having moved past various obstacles, it was about to bump itself against the wall of the room. Seeing this, the man blew a whistle, and the contraption stopped dead. Just as it was about to move again, the visitor switched a flashlight on it. The contraption, at first with hesitation, and then more firmly, started to move toward the light. Mr. Tompkins continued to stare with astonishment.

"One of my pet tortoises," said the visitor, turning to Mr. Tompkins. "I knew it had escaped somewhere."

"It does look like a tortoise," said Mr. Tompkins. "But could you explain to me what this is all about?"

"Well, it so happens that I am interested in the brain, and it occurred to me that though the brain is very complicated, even simple systems, if properly put together, might have a rather complex behavior. So I built a number of electronic pets. One of them is this tortoise, a member of the mock turtle family. She is a descendant of Elsie, the first of the lot. The scientific names of animals are always two Latin words, so I call her *Machina speculatrix,* the speculating machine. It is not that she thinks much, but she is always curious and keeps bumping around to find out what her surroundings are like. That is the big difference between this tortoise and Maniac. Maniac is quick on the draw, but he never goes around looking for problems to solve, he is quite content to wait passively till someone tells him what to do. Not so *Machina speculatrix;* she is curious just like a real animal."

Machina speculatrix is the name of this species.

"She certainly reminds one of a real animal," said Mr. Tompkins. "How did you make her?"

"Her construction is very simple," said the visitor. "But before I describe it, let's trap her so she is not a continual nuisance."

Using his flashlight, the visitor maneuvered the tortoise in front of one of Maniac's panels, which reflected light like a mirror.

Catching sight of the reflection of her pilot light, the tortoise commenced a curious dance. First she would move toward the reflection of her light. As she did so, her light would go out, and she would lose interest and start to move away. This, however, would cause her pilot lamp to go on again, and the cycle would start all over again.

"A narcissistic tendency, as the Freudians say," remarked the visitor. "She is stuck for good admiring herself, so now I have time to tell you about her.

"The tortoise runs on a storage battery. When well charged, she is pretty sluggish, but as the voltage begins to fall, she gets hungry and comes to life. She moves primarily by a motor which turns her rear wheels. Her single front wheel, however, is continuously turned around a vertical axis by another motor, which also turns her turret. When the photocell in her turret picks up a bright light, the front wheel and turret stop turning, and her pilot light goes out. Since her front wheel is now pointed toward the light, she heads for it. If the light gets too bright, or if she hits an obstacle that jolts a contact, the front motor starts to turn again, and she heads off in a new direction."

"But what is she trying to do?" asked Mr. Tompkins.

"She is trying to recharge her battery. There is a hole in the wall, which usually has a light in it. If she can crawl into this hole, she plugs herself in and recharges herself. The current is her food, you might say. After feeding, she lies low for a while and then starts looking for food again.

"You might say, of course, that my tortoise is just a toy. This is true, but I built her to show how you can get fairly complex behavior with very simple components. I have used just two vacuum tubes, two relays, two capacitators, two motors, and two batteries."

"There is something you did not mention," said Mr. Tompkins. "When you blew the whistle, she stopped just like a trained dog."

"Of course," replied the visitor, "but she is not a trained dog, she is a trained tortoise."

"You mean that she has learned to do this?" asked Mr. Tompkins in astonishment.

"Yes. The famous Russian physiologist Pavlov showed quite a while back that a dog, for example, can learn to salivate at the sound of a bell. Normally the flow of saliva starts at the sight of food, and this is a reflex that needs no training. If you ring a bell a few times just before dinner, the dog will begin to salivate even if no food is present. He has learned that the bell symbolizes food. We call this sort of learning a conditioned reflex.

"I decided that I wanted my tortoise to learn in the same way, and I managed, after a few trials, to build a learning device. The principle is that the tortoise computes the statistical relation between two events, say a bump against the wall and the sound of my whistle. If there is a close relation, she begins to respond to the whistle as he would to the bump. Of course, in the beginning I had to train her, and since she forgets, I repeat the training now and then. I will not bore you with the details of the circuitry, but you can take my word for it that it is quite simple."

"Does this have anything to do with how a real animal learns?"

"Possibly. My point has been to investigate the minimal number of components for a learning circuit, since this will give us some idea of the minimal complexity of a neural circuit. However, there are now other kinds of learning machines, and there is no easy way to solve the problems of the brain. Actually most of my time is spent not on these gadgets, but on brain waves. As you no doubt know, all sorts of electrical impulses course through the neurons of a brain."

"But if the brain is essentially an electric-circuit system," said Mr. Tompkins, "doesn't it emit radio waves to the outside world? This would be an excellent explanation of such things as mind-reading, wouldn't it?"

"I don't know," said the visitor cautiously. "There is, of course, a good deal of discussion on the subject of telepathy, but I have not seen a single experiment yet that would confirm it with what I would call scientific accuracy. On the other hand, it would be quite unscientific to deny the phenomenon *a priori*. One thing is clear, however. The electrical currents in a brain are so weak that they cannot

Brainwaves are recorded on a paper tape.

be detected by even the most sensitive apparatus more than a few millimeters away from the skull. So if telepathy should prove to be a fact, something else would be required to account for it.

"But it is certainly true, though much less exciting, that electric processes in the cerebral cortex show up outside the skull. In fact, if one presses electric contacts to several different points on the skull, one notices an oscillating electric potential with a period of about a tenth of a second, and an amplitude of about twenty microvolts. The electric tension can be amplified by a system of vacuum tubes and recorded on a roll of paper. These particular brain waves are easily noticeable when the person is asleep or at least in a state of complete rest; they fade considerably as soon as the subject begins to think."

"Shouldn't it be the other way round, if thinking is an electric phenomenon?" asked Mr. Tompkins in surprise.

"Not necessarily. You can imagine, for example, that in a state of rest all the electric circuits in the brain are operating in unison, and thus collaborate in producing definite electric tensions on its surface. But as soon as mental work begins, the neurons break step, and their effects on the skull cancel out."

"What have you been able to find out by studying brain waves?" said Mr. Tompkins.

"A number of things. First of all a study of brain waves is very useful in locating brain damage due to tumors or other causes. Many hospitals now have equipment to record brain waves for diagnostic purposes. Of more general interest, however, are findings that brain waves are associated with important brain functions.

"Take, for example, the most common kind of rhythmical waves, which have a period of 10 to 20 cycles per second. This is called an alpha rhythm. Alpha rhythms classify people into three groups, according to the way they tend to think.

"About two-thirds of all people show an alpha rhythm when they are quiet with their eyes closed and not thinking, or when they are asleep. As soon as they open their eyes or start thinking, the rhythm disappears and is replaced by irregular fluctuations. Such people are called responsives, or 'R type.' The R-type person is really an intermediate between two extremes: the P and M types.

"The P type are so called because their alpha rhythm persists even when their eyes are open or they are thinking. The reason seems to be that the alpha rhythm is interrupted by visual imagery, and the

P-type person uses very little visual imagery, even when he is looking at something. So his alpha rhythm just keeps going. On the other hand, the M type (M standing for 'minus') thinks so vividly in pictures and colors that he has no alpha rhythm at all! Most people are, as I said, a blend between the two; they think visually enough to interrupt the alpha rhythm when their eyes are open, but not enough to abolish it altogether. As you might expect, M types are very good at problems that require visualization, but not so good at abstract problems. P types are better at abstractions or thinking in terms of sounds or movements. The R types are best when a combination of qualities is required. Your vivid dreams, Mr. Tompkins, make me suspect that you are an M type."

Mr. Tompkins felt that he was learning something really interesting now. "Brain waves, if I understand you correctly, are mainly concerned with sight?" he asked.

"Not entirely. A primitive part of your brain, the thalamus, produces a slower type of rhythm called theta, which is associated with anger or a sudden cessation of a pleasant sensation. But sight is certainly very important. It is possible, for instance, to hook up a device in such a way that the brain waves themselves control a flickering light, so that a subject sees light flashes in synchrony with his brain waves. In such cases many people experience intense visual hallucinations, such as gorgeously colored fireworks flashing through the sky and spinning Catherine wheels. But for others the sensations may not be so pleasant. Faintness, dizziness, loss of consciousness, or sometimes even convulsions can occur as a result of watching a flicker of the right frequency. In fact, such flickering lights used in conjunction with recordings of brain waves are helpful in diagnosing epilepsy.

"But we are only beginning to understand this subject. After all, there are as many cells in your brain as there are stars in the galaxy. So many signals are coursing through the brain that it is hard to sort them out. It is all very confusing."

"It is almost as bad as phychoanalysis," said Mr. Tompkins, who was beginning to feel that he had absorbed enough information for one day.

"Speaking of psychoanalysis," said the visitor, "there is a lot of bluff in it, but there are also many points that are certainly based on the real physiology of our brain. For example the notion of suppressed memories introduced by Sigmund Freud is most probably connected with short-circuited neuron chains in the cerebral cortex. Memory signals are going round and round causing a constant disturbance in your brain until they are brought out and dealt with in a rational way."

"Do you think I might have suppressed memories too?" asked Mr. Tompkins. "This might be a good opportunity to straighten these things out."

"Tell me," said the visitor looking him straight in the eyes, "is there anything that troubles your subconscious? Anything you are afraid of without any apparent reason?"

"There is," said Mr. Tompkins. "I hate to sit on hard chairs. And whenever I sit on a soft one, I inevitably fall asleep. Do you think the fear of hard chairs could have something to do with suppressed unpleasant memories of my childhood?"

"Possibly," said the visitor. "Listen carefully to the noise your neurons are making in your head."

Listening carefully, Mr. Tompkins was able to recognize the high voice of his dear old mother through the din.

"You bad boy," she was saying. "How many times have I told you not to touch that jar of strawberry jam in the kitchen! Bring me my hairbrush and pull down your pants."

"I won't do it again, Mummy!" pleaded Mr. Tompkins. "I promise I won't."

But it was too late, and the terrible brush was coming down at him, like an angel of vengeance . . .

"Ouch!" shouted Mr. Tompkins as thousands of sharp pins shot into his tender skin. "Ouch!"

"What's the matter?" The young mathematician, attracted by Mr. Tompkins's screams, rushed out from the storage room. "Have you hurt yourself?"

"I won't do it again, I promise," said Mr. Tompkins, rising from the flattened box.

"Oh, that's where they were, and you've squashed them!" said the mathematician, looking ruefully at the pile of broken glass. "A bide5 lo! Now we'll have no memories until the next delivery on Wednesday."

"I'll have to sleep on my stomach for the next few nights," said Mr. Tompkins, trying to brush the sharp glass fragments from the seat of his trousers. "But I shall have memories for a long time to come."

"Well, accidents do happen," said the mathematician philosophically.

"What does 'A bide5 lo' mean?" asked Mr. Tompkins trying to look unruffled.

"Oh, that is just a jocular swear-word in Maniacal language," answered the mathematician. "You see, when an electronic computer operates, a broad tape covered with long lines of figures comes out. In addition to the numbers some letters of the alphabet are printed, each letter indicating a certain instruction, but there are just a few of them and you cannot use them for letter-writing. When the machine works, it constantly checks itself—division by multiplication, for example—and if something is wrong the outgoing tape carries a monotonous repetition of the same group of numbers or letters such as: ooooo...oo or a5a5a5...a5, or anything else so the attendant can know about it. Some wits who were constructing the Eniac at the Bureau of Standards, in Washington, D.C., arranged an error signal to be a repetition of the sentence: 'Call cab, call cab, call cab,' and so on. The competing group, building a similar computer in Los Alamos, wanted to do better, and two young women working in the laboratory invented the sentence: 'A bide5 lo' which is nearest they could get to the Hungarian swear word, '*A büdos lo,*' meaning 'a stinky horse.'"

"But why did they use Hungarian?" asked Mr. Tompkins in surprise.

"Well," said the mathematician, "one of them was Klari, the wife of John von Neumann, inventor of the electronic computer, and the other was Mici, the wife of Edward Teller, who is often called the father of the H-bomb. Both girls were born and brought up in Budapest."

"It is always so nice to hear that scientists have a sense of humor," said Mr. Tompkins. "But may I ask you a last question: what is the future of electronic computers as they grow larger and larger and more and more complicated?"

"Let me tell you a little story," said the mathematician with a wry smile. "Humanity was celebrating the beginning of the twenty-first century, by which time technology had made tremendous advances. A giant super-transistor electronic brain was constructed, which occupied the entire inner court of the Pentagon building. It contained 10^m transistors and 10^n memory centers. The memory was supplied daily with economic, sociological, and military information collected by 10^5 secret agencies all over the world, and was supposed to be able to predict world developments for 10^2 years ahead. The grand opening was attended by the then President of the United States and by all political and military dignitaries. Just as at the beginning of a baseball season the President throws the first ball, so in this case he was requested to ask the electronic computer the first question.

" 'Will you tell me, please,' he asked the computer, 'will there be war or peace within the next five years?'

"Because of the complexity of the question, the computer took almost ten minutes to consider it. The answer was very short: 'Yes.'

"The embarrassed designer rapidly fed into the computer another question: 'Yes *what?*'

"This time, within one microsecond, the computer came back with the right answer: 'Yes, sir.' "

Mr. Tompkins saw the point. "Excuse me, please," he said, "but you must be very busy and I don't want to bother you any more. Thank you very much for all this information." He shook the mathematician's hand and took his leave.

» 9 «

Brainy Stuff

THE memory of the metallic voice of Maniac continued to bother
Mr. Tompkins. Unlike some of his fellow workers at the bank, he
was not much concerned about losing his job to a machine. The vice
president in charge of personnel had given a rather persuasive talk to
the bank employees, pointing out that while some jobs might change
with the introduction of computers, the over-all need for manpower
would not decrease. The machine would only make it possible to do
more and better work with the same number of employees.

What bothered Mr. Tompkins was the rather uncanny resemblance
of Maniac to a person (to say nothing of the resemblance of a person to
a maniac). In essence, it was nothing but a suitably connected pile of
relays, yet it seemed to do many of the same things Mr. Tompkins did
—counting, remembering, and so on. And while the mathematician
had warned him that the brain might not function in the same way as
the computer, his tortoise-building colleague did give the impression
that you could build a brain with electronic devices if only you knew
what the circuits were.

Mr. Tompkins kept pondering whether he really was nothing but a
mass of relays, but he seemed to be getting nowhere with the problem.
He was therefore delighted when his father-in-law invited Maud and
him over for dinner one evening. A couple of faculty people from the
University would also be there, and he would meet the new professor

of neurology. "Perhaps," thought Mr. Tompkins, "they can tell me some of the things I want to know."

After dinner the conversation turned to scientific matters, and everyone listened with a mixture of interest and amusement as Mr. Tompkins described his visit to the Maniac.

"I fully agree," said the neurologist, "that our brain cannot operate precisely the way the Maniac does. Take the matter of accuracy, for example. The Maniac's components have to be almost infallible, since even a small error can make his results quite useless. But in the brain it is quite different. For one thing, about ten neurons die in our brain every minute and are never replaced, yet in spite of this, the brain continues to function quite well, even at an advanced age. Furthermore we know that the components of the brain, the neurons, work on a statistical basis. For example, if an impulse reaches a synapse, it may cause the next neuron to fire only 60 or 80 per cent of the time. Clearly this would never do in a computer like the Maniac."

"Of course," interrupted another guest, who was an electronic engineer, "it is possible that the brain works on the principle of redundancy. Suppose that the Maniac's components were very unreliable. You could still make him compute reliably by having many copies of each circuit, and then using only the majority opinion, so to speak. But I am more inclined to suspect that the brain is not a digital computer, but rather an analogue one."

"What is the difference between the two?" asked Mr. Tompkins.

"In a digital computer," replied the engineer, "discrete pulses, which are either present or absent, represent numbers or logical operations. That is the Maniac. But in an analogue computer, numbers are represented by some physical quantity—for example, a voltage. If 20 is represented by 20 volts, and 40 by 40 volts, to add 20 to 40 you add the two voltages and get 60 volts if you have designed your circuit properly. By various tricks you can also subtract, multiply, divide, and do more complicated things. In general, analogue computers are less accurate but much faster than digital computers for many special problems, especially very complicated ones. You are no doubt familiar with a simple analogue computer without knowing it is one. It is a slide rule, where numbers are represented not by voltages but by lengths."

"But from what I have learned so far," said Mr. Tompkins, "a neuron either fires or not; there is no state in between, whereas there's a whole range of possible voltages in a wire. In the brain each impulse is the same. If we hear a louder sound or order a muscle to contract more, it is the number of impulses per second, not the voltage in the nerve, which increases. So I would think the brain is a digital device."

"Not necessarily," said the engineer. "Imagine that you have a tube through which water is flowing. You would say that the flow is a continuously varying quantity. But actually, of course, water is made of discrete molecules and the flow is therefore discontinuous! On even a cruder level the flow of sand through an hourglass may appear continuous. It is the large number of particles which produces the effect of continuity.

"So if a very large number of neurons are firing, which is, of course, the case, the average density of impulses can represent a continuously varying quantity. It is also possible that in some places the brain operates like a digital computer and in some places like an analogue computer. But in any case there is no doubt that it is a device for processing signals."

"I think all of us believe," said the neurologist, "that the brain processes signals that come from the outside. These signals are organized and used to decide what the organism is to do. Our big problem is to find precisely how this is done. By designing and studying computers we may obtain hints and ideas, but ultimately the solution can come only from studies of real brains. Recently we have learned quite a bit by studying a rather unusual brain, the brain of the octopus."

"Is this because he has such a simple brain?" asked Mr. Tompkins.

"Not so much because of that. Of course the brain of an octopus is smaller than the human brain. He has a few hundred million neurons, while we have more like ten thousand million. The real reason is that the octopus brain has evolved in such a way that it consists of well-defined lobes, of course all connected together. It is therefore rather easy to remove surgically such lobes as we wish and observe what then happens to the mind of an octopus."

"How do you talk to an octopus to find out what he thinks?" asked the engineer.

"Of course you don't talk, but you can ask questions, and if you ask them right, the octopus will answer. The questions you ask are what the octopus can learn, and what he forgets.

"Octopuses, like some people, enjoy crabs, and if they see one, they make a grab for it. The investigator exploits this reaction. He wires the crab so that the octopus may get a slight shock when touching the crab.

How do you talk to an octopus to find out what he thinks?

This, of course, he does not like. In this way you can teach an octopus to recognize a white disk by showing it when the crab is shocking, and not showing it when the crab isn't. After a few trials the octopus catches on. You can readily see how this sort of experiment can be extended. A circle can be used to signify danger, a triangle safety. In this way you can find out what shapes an octopus can distinguish, how soon he forgets, and so on. You then combine this with brain surgery; after removing a lobe, you can test for learning ability, memory, pattern discrimination, and others. The little octopuses make some people shudder, but they are really both interesting and charming."

"What have we learned from this?" asked the engineer.

"In part, more about our own ignorance. Even the octopus brain is very complicated, and it is not built on what we would call straight-forward principles. There is no single group of neurons which says 'aha, a circle,' or 'attack that crab.' The various groups of cells concerned with attacking a crab or with any other activity form a system of interconnected centers that mutually stimulate and inhibit one another. The whole system is poised, so to speak, on a knife edge. Certain centers shift the balance after processing all available information in a rather complex way. For instance, one of the lobes is concerned with the difference between 'successive' and 'simultaneous.' A normal octopus who has learned the difference between two figures shown simultaneously will also tell them apart if they are shown one after the other. But if a particular lobe is removed it cannot do this. Other lobes decide whether it is worth while putting something into the memory, or retrieving it, whether something is painful or pleasant, and many other things."

The conversation continued for a while, and when it was time to leave, Maud volunteered to drive the guests back home, and her father went along for the ride. Mr. Tompkins decided to wait, mainly because he felt like enjoying some more of his father-in-law's excellent brandy. After pouring himself another glass, he closed his eyes to savor its excellence. . . .

When he opened them again, he was surprised to see the neurologist still there, standing next to the large mirror hanging on the wall.

"Since you are so interested in the brain," he said, "why don't you look at your own in this mirror. It amplifies all the principal features of your brain, but reduces all the other parts of the body, turning them into small appendices attached to the surface of the brain where the corresponding nervous centers are."

Mr. Tompkins walked over to the mirror, but after one glance backed away in horror; the creature that looked at him from behind the glass defied all human imagination. It resembled a large sack of some gray material with its surface folded up in numerous fissures. Attached to this shapeless body were short stocky arms and legs, a large pair of lips with a tongue hanging below them, and a pair of eyes protruding from behind the ears. The whole thing looked like the well-known picture of a Martian in an illustration for H. G. Wells' fantastic novel *The War between Worlds*.

"Is that *me?*" exclaimed Mr. Tompkins in disgust.

"Certainly it's you," said the neurologist. "And, in fact, this mirror amplifying your brain features does not make you look much worse than some curved mirrors you can find in amusement parks. Or at least it does you more justice."

Mr. Tompkins went back to the mirror. He could now recognize the basic features of the brain, which he had seen before in anatomy books.

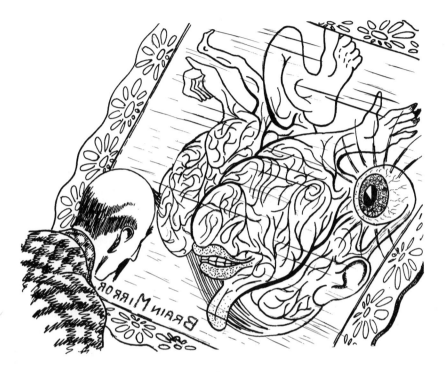

"Is that me?" exclaimed Mr. Tompkins in disgust.

There was a deep central fissure separating the brain into a right and a left hemisphere, and another fissure running upward and toward the back along each hemisphere, separating the brain into the frontal and occipital lobes.

"You will notice that your legs, arms, mouth, and tongue are attached to the frontal lobe of your brain, since, in fact, that is where most of the motor centers governing your motions are located. Sensory centers, like eyes and ears, are located at the back of your head."

"Isn't my tongue also a sensory organ?" said Mr. Tompkins, protesting.

"Well, nobody knows exactly where the taste centers are, and they might just as well be in the back lobe. But the main motor function of the tongue is the moving of food, and, of course, speech; this is certainly located in the frontal lobe. You may also notice that your lips and tongue are located essentially in the left hemisphere, showing that you are a normal right-handed person."

"When you speak of centers," said Mr. Tompkins, "do you mean that the brain is divided into compartments, each of which is concerned with some part of the body, or some sensation such as hearing?"

"No, that is not quite what I mean. Take, for example, the movement of your foot. Many parts of the brain may participate in the decision to move it. But all their signals ultimately converge at one region, which we call the motor center for the movement. Similarly, signals from the sense organs first pass to special areas for initial processing, but from there they may go to many other parts of the brain. We locate these more specific centers because damage to them abolishes movements in certain parts of the body, or deprives the victim of certain sensations. Damage to other parts of the brain has less specific effects. Another way of locating such centers is to observe the effects of weak electrical currents applied to small areas of the brain. Such experiments have been done on people whose brains were exposed for surgery. They would then move some part of their body, or report sensations of light or sound. Incidentally, this is possible because the brain itself feels no pain when touched or cut."

"It would be so nice to get in there and do a bit more exploring," Mr. Tompkins said dreamily; for, ever since his journey through the blood stream, he had regretted that hunger had prevented him from visiting his brain.

"Why don't you go in there?" said the neurologist.

"You mean through the glass?" said Mr. Tompkins in surprise.

"And why not? Haven't you ever heard of Alice?"

Fascinated by this idea, Mr. Tompkins put his forehead against the cold, smooth surface of the mirror, and pushed forward.

"Let's pretend the glass has gone soft like gauze," thought Mr. Tompkins, "so that I can get through. Why, it's turning into a sort of mist now, I declare! It'll be easy enough to get through. . . ." And certainly the glass was beginning to melt away, just like a bright, silvery mist. In another moment Mr. Tompkins was through the glass, and found himself walking along a rather narrow canyon with steep gray walls. The walls of the canyon were covered with a large number of darkish shadows, which Mr. Tompkins mistook for some kind of desert plant.

Suddenly he found himself surrounded by ten or fifteen loudly barking dogs, all of different sizes and breeds.

"Nitchevo," said the old man, extending his hand. (Courtesy of Dr. J. Z. Young, University College, London)

"At least they are not as aggressive as my digestive enzymes!" thought Mr. Tompkins. "But what on earth are all these dogs doing in my brain anyway?"

"*Nazad, agolteleey!*" shouted somebody behind him, and the dogs obediently backed away without touching him. Turning around, Mr. Tompkins saw a very old man with a bushy white beard who was approaching him from the bottom of the canyon.

"*Nitchevo, oni nehye koosayoutsia. Rad vas vidyet!*" said the old man, extending his hand, and—noticing the embarrassment on Mr. Tompkins's face—continued. "Translated into English, I said, 'The dogs don't bite. They are nice experimental dogs. Welcome to the Land of Cerebrum.' "

"Cerebrum," said Mr. Tompkins. "Isn't that the learned name for the brain? Do you mean to say that I am actually inside my own skull, and that these desert plants covering the walls of the canyon are the nerve cells which control all my memories, thoughts, and desires?"

"Right," said the old man. "You are at the bottom of what we call the Sylvian fissure, a deep gorge in the cerebral cortex originating at the lower part of each brain hemisphere, and curving upward and back along its side. A great many of your sensory and motor centers are located in this region. As you see, each neuron has a number of branching tentacles or fibers running in all directions; they really do look like some fantastic desert plant when you think about it. Some of these fibers are comparatively short, serving as intercommunication lines between the several thousand million neurons forming your brain. Others are very long and run inside your spinal column to the most distant parts of your body, connecting the brain with various sensory organs as well as with the muscles. Every bit of information obtained by your senses is sent into the brain through the incoming fibers known as dendrites. As soon as that information reaches the cerebral cortex, the central neuron council gets busy to decide what to do about it, and when the decision is made orders are sent to the muscles through long outgoing motor fibers called axons."

"Very much like the electronic machines with their input and output channels leading to the central computing unit," said Mr. Tompkins. "I would like to see how it really works."

"That's very easy. Now watch!" said the old man, suddenly stamping his heavy boot right on Mr. Tompkins's pet corn. "In a minute you will see your own feeling of pain."

And indeed Mr. Tompkins could see an excitation seizing the entire slope of the Sylvian canyon. His sensory centers had already received the danger signal from his toes, and were now asking his motor centers to do something about it. A number of alarm signals were converging toward the neuron along its branching dendrites. When the incoming signals had finally entered the main body of the neuron, a long-distance impulse started outward along the axon.

"The signals travel at about two hundred miles per hour," said the old man, "but of course you see it all in a different time scale. They are probably just reaching their destination now."

"Ouch!" exclaimed Mr. Tompkins suddenly, and jerked his foot from under the old man's boot.

"I did not mean to hurt you," said the old man with a smile, "but you told me yourself you wanted to see how your nervous system operates. This particular neuron is connected with your speech organs, and the signal you have just seen going out was sent to your vocal cords, ordering them to produce a loud sound, presumably with the purpose of scaring away whoever was hurting you."

"And also to my foot, to jerk it away," added Mr. Tompkins.

"No, you are wrong there. Such elementary action as that can be dealt with by lower parts of your neuron council. These comprise the spinal brain, or spinal cord, which runs all the way down through your vertebrae. In fact, even if your head had been cut off, you would probably jerk your leg just the same. At least frogs do so. But, of course, without your head you could not possibly say 'ouch.'

"You have quite rightly compared the neuron system of the brain with the system of relays in electronic machines, known in biology as synapses. Many such connections were established as a result of spontaneous mutations far back in evolutionary history, and, being found useful by the organism, were carried from generation to generation through regular hereditary processes and natural selection. You do not need to learn to jerk your foot away if it is hurt. That is known as an instinctive or innate reflex. But other, more complicated actions—such as saying 'pardon me' if you step on somebody else's foot—are not hereditary, and have to be learned from experience in each particular case; I call them conditional reflexes.*

---

* EDITOR'S NOTE: The original term *conditional* reflex, introduced by the famous Russian physiologist, Ivan Pavlov, evolved into *conditioned* reflex in English-language scientific literature.

"Take this Barbosik, for example," continued the old man, putting his hand lovingly on the head of a fine Irish setter sitting at his side. "He learned to recognize a certain musical note for the sake of food. For a while my assistant played the note on his violin when Barbosik's food was served. Thus the signals sent by the taste buds of his tongue to the taste neurons in his brain arrived simultaneously with the sound signals coming to the auditory neurons, and a connection between the two was somehow established. You may imagine that this simultaneous excitation of both neurons, which as we know is electric in nature, could produce some kind of conduction channels between their previously insulated fibers. And once the insulation is broken through, the connection becomes permanent, and the sound impulse is, so to speak, mistaken for taste impulse. Since every dog possesses an instinctive reflex which causes the salivary glands to secrete saliva as soon as the tongue feels the taste of food, Barbosik's mouth waters now each time he hears that note on the violin.

"Of course, this is only a small example, but I am quite sure that all our actions, even the most intricate ones, are based on such reflexes which are acquired either in the evolutionary history of the animal, or in the personal history of any given individual. After all, at least a great part of learning is based on associating two or more things together, a red light with stepping on the brake, or 2 + 3 with 5. Such associations have been studied in many ways, but I am proud that my dogs here have laid the basis for understanding so much of what goes on in the brain."

"But," said Mr. Tompkins thoughtfully, "in the case of electronic machines, all the wiring scheme of relays is conceived in the brains of the people who design them. But who designed the human brain itself? Mustn't we assume the existence of some superbeing who conceived all these intricate connections between the neurons in the brain?"

"It's a good question," said the old man, "and I can answer it, even though only in a general way. You must remember first of all that it takes only a few years to build the most complicated electronic machines, whereas it took at least a billion years of organic evolution to develop a brain system as advanced as ours. As in any other evolutionary progress, the development here was carried forward by trial and error."

"Could you give me a more concrete description?" asked Mr. Tompkins.

"Well," said the old man, "I can give you a brief lecture. The human brain has about 10^{10} components, a fantastic number for any computer engineer, and at first sight it might seem hopeless to understand how it functions. However, there are many simpler brains which we can study, and we can learn quite a bit by studying how brains evolved.

"Originally the nervous system had nothing to do with thinking; its function was and to a great degree still is the activation and coordination of the muscles. The first muscles appeared in sponges, where they open and close the pores that let in the water which the animal filters to obtain its food. Sponges do not have nerves; the muscle cells themselves are sensitive to such things as the chemical composition of the water and react by contracting and relaxing.

"Certain cells later became specialized to transmit pulses from sensory cells to muscles. When a sensory cell was exposed to light, or an odor or some other stimulation, it would send a message via such specialized cells to a group of muscles, ordering them to contract or relax. This is what we call a reflex arc, and in its simplest form it is quite automatic. The smell of food which causes Barbosik's mouth to water operates through such a reflex arc.

"As organisms became more complicated, groups of such nerves became connected to coordinate activities. An excellent example is an eel, which swims by waves of muscular contractions that proceed along its body. At any given moment, the muscles of a segment are contracted on one side and relaxed on the other. This seems very simple, but in fact it requires a considerable amount of neural circuitry, as you will quickly see if you try to build something like it yourself. The muscles have two kinds of nerves. One set, the motor nerves, gives the signals to contract; sensory nerves signal whether the muscles are contracted or relaxed. Both sets of nerves go to a special center called a ganglion, where signals and orders are processed. If signals indicate that one side is contracted, orders go out to relax that side, and simultaneously other orders go out to begin contracting the other side.

"Each body segment has its own center in the spinal cord and this center is actually a miniature brain. But since the segments have to work in a coordinated fashion, the centers are again connected together and signal to each other so that a wave of contraction and not just random movements is produced.

"The undulations are now a unit of action. The sight of a shrimp, which means food, or the shadow of an enemy, which means danger, feeds into the centers as a signal saying 'Speed up undulatory motion.'

Other signals stop or slow down the motion. It is like the engine of a car which has only one response to pressure on the accelerator and is not at all concerned with why the accelerator is pressed down.

"You are quite familiar with such a unit system: walking or running is quite automatic, once you have given the signal. It is only when you suffer from some neurological disorder that you realize how complicated walking really is.

"Next, several such unit actions are coordinated into a higher unit of action, for example, the action 'feed.' This involves lower unit actions 'swim,' 'bite,' 'swallow.' A higher center controls and coordinates the lower 'swim,' 'bite,' and 'swallow' centers, so that the single signal 'feed' activates subordinate signals in proper order.

"The principle here is that of hierarchical order, familiar in human organizations. An order on an aircraft carrier—'launch an attack'—immediately brings into action several subroutines, such as 'change course into the wind,' 'arm planes,' 'brief pilots.' Each major subroutine is in turn composed of more minor ones, ending with elementary unit actions, such as pushing buttons to activate elevators or launching catapults. All subroutines are connected by signals to centers, human or otherwise, which ensures simultaneous or successive operations as required.

"Of course, as I just explained, the action of the reflex arcs can be modified by conditioning, so that an organism is plastic and adaptable. In general, the larger the brain, the more adaptable it is."

"From what you said," said Mr. Tompkins, "I gather that the ultimate control is exercised by signals from the sense organs."

"I would rather say on the basis of such signals," replied the old man. "The brain pays attention only to processed signals. The eye, for example, does not only transmit what it sees to the brain. It thinks about what it sees, and tells the brain what it thinks."

"The eye thinks?" Mr. Tompkins asked incredulously.

"This is not so remarkable if you remember that embryologically the eyes arise as outgrowths of the brain, and remain, in fact, part of the brain. When I said the eye thinks, I meant that it processes visual data.

"You have no doubt read that the eye is like a camera; it throws an image on a screen of light-sensitive cells called the retina. The picture is then transmitted to the brain as a series of dots of varying brightness, as if from a television camera. Now this is not quite correct. The cells of the retina do form a light-sensitive mosaic, but a field of spots will give the brain no information unless it is analyzed. Analysis means two things; one is the interrelation of the spots, the other is picking out what is significant in the visual field.

"The retina has a network of nerve cells which connect to the light-sensitive rods and cones, and to one another. Small areas of the retina are so connected that they respond to one of the following aspects of the image:

    a. Signal if there is a sharp boundary between light and dark in the area.

    b. Signal if a convex boundary, darker on the convex side, is moving across the area.

    c. Signal if the contrast between points in the area is changing.

    d. Signal if light is dimming in area.

    e. Signal at a rate proportional to the average illumination of the eye.

"These areas of the retina overlap so that the brain is informed of all these aspects in any given area.

"The brain, as you can see, receives information from the eye which in large measure is already processed, and processing is then carried on further in the brain itself. Hints about how this is done are provided by so-called optical illusions, with some of which, no doubt, you are familiar. For example, lines on a flat sheet of paper are processed to mean 'cube in three-dimensional space.' Since two cubes have the same representation, during prolonged staring the meaning shifts from one cube to another.

"Even more informative is the 'waterfall illusion.' If you stare for a while at some continuous motion, a waterfall, or spots on a moving belt, and then look at some stationary object, you see it moving. The curious thing is that although you see it moving, you also see quite clearly that it is not changing position in space.

"The lesson here is that at a certain level of the brain, 'motion' has nothing to do with 'change in position.' We associate the two because usually visual data processing reads out 'motion' and 'change in position' from the same set of data. But this is not always the case, and we then call it an illusion. Actually, it is merely normal processing of slightly unusual data. The way we see things and analyze them into categories of perception, such as 'motion,' 'three-dimensional space,' 'discrete object,' is determined by the method of data processing our brain uses."

"I presume," said Mr. Tompkins, "that it is only data from the eye which need such complicated processing. Sounds should need no analysis."

"I am afraid this is not so," said the old man. "Take, for example, music. If you can only hear individual sounds, music does not exist for you. Dogs never listen to hi-fi for pleasure, although they may recognize some simple tunes. To appreciate music, you have to be able to abstract a pattern in time from the individual sounds, as you have to abstract a pattern of lines in space to see a figure. This requires training. Thus some people can abstract nothing more complicated than a simple rhythm of beating drums. Devotees of the symphony can abstract more complicated patterns which include drums and also much more.

"You can easily see why this is so by considering a nonmusical example. If you write a series of numbers, 1, 2, 3, 4, 5, 6, 7, 8, 9, . . . almost anyone will recognize the pattern. Each successive number is merely one larger than the previous one. Now write: 1, 4, 9, 16, 25, 36, 49, ... This is still easy. It is the previous series of numbers, each squared. Now try: 1, 2, 4 1/2, 16 2/7, 26 1/24. . . .

"Most people will have trouble with this. Actually it is $n^n/n!$, that is, each of the series of integers is raised to the power of itself, as $3^3 = 27$, and then divided by $n!$, which is the number multiplied by all the preceding integers. Thus 3! means 1 x 2 x 3. It is quite easy to devise a pattern so complex that even the most skilled mathematician will not find it.

"But this reminds me of a story. A physicist working in Washington, D.C., liked to work on this sort of problem. His son, then a student at Columbia University in New York, sent him the following series of numbers: 14, 23, 28, 34, 42, 49, 57, . . . and the question: 'What comes next?' After working on the question for a week, the father wired, 'I give up, what is it?' The answer that came back was 'Central Park,' since the series of numbers were the numbers of the subway stations of the line going uptown to the park station. A little lacking in respect toward a father, perhaps.

"Getting back to music, we can see the pattern must not be so simple that it is dull, and at the same time not so complex that it is incomprehensible. The human brain is limited. It might be possible to compose symphonies far surpassing any of Beethoven's in subtlety and beauty, but if the pattern is beyond recognition by the human brain it will be merely noise to us. As a matter of fact, Beethoven sounds like noise not merely to chimpanzees but to many people untrained in music, because they are unable to grasp sufficiently complex patterns. It is all a matter of ability to process data."

"Why does the brain have to abstract patterns?" asked Mr. Tompkins. "Couldn't it use the sense impressions just as they are?"

"There are just too many of them, and besides, most of them are of no importance for the matter at hand, or as we say, they are irrelevant. You are quite familiar with this sort of thing from your own experience. If you play tennis, your eyes receive images of innumerable things, but data processing ensures that you will react—subjectively 'pay attention' —only to the relevant, which is the ball and the opponent. An even better example is driving a car. If you notice the irrelevant scenery rather than the relevant traffic, you are not likely to drive long.

"For us many things are relevant at one time or another, but for simpler animals the data relevant to action are often few. The frog, for example, pays virtually no attention to any object which is not moving. 'Small object moving' is relevant because it signifies food; 'large object moving' is an enemy. This simplification of the situation leads at times to fatal accidents, since a heron, standing very still, can pass from being irrelevant to being a very relevant enemy in a very short time. Generally, however, this simple distinction is sufficient for the frog's needs.

"In some very simple animals data processing is so restricted that they can keep only one thing in mind at a time and respond to signals only in a certain fixed order. There is, for example, a wasp that preys on bees. The smell of a honeybee at first provokes no interest, since initially the wasp reacts only if it sees a moving object the size of a bee. On seeing such an object, it flies downwind of it. At this point smell takes over. Only if it smells like a bee will the wasp attack. Once it has grasped the object, smell becomes irrelevant and it will sting only if its sense of touch tells it it holds a bee. Here sight, smell, and touch sensations mutually exclude each other."

"So," said Mr. Tompkins, "once the brain has processed signals and decided they are relevant, it tells the body what to do!"

"Quite so," said the old man. "Although at times the only action may be to store the signals in the memory. Incidentally, it often happens that the stronger the signal that reaches the brain, the stronger the action. Thus an unexpected big bang is likely to make us wince or jump more than a small one. Sometimes this leads to amusing consequences. A stimulus which produces a complex activity is called releaser. For ex-

A bird may abandon its own clutch in favor of a giant egg.

ample, a round object resembling an egg releases, under proper conditions, nesting behavior in birds. If some birds are presented with a giant egg, they will abandon their own clutch in favor of the giant. This is an example of 'the bigger, the better' point of view, well known to man and one of the bases of Hollywood's prosperity. Men find a certain curvature of the female figure attractive, and Hollywood has exploited the fact that an even greater curvature is even more acceptable."

"I see now that there are some significant differences between the Maniac and a brain," said Mr. Tompkins.

"There are, of course," replied the old man. "One important difference is that a brain, unlike our computers, has an internal drive. As I told you before, a brain is, among other things, a coordinated system of centers controlling unit actions. Sufficiently complex systems of unit actions are called instincts, of which eating, mating, building spider webs, or migrating south in winter are examples. The brain is so organized that each of these systems or instincts tends, as time goes by, to become spontaneously active, and the tendency toward activity increases with time. Once the activity is accomplished, the drive is dissipated and then gradually builds up again.

"The pecking activity of a hen, for example, is released by the sight of grain. A satiated hen will scarcely peck at all. If it is normally hungry, it will peck at grain, but if it is very hungry, it will peck at the ground even if grain is not present. We call this a 'vacuum activity,' which indicates that the internal drive has become so strong that action occurs even in the absence of a releaser.

"An important fact is that if an internal drive cannot dissipate itself in the normal way, it may dissipate itself via another action system. For example, there is a little fish called the stickleback, which guards its territory against other males of the same species. In general, a male fights another more and more vigorously, the nearer he is to the center of his own territory. Conversely, the farther he penetrates someone else's territory, the less vigorously he fights and the more likely he is to flee, as though he had a guilty conscience. As a result, a fairly sharp boundary is established between the territories of two males.

"However, if the males are in a crowded area, their territories are smaller than they should be. At the boundary, the males are torn between two action systems, to fight or flee, each of which inhibits the other. Not being able to do either, their drives then spill over into a third action system, which is digging out a nest in the sand. This activity is not in the least appropriate; it merely provides a way of getting rid of an internal drive which cannot find its normal outlet.

"This is called a displacement activity, and is well known in man. When frustrated, a man may wring his hands in despair, or he may scratch his head when puzzled. Less trivial examples are common and are often called 'sublimations' by psychiatrists. When Dante found Beatrice unapproachable, his displacement activity was to write poetry describing his visits to heaven and hell."

"But," said Mr. Tompkins, "there seems to be something wrong here! You just said that internal drives activate instincts. People are not driven by instincts; they are rational animals."

"There is no doubt," said the old man, "that the activities of people are different from those of lower animals, but it is really a matter of degree. One might say that the difference between man and lower forms is somewhat like that between a desk calculator and an electronic computer. A desk calculator can add, subtract, multiply, and divide. In addition to these operations a computer can store intermediate results and refer to them in a complicated way, so it can solve more complicated problems. But this is all still done by repetition of elementary operations such as addition and multiplication. If the system is made more complex, all sorts of new aspects emerge that you would not have expected from studying the simpler system.

"We have our instinctive drives just as other animals do and ultimately our activities are directed toward gratifying them. The difference is in the way we gratify them. Since the number of controlling centers, and their interconnections, is much greater in a man than in a fish, it is possible for man to do this in much more subtle ways. For one thing, we can feed into the computing centers of our brain much larger amounts of data, present and remembered, and we can carry out what a computer operator would call a simulation; that is, we imagine the details of a proposed course of action. This makes it possible to determine what obstacles exist without actually having to go through the activity. If obstacles are found, we try other simulations until we hit on the right solution. Of course, to a degree animals can do this too. If a dog is blocked by a fence which is open at one end, he will quickly notice this and run around it. A chicken, however, is not that intelligent: he may run straight toward the fence and beat himself against it in a vain attempt to get through.

"As a result of this ability to simulate situations, the human brain has developed to a high degree the power of gratifying instinctive drives indirectly by proceeding to the primary goal via secondary goals. Both men and chickens, for example, have an instinct to eat. But all a chicken can do to gratify this drive is to peck at food if it is there. Men, however, can obtain food even if it is not immediately available. They may first build a boat, then go fishing, and only then eat. Building a boat is a secondary goal, which is done only to achieve the primary goal of eating.

"However, by introducing secondary goals to reach the objective of gratifying primary instinctive drives, man has often made the secondary goals so important that the primary drive has spilled over into them, as a sort of displacement activity. Science is a good example. Many scientists do research as an end in itself, quite without reference to any practical result or private gain. There are any number of other possible examples from the arts, business, and politics."

"And in banking, too, I suppose," Mr. Tompkins added thoughtfully. "Computers have a memory, since they have to remember the results of intermediate calculations. I guess the brain also has the equivalent of a filing cabinet or something like it. Is the memory store near this Sylvian canyon?"

"Unfortunately, I cannot tell you much about it," replied the old man. "There is a store all right, but it is not at all like a filing cabinet or the memory of a computer. Any single memory is not localized; it seems to be stored all over the brain. If part of the brain is removed by surgery, memory for everything becomes poorer by about the amount of brain tissue removed but no specific item is lost. It is not as if some cards were removed and others remained.

"Although we know almost nothing about the changes that occur in the brain when it remembers something, we do know that there are a short-term and a long-term memory. Something which is remembered goes first into the short-term memory, and stays there about twenty minutes. If you go into a coma and then recover, you will remember nothing that happened in the last twenty minutes of consciousness. Mainly for this reason it is thought that the short-term memory is neural impulses traveling back and forth in a circuit, like an echo reverberating between two cliffs. After twenty minutes the memory is 'fixed,' and may last one hundred years if you live that long. The long-term memory is apparently some kind of structural change, possibly an opening of new conducting pathways by providing new synapses between neurons. But we really do not know."

"Can I ask you a personal question?" said Mr. Tompkins. "You said that once some numbers, names, verses, or what not, are imbedded in the brain, they remain there 'fixed' and may be remembered a century later if the person lives that long. Well, I wonder if you recall a young man named Antonovich, who is a bit over sixty years old? He told me that when he was a young student he took a course in elementary physics from your son, who was then a professor at his university. He often visited your home, and you taught him to play *babki,* which I gather is a game something like knucklebones."

"Certainly I remember him," said the old man, "a thin, tall, blond fellow whom my son often brought home for supper. That was almost half a century ago, but I still remember how bad he was at this game. In addition to physics and astronomy, the fellow had a passion for yachting and quoting poetry. He knew by heart endless verses which he learned in kindergarten, school, and the university, and all of them seemed stuck in his memory like phonograph records."

"He told me that a few years ago he made a bet that he could quote by heart verses for two whole hours nonstop," said Mr. Tompkins. "He won the bet, got laryngitis, and had to cancel his lectures for the next few days. But he also told me that while in his youth he could memorize a long poem just by reading it a few times, he cannot do it any more. Although he loves one poem of a modern Russian poet—Kosimonov, I think, is the name—after reading and rereading it many times, he cannot quote by heart more than a few stanzas. And although he remembers very well the names of his school friends and school teachers, it is very difficult for him now to memorize the names of his university colleagues and the students in his classes. Does this mean that while the memories of youthful days remain and do not wear out as do old phonograph records, the ability to memorize new things decreases with age? Or does it mean that the brain becomes so crowded with old memories that there is no place left to put the new ones in securely?"

"It is a very interesting and also a very difficult question," said the old man. "It is difficult because as I just told you we really do not understand how our memory operates. However, it is a general finding that if cells do not divide they deteriorate with age in various ways, and eventually they die. Now brain cells never divide after the brain is fully formed. So if memory requires the establishment of new connections by growth of branches between cells, it is not unreasonable that the brain cells of an older person may not form such connections as readily as the brain cells of a younger person. In addition there are probably other factors. An older person, owing to previous experience, has developed his interests and capabilities in certain directions, or to put it in a less flattering manner he is more set in his ways. Thus he may often fail to remember some things because consciously or unconsciously these things now appear to him to be less important. But let's wait to answer your question when we understand better what memory really is."

By now Mr. Tompkins was quite fascinated, and, for the first time since he started these sightseeing trips through his own flesh, he began to feel that living matter, even though immensely more complicated than ordinary inorganic materials, is ruled by the same fundamental physical laws which govern all the other processes in the universe. Nevertheless, he was wondering how the terms, like 'consciousness,' 'soul,' and

'I,' used by philosophers fitted into the picture he had seen with his own eyes.

"There is one thing that is bothering me," said Mr. Tompkins, turning again to the old man. "I see very well now how my body, my heart, my lungs, my stomach, my muscles, my nerves, and even my brain operate. But who am I? It seems that I have never met myself inside my own body!"

"Oh!" said the old man, and smiled through his whiskers. "Let me answer your question by asking you a question. Suppose that in your city there appears a new fashionable Dr. X. who claims that he has discovered the secret of rejuvenation. He establishes a clinic where he promises to restore youth to any person within a few weeks, and for a reasonable fee. At first people are very skeptical, but they soon find out that Dr. X. really is as good as his word. There is the case of a professor emeritus of the local university, the well-known Dr. M., who after three weeks of treatment took back his old playing position in the university's football team. There is also the case of a society matron, Mrs. R., who at her own request became so young that only her parents, but not her husband, could recognize her. There are also many other cases where the patients seem to lose a rather less striking number of years, yet who feel nice and vigorous after the treatment. But the treatment itself remains a mystery. After being accepted by the clinic the patients are immediately put to sleep, and the first thing they know is that the bill and a mirror are presented to them on their way out of the clinic. Suppose you wish to take twenty or thirty years off your shoulders, and you register at that clinic. But this time something goes wrong and, before you are put to sleep, you overhear a conversation between two nurses which reveals the method used by Dr. X. You find that what is being done is essentially the following. The clinic maintains, somewhere out in the country, a secret farm on which a great number of human babies, acquired by various semilegal means, are being reared. These young people of different ages are developed according to the best medical standards in respect of all their physical abilities. But their brains are kept absolutely blank. When a new patient enters the clinic and states the age to which he or she would like to return, a young person of suitable age and appearance is selected from the farm. If necessary, plastic surgery is performed to make that 'brainless' body look exactly like old photographs of the patient. Now comes the most important part of the treatment, which is really creditable to the scientific achievements of Dr. X. Your new body and yourself are placed side by side on a hospital bed, and by an intricate electronic system all the synapses existing between the neurons in your brain are copied into the brain of the younger person. In principle, you see, it is quite possible. Thus you get an 'identical twin' who, though younger than you, possesses all your memories, all your knowledge, and all your other mental characteristics. Well, after that they kill your old body one way or another, and it is disposed of, while the new body, looking and behaving exactly like yourself, is released from the clinic to your family and friends."

"But that's cheating!" said Mr. Tompkins. "A doctor like that should be sent to jail!"

"Don't get excited," said the old man. "After all that is only an imaginary case. It is quite true that the existing laws would consider such practices as criminal. But let's think about it for a moment. Suppose Dr. X.'s discovery consists of a method by which the cells in your body could be replaced by new cells one by one. This isn't much different from ordinary blood transfusion, is it? But I am not speaking about the legal aspect of the problem, and give it to you only to ask a question. After finding out what Dr. X. is going to do to you, would you or would you not run out of that clinic and never, never come back?"

"I certainly would!" said Mr. Tompkins with conviction.

"Now you are being irrational," said the old man with a smile. "If you consider yourself not as the collection of the material cells of your body, but rather as a complex of your abstract memories, thoughts, and desires, why should you object to the transference of all the contents of that inner self to a new material background? After all, nobody could object to transferring the contents of an old notebook into a new and better one, if all the information is copied without any change."

"I suppose you are right," admitted Mr. Tompkins, "and I think I ought to have gone on with that operation. But, in fact, I don't think I would."

"Well, when you finally make up your mind about that question," said the old man, "you'll probably know your attitude towards the philosophical questions you are worrying about."

"I see what you mean," replied Mr. Tompkins, "but what bothers me is whether I am merely a complex of abstract memories, thoughts, and desires, as you put it. A memory, a thought, perhaps even a desire can be recorded on a computer tape. But somehow I am convinced that a desire on tape is not quite the same as a desire in my mind. At least, I do not think it feels quite the same. What is it that makes me feel I am me?"

"Science has very little use for such questions," retorted the old man. "The standard answer is to ignore them. But this is really not quite fair; we should at least examine why such questions are so hard to answer.

"When we investigate something as scientists, we divide the universe sharply into two parts: one is the subject, or observer, and the other is the object, which is the universe minus the observer. We then forget about the subject, which is ourselves, and proceed to examine the universe as if we were not a part of it.

"This is an excellent procedure that has given us great insight into the nature of the universe and a great deal of control over our environment through the technology it has made possible. But it does have rather subtle limits, which are well illustrated by the questions you are now asking.

"When you begin to ask questions about the nature of your 'I' and so on, these questions may appear to have the form of scientific questions, but in fact they are not. Science deals only with things that can be described objectively—that is, things that can be communicated by anyone to anyone else. For example, the weight, dimensions, or velocity of an object can be described in purely objective terms and in principle anyone can check such statements for himself. But the nature of your 'I' is known only to yourself and is therefore not an object of scientific study in the same way as is physics. Suppose you say that the statue of 'The Thinker' by Rodin is beautiful, and someone else claims it is ugly. All that this tells me, strictly speaking, is that you are likely to spend more time looking at it than the other fellow, but I have no idea of exactly what sort of subjective sensations you are experiencing. You can see this very clearly if instead of people you consider lower animals. Ants are certainly attracted to honey, and this is an objectively describable fact. But it is quite meaningless to ask whether honey tastes to them as it does to us, or whether their experience is more similar to ours when we eat Parmesan cheese. There is no scientific operation which could decide the question even in principle. In the case of other people, we think we know how they feel because they react to things in about the same way as we do, but this belief cannot really be verified by any scientifically acceptable method. Of course it would be quite wrong to conclude from this that a subjective sensation is unimportant or unreal. Quite the contrary; sensations are the primary things and the only things we really know. That a universe exists around us is only a hypothetical deduction from our subjective sensations.

"Some philosophers and logicians have suggested another reason why it is so difficult to discuss scientifically problems about the nature of the inner 'I.' This difficulty is sometimes called the 'self-reference problem' and arises from the fact that in certain cases a part cannot completely describe the whole of which it is the part. The ancient Greeks were the first to discover this. Thus it is reported that Epimenides the Cretan said that all Cretans are liars. Since Epimenides is a Cretan himself, he must be telling the truth when he is lying, which is self-contradictory. This logical impasse arises because Epimenides is describing a system of which he is a part. There are a number of such paradoxes, some of great importance in mathematics and logic. You are well aware of one such situation: it is logically impossible for you to be injected into your own blood stream, since then a part of you, your blood stream, would include the whole, which is you. If this is so it can then be argued that since the understanding or description of anything is a *part* of our inner 'I,' the understanding of the 'I' by itself is logically self-contradictory. Of course, one is here referring to the subjective 'I' known only to oneself. There is no difficulty in principle in studying brains objectively by physical methods, since here one stands outside the system one is studying. But the subject is a difficult one and does not really concern me as a scientist studying objective reality. You run into these troubles only if you include, as part of the universe which you study, your subjective 'I' and things equivalent to it, such as knowledge. No troubles arise if you study the universe, including the brains in it, as a spectator."

"I take it, then," said Mr. Tompkins, "that science cannot answer my question."

"I believe you are right," said the old man. "Science treats only situations where a clear separation of subject and object is possible. Through sound instinct it refuses even to consider your question 'what am I?' This does not mean that because the question is scientifically meaningless it is necessarily meaningless in general. But you will not get the answer from science."

Just then Mr. Tompkins heard Maud and her father talking in the foyer, and he realized that he had been dozing in his chair. It was time for him to go home.

» 10 «

The Lake of Dreams

MR. TOMPKINS'S son Wilfred was now a junior faculty member at a nearby university, and his reputation as a scientist was growing. Thus Mr. Tompkins always felt a touch of pride when his son paid him a visit. It was now summer, and he looked forward eagerly to seeing him again. Wilfred duly arrived, obviously rather tired, and they determined to spend a relaxed weekend.

On Sunday they decided to go fishing on a nearby lake. They hired a small rowboat and the necessary fishing equipment, and pulled off across the mirror-like waters. The setting sun was casting grotesque shadows of the weeping willows, the wind whispered gently in the reeds, and the clouds began to assume fantastic shapes. Fishing is conducive to contemplation, and while Wilfred, an expert oarsman on his racing team at college, leisurely guided the boat across the lake, Mr. Tompkins leaned against the stern, holding in his hand a fishing pole, waiting for a bite. His thoughts, as usual, turned to science.

"I have often wondered," said Mr. Tompkins to his son, "why your grandfather becomes so excited whenever he talks about the effect of the sun's rays on the growth of plants. I once attended a lecture he gave on the subject, and it had something to do with entropy, as he called it. Although I had heard the word before, it has never been quite clear to me what it means. What was the point he was trying to make?"

"Oh, yes," said Wilfred. "He sent me a reprint of that lecture while I was abroad, and I remember his point very well. It has to do with a

The clouds began to assume fantastic shapes.

fundamental difference in the way people have looked at life. You see, the problem of life has always been, and still is, the foremost challenge to the mind of any thinking man. For a long time there have existed two opposing schools of thought: the vitalistic and the mechanistic. The former school, which not so long ago was the largest, but is now rapidly shrinking, thinks of the phenomenon of life as something entirely different from the phenomena observed in the inorganic world. The difference is supposedly due to a mysterious force of life, or *vis vitalis*, which is present in all living organisms and is responsible for all the differences between living and nonliving matter. The supporters of this school consider it fundamentally impossible to explain all the properties of living creatures on the basis of purely physical and chemical interactions.

"The mechanistic point of view is that all phenomena observed in the living organism can be reduced in the end to regular physical laws governing the atoms of which the organism is composed, and that the difference lies entirely in the relative complexity of living and non-living matter. According to this point of view, basic manifestations of life, like growth, motion, reproduction, and even thinking, depend entirely on the complexity of the molecular structures forming living organisms, and can be accounted for, at least in principle, by the same basic laws of physics which determine ordinary inorganic processes."

Mr. Tompkins noted with some amusement that his son had already acquired the habit of speaking as though he were lecturing to an audience. "I see the difference," he said, "but what has it to do with the sun's rays and the growth of plants?"

"Because at first sight it would seem that all living organisms defy one of the most fundamental laws of physics: the law of ever-increasing entropy," Wilfred said.

"But what is this entropy, and why is it supposed to increase?" said Mr. Tompkins.

"Well, it is an idea related to the concept of disorder. All material bodies dealt with in physics are composed of an immense number of individual molecules involved in violent thermal motion. The air is nothing but a swarm of oxygen, nitrogen, and carbon dioxide molecules rushing wildly in all directions and colliding all the time with one another and with the walls of the room. The water molecules in this lake are loosely glued to each other by intermolecular forces, so that their thermal motion is like the aimless crawling of tightly packed worms in a fisherman's can. The molecules forming the oars I hold in my hand occupy fixed positions, since they are solid bodies, but even they are involved in a wild thermal dance, jerking and swinging around these positions. The most characteristic feature of thermal motion is its lack of order—its state of elementary disorder, as the physicists call it."

"Does this motion always have to be so disorderly?" said Mr. Tompkins.

"No. You could imagine that one-third of all the air molecules in a room move vertically up and down between the floor and the ceiling, one-third horizontally from the front wall to the rear wall, and the remaining third also horizontally between the wall on the right and the one on the left. But if at any time you had such a distribution, mutual collisions between the molecules would tend to scatter their velocities in all possible directions. The possibility of such a distribution is not completely excluded, and there is always a chance that it may actually take place once in a long while and for a brief moment. But this is highly improbable, and you would not bet on such a chance any more than you would bet on the chance of throwing a few hundred heads in succession while tossing a coin, although this too will happen once in a blue moon.

"The degree of disorder, of randomness of molecular motion, is measured in physics in terms of entropy, which is defined for technical reasons as the logarithm of the probability ascribed to any particular type of motion. So the highest value of entropy is given to the most probable, completely orderless motion, while types of molecular motion showing some degree of order are given lower entropy values."

"And what about this law of increasing entropy?" said Mr. Tompkins.

"Well, the law of ever-increasing entropy simple states that the natural tendency of events is to proceed from less probable or ordered distributions to more probable distributions with greater degrees of disorder. My wife, Vera, like every housewife, knows this law well. While it takes any amount of work to keep a house in order, no effort is needed to make it untidy; you just stop doing anything about it for a day or two. Every highway commissioner knows that no maintenance equipment is needed to make the roads impassable. And every army officer knows that, for all the effort that must be spent in training soldiers to march in step, they easily turn into a mob as soon as discipline is broken."

Mr. Tompkins laughed. "Is there no way of getting around this sad fact of life?" he asked.

"Alas, no. But if the law of increasing disorder did not hold for thermal motion in material bodies, some most unusual engineering feats would be possible. If one could 'persuade' the molecules of air to assume sufficiently often the three-directional velocity distribution I have described, one could build jet planes that would fly without any fuel. Indeed, one-third of all the molecules moving in the same direction would form a perfect 'natural' jet. We should also be able to construct a fuelless car that sucked in the orderless heat motion from the surface of the road—every road surface is very hot as compared with absolute zero—and 'straightened it out' into an orderly motion of wheels. Such cars would also help to make city streets more comfortable in summer, since they would cool the pavement by sucking the heat out of it. However, such machines, though completely consistent with the law of conservation of energy, cannot be built, because they would violate the law of ever-increasing entropy. They are often called perpetual-motion machines of the second kind, the phrase 'perpetual motion of the first kind' being reserved for machines violating the energy-conservation law."

"But let's get back to the plants," said Mr. Tompkins.

"Right. Suppose you put an acorn into the ground and a great oak grows out of it. The complex organic molecules constituting the body of the oak are made up of the atoms which previously formed the molecules of carbon dioxide absorbed by its leaves, and the molecules of water and a few simple inorganic salts sucked in by its roots. We have here a transformation from the simple molecular structures of air and water solutions of salts into a highly organized structure of protein molecules and plant cells. There is no doubt that the second structure is *per se* much more ordered than the earlier ones, and that entropy had decreased in the process of growing.

" 'That is that!' a vitalist would say. 'This definitely proves that we must introduce a notion of *vis vitalis,* an organizing force of life, which opposes the tendency to disorder of inorganic materials. As long as this

Energy and negative entropy pull a wagon.

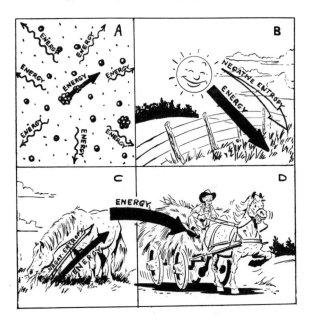

Energy and negative entropy feed a farmer.

vis vitalis is present in the body of a plant or an animal, its development goes against the laws of ordinary physics. But as soon as death comes, and the *vis vitalis* flies out of the body like a white dove, the laws of physics come into force again, and the organic matter rots and decays into its primary elements.'

"This argument seems very persuasive indeed, but wait a minute. Is there nothing else absorbed by a growing plant except carbon dioxide, water, and salts? What about sunlight, without which no plant can grow? Of course, nobody would deny that the sun's rays bring in the energy which is necessary to build complex organic molecules out of the much simpler molecules of carbon dioxide and water. As the plant grows, solar energy is absorbed and stored in its body. It can be liberated again when we use the plant as firewood, or when the plants, used as food by animals, serve as the sources of mechanical energy. Incidentally, if you look at it this way, you will see at once that a horse is an atomic-powered motor since it gets its energy from eating grass, which received the energy from the sun's rays, and solar radiation is maintained by thermonuclear reactions taking place in the sun's interior. In fact, the horse is even better than our nuclear reactors, since it produces no dangerous radioactive by-products. In the case of a farmer whose diet includes both vegetables and meat, the situation is slightly more complicated but nevertheless the same in principle."

"But can the sun's rays also account for the increasing molecular order, or the decreased entropy, which characterizes the growth of a plant?" said Mr. Tompkins.

"Any physicist of whom you ask this question will say yes. He will tell you, in fact, that solar radiation, reaching the earth, shows a very high deficiency of entropy content, and that plants are welcome to use the entropy deficiency of solar radiation in order to reduce their own entropy. To understand this point you have to know a little about the properties of radiation.

"No matter how cold a body is—except of course at absolute zero—it gives off a certain thermal radiation with a certain prevailing wavelength. As the temperature of the body increases, radiation becomes more intensive, and its prevailing wavelength becomes shorter. A piece of ice gives very little heat, so that when you stand near an ice block you feel cool because your skin radiates more heat into the ice than the ice radiates into you. On the other hand, a stove, having a higher

Energy spectrum at different temperatures.

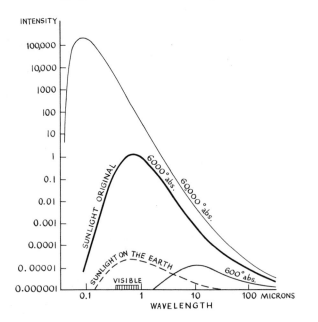

temperature than your body, emits more thermal radiation than your skin does and you feel a pleasant warmth coming from it. As long as the temperature remains below eight hundred degrees centigrade, the wavelength of radiation is too long to affect the retina of your eyes so that you do not see, but only feel, it. It is often called 'heat rays.' With an increase in temperature the prevailing wavelength decreases, and the radiation becomes 'visible.' You will see the heated body first as red hot, then as yellow hot, white hot, and finally blue hot." Wilfred took from his pocket a cigarette box and drew a diagram on its back.

"See, Dad," said he, "I have plotted here the energy distributions in the thermal radiation spectrum for different temperatures of the emitter. I need not explain the diagram, since it speaks for itself. But I want to call attention to the fact that at any given temperature there is a well-defined spectral distribution, and also a well-defined total intensity, or the amount of radiation energy per unit volume. The observed properties of thermal radiation can be derived theoretically from the assumption that the light vibrations are taking place completely at random in both their directions and amplitudes. This assumption is identical with the one concerning the randomness of molecular motion in a gas. Thus, just as in the case of a gas, the normal state of thermal radiation is that of elementary disorder, and its entropy has the maximum value.

"However, this statement holds only as long as the thermal radiation is in immediate contact with the surface of the hot body from which it is emitted. As the radiation from the sun's surface spreads out into the surrounding space it is rapidly diluted, and its energy density decreases in inverse proportion to the square of its distance from the sun. Since the distance from the sun to the earth exceeds the radius of the sun by a factor of 214, solar radiation reaching the earth contains 46,000 (or 214^2) times less energy per unit volume than it did while leaving the photosphere of the sun. This decrease of energy density is not accompanied, however, by corresponding changes in spectral distribution, since while traveling through the space between the sun and the earth, the radiation does not have any chance to exchange the energy contents between its different wavelengths.

"Thus, solar radiation reaching the earth is in some kind of hybrid state, possessing a spectral distribution which corresponds to the very high temperature of the solar surface (6000° C.), and the energy density corresponding to the much lower temperature of a hot sunny day. One can easily show that such a state of affairs is not at all a 'most probable' one, or that, in other words, the entropy of solar radiation reaching the earth is not at its maximum. This does not mean, however, that the entropy of sunlight decreases as it travels toward the earth, since, in fact, such a decrease would violate the law of entropy. What actually happens is that solar radiation, which is expected to gain in its entropy while traveling away from the sun, does not gain enough. The case is similar to the case of a taxpayer who finds that his income during the year was less than the amount he put into his declaration of the estimated tax at the beginning of that year. Well, one way or other, the sun's rays falling on the surface of green leaves can, so to speak, suck out the excess entropy, thus helping to bring down the total entropy content of the plant. Of course, the process would not necessarily go on of itself, and it is up to the plant to use the opportunity of getting negative entropy from radiation. In the same way in the business world, a 'financial opportunity' would not necessarily enrich a person unless he is smart enough to seize it. When solar radiation carrying the opportunity to reduce entropy falls on the iron roof of a house, the opportunity is simply lost because iron is 'too stupid' to know how to use it. The roof will be heated and will send back solar radiation in the high-entropy form of heat rays. But the plants are smart in that way, and use a special process known as photosynthesis, which utilizes both the energy and the entropy deficiency of solar rays for building up complex organic structures from much simpler inorganic ones."

"But how," objected Mr. Tompkins, "can an entropy deficiency—or negative entropy—be used by growing plants? It's hard to see how a deficiency of something can be helpful for anything. How can something negative be used for doing something positive?"

"Well," replied Wilfred, "if you think for a moment you will see that it is just the result of terminology, the result of our original definition of entropy as a degree of disorder and not a degree of order. In fact, the statement that entropy deficiency in absorbed radiation is necessary for plant life is similar to the statement that arsenic deficiency in absorbed food is necessary for the life of human beings.

"Most of the entropy—and energy—collected by plants from the sun's rays goes to waste when the plants die and rot, but when a horse or a cow eats grass, or when we eat salad, the entropy deficiency of the plant serves to reduce the entropy of animal tissues. And of course, when we eat a steak, we are getting the necessary entropy deficiency second hand, or rather third hand in a somewhat more digestible or at least in a more tasty form. An Austrian friend of mine liked to say that in modern and scientifically organized restaurants the menus should include not only the columns of prices and calories (energy content), but also an additional column telling the customer how much entropy he can get rid of by eating different dishes.

"Summing up, we can say that the old idea of *vis vitalis* can be given the following simple physical interpretation: (*vis vitalis*) = (entropy deficiency) = − (entropy) = − k × log (probability of material structure and motion). That living things obey the laws of physics can be called the first fundamental principle of biology."

"This principle, I take it, is quite an advance," remarked Mr. Tompkins. "Now nature is no longer split into two fundamentally different parts, the living and the nonliving. Intellectually this is much more satisfying than the old ideas, and it shows, I think, that we are making real progress in our thinking."

"Well, it is progress all right," replied Wilfred, "but from a certain point of view it is also a return to ideas current very long ago. The idea that the universe is composed of two components, matter and spirit, is not so very old, and originated, I believe, in late classical times. Before that time it was taken for granted that the universe was one— for example, the ancient Egyptians thought that men and gods, bodies and souls, animals and plants, and earth and sky were consubstantial, or made of the same substance. It did not matter whether you called this substance matter or spirit. So you see that our modern view of the unity of the universe has very deep roots, and the idea of a duality is really just a brief episode in the history of thought."

This comment on ancient ideas made Mr. Tompkins think of something he had read recently. "Your description of the growth of plants sounds similar," he remarked, "to the ancient Greek idea that plants grow by putting together the stone-atoms from the ground, water-atoms from the rain, and fire-atoms from the sun's rays."

"Yes, Dad," said Wilfred. "Those ancient Greek philosophers were quite clever—and conceived quite reasonable ideas even though they were, so to speak, just philosophizing without any empirical evidence. They recognized the existence of four different kinds of atoms—those of air, water, stone, and fire—and considered the soil to be a mixture of stone and water atoms—that is, mud. We know now that although correct in principle, they were wrong in the details. Air is a mixture of nitrogen and oxygen with a small percentage of carbon dioxide, a chemical combination of carbon and oxygen. Water is a chemical compound of oxygen and hydrogen, and stones are complex combinations of oxygen, silicon, aluminum, iron, alkali metals, and what not. On the other hand, the Greek idea of atoms of fire, which come with the sun's light or are released by burning wood, was in a way more correct than was modern science up to the year 1900, when Max Planck introduced the notion of light quanta. The light quanta, now usually referred to as photons, are considered today to be a kind of particle, on an equal standing with neutrinos, electrons, nucleons, and the other elementary particles of nuclear physics. Here the ancient Greeks were, after all, not far from the truth. But they were mistaken in their view that air plays no role in the growth of the plants. We know now that a growing plant gets its carbon from the carbon dioxide of the air, its hydrogen and oxygen from the water in the soil. The soil is not just wet sand but contains small amounts of various salts and organic materials formed as a result of the decay of earlier plants."

"Like petrified wood?" interrupted Mr. Tompkins.

"Oh no! Petrified wood is really a mineral in which the original organic compounds of wood were replaced under special conditions by inorganic silicon compounds. Petrified wood retains the shape of the trunks of trees fallen millions of years ago, but does not retain their chemical constitution. If you grind up a piece of petrified wood and mix it with water, you do not get good soil. Essential for plant growth are the minute amounts of earlier vegetation, and the salts which form the ashes which are left over when firewood is burned. However, the main weight of a growing plant is obtained from the carbon dioxide of the air, and the water in the ground."

"It seems difficult to believe," said Mr. Tompkins to his son, "that the main body of a plant is derived from the air, and not from the soil."

"Well, look at it this way," said Wilfred. "Suppose a mighty oak grows in your garden. If its thick stem and branches were made of the soil in which it grows, there should be a deep hole in the ground around it. Obviously this is not the case."

Mr. Tompkins had to admit that this was a persuasive argument. "But where does the carbon dioxide of the air come from?" he asked.

"Partially from wood fires, the decay of fallen plants, and the breathing of animals, but mostly from volcanic eruptions, which also eject the various phosphorus and sulphur compounds needed for life from the earth's interior. Of course this carbon dioxide is continuously broken up by plants with liberation of free oxygen. However, if plant life on earth were to be destroyed in some future nuclear war, the oxygen of the air would gradually be used up by various oxidation processes and, not being renewed by the photosynthetic activity of plants, our atmosphere would become a mixture of nitrogen and carbon dioxide only. The fact that recent studies of the atmosphere of the planet Mars show that it has a high concentration of carbon dioxide but no free oxygen suggests that there apparently is no plant life—and, consequently, no animal life—on that planet."

"I know, of course, that plants carry on a process called photosynthesis, and produce oxygen," said Mr. Tompkins, "but how do they do it?"

"The main agent in performing the marvelous trick of turning water and carbon dioxide into complex organic materials with the help of light is the green substance called chlorophyll, which gives plants their characteristic color," replied Wilfred. "Microscopic examinations of plant leaves show that each cell contains green particles known as chloroplasts, which, in their turn, consist of still smaller units known as grana. These grana, which are apparently individual conversion factories of solar energy, contain chlorophyll, and a task force of enzymes that help the chlorophyll to do its job.

"From a chemical point of view, photosynthesis is a reversal of the process of respiration, or ordinary burning. While in the burning process complex organic molecules (formed essentially of carbon and hydrogen) react with atmospheric oxygen, liberating energy and forming simple molecules of carbon dioxide and water, the photosynthetic process puts together the molecules of atmospheric carbon dioxide and ground water and produces complex organic molecules, liberating the excess oxygen into the atmosphere. But whereas the burning process easily goes on of its own accord, since it represents the natural direction of chemical reactions, photosynthesis must go, so to speak, uphill. To build organic materials in that way, it is necessary to detach the hydrogen atoms from the oxygen atoms in water molecules, and to attach them, in proper proportions, to the molecules of carbon dioxide. Since breaking the chemical bond between hydrogen and oxygen in water requires more energy than one gets back when a hydrogen atom attaches itself to carbon, the process requires external energy. The organic substances formed in the process have a more elaborate structure than air and water, and so the process also requires the injection of negative entropy. Both of these are, of course, supplied by sun rays.

"Organic molecules constructed by the photosynthetic process are known under the general name of carbohydrates, since they contain oxygen and hydrogen in the same proportion as water; in chemists' shorthand these compounds are written as $C_mH_{2n}O_n$. The sugar which is first formed in photosynthesis is a simple sugar called glucose (or corn sugar), written as $C_6H_{12}O_6$. Two molecules of a simple sugar joined together form sucrose, $C_{12}H_{22}O_{11}$, which is the ordinary sugar you use with your coffee. By joining together simple sugars into long chains— or polymerizing, to use the technical term—one can form starch, and also cellulose, which is the main component of plant structures such as wood and cotton. The difference between these polymers depends on slight differences in the way the simple sugar molecules are joined together. Further reactions between the energy-rich and entropy-poor compounds formed by photosynthesis lead to the formation of all other complex organic molecules, in particular, the proteins from which all plant and animal bodies are constructed.

"Of course, besides their photosynthetic ability, all plants also possess a respiratory mechanism similar to that of the animals. In fact, photosynthesis in plants should be compared with the feeding of animals, and takes place only when food—in this case, sunlight—is available. The respiration of plants takes place all the time, just as with animals; and during the night, when photosynthesis stops, respiration forms the main part of their biochemical activity."

"From all you say," commented Mr. Tompkins, "I gather that biology is now becoming a very much more exact science than it used to be—a bit more like physics and chemistry."

"I would agree," answered Wilfred. "Biology, which until recently was a purely descriptive science, is now rapidly developing into an exact discipline. That stage, which every branch of science reaches sooner or later (depending on the complexity of the field of its studies), is characterized by the discovery of the basic elementary processes which underlie the apparent complexity of macroscopic phenomena. If you look into the state of physical knowledge about a century ago, you will find that it was essentially composed of a large quantity of seemingly unrelated information concerning the mechanical, chemical, thermal, optical, electrical, magnetic, and other properties of material bodies—a kind of classified directory, I would say. With the establishment of molecular and atomic theories, and with the progress of our inquiry into the internal structure of individual atoms and their nuclei, the situation has changed quite a lot, and we are now able to reduce the multitude of complicated large-scale phenomena to the motions and interactions of the constituent particles from which all material bodies are constructed. We find, indeed, that the laws governing these elementary phenomena are comparatively few and rather simple, so that the entire structure of physical science can be based on a limited number of fundamental notions and laws, much in the same way as the system of Euclidean geometry is based on a few fundamental definitions and axioms. We have dug here to the very bottom of the complicated structure which faced the earlier explorers.

"It is not surprising that it has taken somewhat longer for biology than for physics to discover its elementary laws and principles, since the phenomena it studies are immensely more complicated. But we now seem to be on firm ground, and progress is certainly very rapid. Soon, I think, we should be able to solve the ancient riddle of life, at least as the riddle has been understood up to now."

"Are there any other basic principles of biology we now know," asked Mr. Tompkins, "besides the one that living matters obeys the laws of physics?"

"While it is true," said Wilfred, "that the old *vis vitalis* has been redefined in physical terms as the ability of living things to utilize negative entropy, our recognition that the principles of thermodynamics apply also to living matter does not solve all the problems of biology. Wood and coal have been burned for a long time, but it was not until the steam engine was invented that burning fuel became a motive force. Here something new happened when matter was organized into an engine, and something new happens when matter is organized into a living thing. What we have learned concerns this matter of organization.

"For a long time we have thought, quite correctly, that an organism is extremely complicated. But we now realize that behind this complexity there is a basic simplicity. An organism is complicated, to be sure, but it is only complicated in the sense that a computer is complicated. A computer is built of simple standard parts; essentially it is nothing but a mass of relays, and the apparent complexity is due to the way these are interconnected. So it is with the organism, which is essentially also built of *twenty* similar kinds of parts, which are chemicals called amino acids. A string of amino acids joined together forms a protein. Of course there are many thousands of different proteins in an organism, but the differences between them are simply differences of the order in which the amino acids are strung together. Even a string only a hundred amino acids long can be made in 20^{100} different ways, and this variety makes possible the varied things that proteins do."

"Yes, I've learned a little about that, recently," said Mr. Tompkins.

"Then you know that one thing they do is to interact with each other in many different ways to form more complicated structures, and this determines the form the organism will take. Whether you are a skunk or a rose, a cabbage or a man, ultimately depends on the sequence of amino acids in your proteins.

"Another function is even more important. Many proteins catalyze, or speed up, chemical reactions. In fact, many of the reactions they catalyze are otherwise so slow that we can say that they cause certain reactions to proceed which otherwise would not, and thus they determine what sort of chemical reactions are going to take place in the organism. For example, by their presence or absence they determine what foods will be digested, which kinds of sugars can be used as food, and which kinds of vitamins will be made in the body (any that cannot be made will be required as food). As you know, such proteins are called enzymes.

"As a result of their variety, proteins can produce effects which at first sight are strange and unexpected. Plants, as I have just said, absorb light which they use as food. As is well known to oceanographers, there are other organisms which use food to produce light. It is easy to calculate that below a few hundred feet of sea water all the light from the sun is absorbed, and theoretically the ocean there should be in utter darkness. Yet when photographic plates were first lowered to great depths and exposed, they unexpectedly came up fogged. We now know that this is because deep in the ocean there are all sorts of strange animals, ranging from one-celled protozoa to fish and squids, some of whose enzymes catalyze reactions producing light. Some species even have lenses, again made of proteins, to focus their light like the headlight of a car. We do not always understand what use light is to them; perhaps this makes it possible for the sexes to recognize each other, and thus helps perpetuate the species. There are also a few species of light-producing organisms on land with whom we are more familiar, such as fireflies, glowworms, and fungi which make decaying wood emit light. In all these cases a certain sequence of amino acids in proteins determines whether light will be produced.

"Thus I would say that the second fundamental biological principle is that the sequence of amino acids specifies the organism."

"I see," said Mr. Tompkins, "that an organism is specified by the order in which amino acids are arranged in proteins. But an organism also has to know how to arrange the amino acids in the proper order if I remember one of my dreams right."

"Ah, that is the third great principle which biologists have unraveled just recently," replied Wilfred. "The information on the sequence of amino acids is written in code in a molecule of DNA, or deoxyribonucleic acid, which is the substance of which genes are made. In spite of its rather formidable name, DNA is actually just a string of four different chemical groups, called bases, in the same way as proteins are strings of twenty different kinds of amino acids. The string of bases determines the order of the amino acids in the proteins. It 'codes' the protein sequences, and we can look at it as a number many millions of digits long which by specifying the proteins specifies the organism. This number of course also includes the instructions to build an enzyme which will copy the number, or, in molecular terms, will build another DNA molecule which is a copy of the original. In this way the blueprint to build the organism is passed on from generation to generation. More than that: the blueprint is improved. Copying of the blueprint is subject to slight errors now and then, and some errors produce blueprints which propagate better than the original.

"All this has been elucidated just within the last few years. We are now confident that the problem of biological organization at the level of molecules and atoms will soon be completely solved."

"Oh yes," said Mr. Tompkins. "I recall all this from the dreams in which I wandered among the genes and DNA, but you certainly summarize this much more succinctly than I could have done. However, is biological organization at the level of molecules and atoms all there is to life?"

"The answer is both yes and no," said Wilfred. "A living thing is made of molecules and atoms, of course, so in a sense there is nothing else. However, there is an important aspect to life which does not immediately follow once we know the molecular organization. A horse that is alive and one that is dead both have a rather similar molecular structure. What makes them different is their behavior, and the most characteristic thing about the behavior of living things is that it is purposive, or 'goal-directed.' A salmon leaping a waterfall, a bird building a nest, or a man playing chess are examples of living objects directing their activities toward a certain objective. Molecular biology fails to explain in a direct way this most fundamental property of living things.

"Until recently it was not fashionable among scientists even to admit the existence of the problem of purpose. If you did so, you were called a 'teleologist,' which is a naughty word."

"What, may I ask, is a teleologist?" said Mr. Tompkins.

"A teleologist," answered Wilfred, "is someone who believes that the purpose or aim of an action is the cause of the action, and who, in general, tends to explain events in terms of ends, not means."

"What is so bad about that?" asked Mr. Tompkins.

"Nothing, really, except that in the early history of science a teleological attitude, when carried to extremes, tended to inhibit an investigation of the mechanisms by which an effect is produced. For example, a teleologically minded physiologist, in those early days, would neglect to study how muscles actually function, and would be satisfied to know their purpose, such as walking or lifting a weight. It was then useful and proper to oppose such a point of view, since it stifled further investigations. Thus purpose began to be considered a 'metaphysical' concept, and the easiest way to explain it was to deny its existence. As some wag put it, it became the chief purpose of many scientists to prove that living things are purposeless.

"Fortunately scientific progress itself has made this denial of the obvious unnecessary. There is no real contradiction between the concepts that an object living or otherwise is goal-seeking, and that it also has mechanisms by which it functions. We now have a new branch of science called cybernetics, which studies purposeful actions of both machines and living things in a strictly scientific way. Goal-seeking, as it is called, is now a respectable subject, and the key to understanding it is the simple principle of feedback. Feedback can be considered the fourth fundamental principle of biology."

"You mean to say that a machine can also be purposive?" said Mr. Tompkins.

"Of course. We have such machines all around us now. It is true that until recently most machines were not capable of goal-seeking action.

Their action was preset, and they would carry it out whether it would lead to the desired result or not. Suppose, for example, that you had a machine tool which had to cut away a certain amount of metal. You could preset it to do so. But if the cutting edge was worn, it would remove less than the required amount, and the only way to correct this was to have a human operator control the operation. Now there are machines which do not need a human operator. They measure the amount of metal removed, and feed the information back to the driving mechanism, which continues to cut until the difference between the amount removed, and the amount it is desired to remove becomes zero. This is the basic principle of feedback, and it has now been applied to all sorts of devices. An antiaircraft missile, for example, computes the difference between its trajectory and the flight path of its target, and then uses this information to reduce the difference to zero, even if the target takes evasive action. It is just like a dog chasing a rabbit. The dog does not run on a preset course; it adjusts its course according to the actions taken by the rabbit, always trying to produce an encounter with its target. These perhaps are trivial examples, but they make it clear that purpose or goal-seeking is a matter of processing information and can be investigated by strictly scientific methods.

"So far as mechanism is concerned, we can see quite clearly that purposive action by living things is also controlled, at least in the simpler cases, by mechanisms not very different from the ones we now build into our goal-seeking machines. Of course, in more complicated cases we do not see this so clearly, but there is at least the hope that eventually we shall have a simple explanation here also."

"But such machines," said Mr. Tompkins, "are purposive only because we have designed them for a certain purpose. What about animals—say, your dog chasing the rabbit? Who has designed him?"

"Evolution, of course," replied Wilfred. "Sifting the good from the bad, so to speak, goal-seeking mechanisms have, quite inevitably, proved to have greater survival value than those which are not. And remember, you yourself are just as much a product of evolution as is a dog, and our superiority is precisely that you can pursue goals more effectively than any other animal.

"I do not doubt that we shall learn much in the immediate future. But there may also be surprises. Remember what happened to celestial mechanics? After Newton everything seemed so clear for a while, and then the planet Mercury began to deviate ever so little, but very definitely, from its predicted orbit. As a result we have had to swallow Einstein's relativity, with its new concepts of time and space. The lesson here is to keep working and never close your eyes to the facts."

"What sort of surprises might we expect?" asked Mr. Tompkins.

"Well, if you expect something it is no surprise," remarked Wilfred. "However, leaving aside such things as telepathy, there is one intriguing idea that is now being considered rather seriously by many scientists. It is possible that we are only one of many intelligent species that exist in the universe, and perhaps we may be able to communicate with the others, and learn what different forms of life are possible."

"You mean in the solar system?"

"No, I do not. Space probes and other investigations have made it very doubtful that there is any sort of life on any planet circling our sun, except, of course, on earth, and certainly there is no civilization here other than our own. But it is quite possible that there are planets circling the vastly more distant suns we call the stars, and that on these planets there is not only life, but intelligent and civilized life."

"A fascinating idea," said Mr. Tompkins. "I know, of course, that such speculations have been proposed in science fiction for a long time, but I gather from what you say that they are now being taken seriously. What has produced this change in attitude?"

"It is the answers we now give to two questions," said Wilfred. "First, are there other inhabitable worlds? This is for astronomers to answer. Second, are other inhabitable worlds, if there are any, actually inhabited? This is a question for a biologist, which he can answer only if he understands how life originated and developed on our earth. We can answer the first question, whether there are other inhabitable planets around other stars, if we know how planetary systems are formed.

"The early theories of the origin of the planetary systems were formulated in the second half of the eighteenth century by a German philosopher, Immanuel Kant, and a French mathematician, Pierre Simon de Laplace, and, though conceived independently, were very similar and became known as the Kant-Laplace hypothesis. According to these views, the young sun was surrounded by a belt of diffuse material, known as the 'solar nebula,' which was either left over from the early stages of the contraction of diffuse matter which formed the sun or ejected during later stages because of the increasing speed of rotation of the main body of the sun. Kant, being a philosopher, formulated this hypothesis in a purely qualitative way. It is surprising that Laplace, although a brilliant mathematician, published it only as a popular booklet and apparently never attempted to put it on a mathematical basis."

"Maybe he tried, but could not get any reasonable results," interrupted Mr. Tompkins.

"Maybe, and indeed I would say quite possibly. But one way or another, the Kant-Laplace hypothesis was not challenged mathematically until the appearance on the scene, about a century later, of a British theoretical physicist, James Clerk Maxwell. Maxwell started his analysis with a comparatively minor problem, the question whether the rings of Saturn are stable rings. Why do they not condense into a single lump of matter, or maybe a few different lumps, thus giving rise to additional satellites of Saturn? He realized that there are two opposite forces acting on the material of Saturn's rings. First, there are the forces of Newtonian gravity between the different parts of the ring, tending to condense it into one or several spherical bodies similar to the other satellites of Saturn. Secondly, there is a disruptive force due to the fact that, according to Kepler's third law, the outer parts of the ring move with a lower angular velocity—that is, a longer rotation period, than do the inner parts. These forces tend to break up the embryonic condensations and spread their material uniformly all around the ring. The final result depends on which of these forces is stronger. Maxwell derived a mathematical formula which gives the answer to the problem if one knows the total mass of the ring, its size, and its rotational velocity. These values are known from observation, and he found that the disruptive forces here prevail over the gravitational forces. Thus Saturn's rings cannot condense into satellites. And so it is.

"As a next step, Maxwell tried to apply his mathematical treatment to the hypothetical ring surrounding the sun during the early stages of its formation. To do this, he assumed that all the matter now condensed into planets was originally scattered uniformly all over the plane of the ecliptic, thus forming the primordial 'solar nebula.' The result was quite shocking: the balance between condensing and disruption forces was the same as in the case of Saturn's rings. Thus if the 'solar nebula' ever existed, it could never have condensed into the planets because its mass would have been too small!

"The only apparent alternative was to assume that our planetary system originated as the result of a collision between the sun and some other star. There are indeed a hundred thousand million stars in the stellar system of the Milky Way. But because of the large distances between the neighboring stars as compared to their diameters, the stellar traffic in the Milky Way is very safe and collisions, or even 'near misses,' are extremely rare. In fact, if a collision produced our planets, our sun and the star with which it collided some five thousand million years ago might well be the only two stars in the Milky Way possessing planetary systems. So life in the Milky Way would also be very rare.

"This collision hypothesis was formulated at the beginning of the twentieth century by Sir James Jeans in England and by Forest Moulton and Thomas Chamberlin in America, but it soon ran into its own difficulties, and the situation became desperate. It was not until the last year of the Second World War that the paradox was apparently resolved by a German physicist, Karl von Weizsäcker. He pointed out that Maxwell's conclusion was wrong, not because he used poor mathematics, but because in his time astronomers had a completely wrong idea about the chemical constitution of the universe. It was generally assumed that the sun, other stars, and interstellar material had the same chemical constitution as our earth, being formed mostly of iron, silicon, and oxygen atoms. It was assumed that hydrogen was practically absent in the sun, and that helium, first discovered in the sun's spectrum and named after it (*helios* is sun in Greek), is as extremely rare as it is on the earth. Only at the end of the third decade of the twentieth century did astronomers, helped by Niels Bohr's quantum theory of the atom, come to the conclusion that this assumption was completely wrong. In fact, we know now that the sun, other stars, and the interstellar material contain about 55 per cent of hydrogen, about 44 per cent of helium, and less than 1 per cent of all other elements. This fact removed Maxwell's objection to the original Kant-Laplace hypothesis, since it meant that at the time of their formation the planets—or as they call them now, protoplanets—also contained vast amounts of hydrogen and helium which have now disappeared. The solar nebula must have been much more massive than Maxwell thought.

"According to the calculations of the Dutch-American astronomer Gerald Kuiper, these protoplanets were formed before the sun itself had condensed enough to become hot and luminous. Thus, as in many other cases, the protoplanets were conceived in darkness. In particular, the protoearth was a giant globe of a mixture of hydrogen and helium, with a tiny rocky kernel forming about 1 per cent of its total mass, on the surface of which we are walking today. When finally the sun had condensed sufficiently so that its central temperature reached twenty million degrees Kelvin,* thermonuclear reactions started in its interior and it began to pour oodles and oodles of radiation into the space around it. This radiation blew away the thick hydrogen-helium primordial atmosphere of Mercury, Venus, earth, and Mars and revealed their rocky cores. In the case of Jupiter and the planets beyond it, which were farther away from the sun and thus experienced less of its radiation pressure, a considerable part of the primordial hydrogen-helium atmosphere is still left, and their rocky cores are hidden from our eyes in their deep interior. Jupiter, for example, has a rocky core only about ten times more massive than the earth, the rest of the mass being accounted for by a thick and tenuous hydrogen-helium atmosphere. If you remember that the total mass of Jupiter is about three hundred times larger than the mass of the earth, you can readily see how unimportant its rocky core is.

"The works of Weizsäcker and Kuiper gave a completely new, or rather very old, aspect to the problem of the origin of planets, offering us old wine in new and better bottles. It is now estimated that the chance for a star to have its own planetary system is better than one in a hundred, so that among some hundred thousand million stars forming the Milky Way a few thousand million stars are expected to possess planetary systems. And even if only 1 per cent of these planetary systems contain a planet comparable to our earth, there must be at least ten million inhabitable planets within the Milky Way.

"In a discussion of the origin of life on these inhabitable planets, it is important to notice that the primary atmosphere of the earth and other inhabitable planets was, as the chemists say, reducing rather than oxidizing, that is, possessing more hydrogen than oxygen. Thus the volatile substances forming these primordial atmospheres must have been hydrogen and its compounds with oxygen, nitrogen, and carbon— that is, water vapor, ammonia, and methane, also known as marsh gas. This is a very important conclusion, because such an atmosphere is precisely the one which will produce a profusion of different organic compounds. Biologists are now convinced that if such organic compounds are present, life is sure to develop. So the answer to our first

* Lord Kelvin's temperature scale starts at the absolute zero temperature, −273 degrees centigrade, which is the lowest limit of possible low temperature.

question, are there many inhabitable worlds?—which is yes—also helps answer our second question, are the inhabitable worlds inhabited? The answer again seems to be yes.

"Our sun and our earth are now about 4,500,000,000 years old, and our civilization is a newborn infant. If it is true that there are many civilizations in our galaxy, then very many of them should be vastly more advanced than we are, since even if some stars were only a few million years older than our sun, life around them would have had that much more time to evolve. Such civilizations would know all we know and much more, and therefore it is not unreasonable to hope to communicate with them."

"How do you propose to get in touch with the inhabitants of other planets which you are so confident exist?" asked Mr. Tompkins.

"The only reasonable method, so far as we now know, is by radio. Unfortunately, it is not quite as simple as twiddling the knobs of your radio receiver and finding a program on the air. The major problems are the great distances, the large number of stars, the time it would take a signal to get there and back, and static.

"Actually distance, by itself, is not really an obstacle. It is, of course, true that a radio signal gets weaker with distance according to the inverse-square law; at twice the distance it is four times as weak, at three times the distance it is nine times as weak. But in large measure we can get around this by beaming our signal like a searchlight. To do this, of course, we need a radio mirror. The larger the mirror is, the sharper our beam, and the farther we can signal. Even now we could signal to quite a distance. The largest fully steerable radio mirror now in existence is at Jodrel Bank in England, and it has a diameter of 250 feet. Using such a mirror and transmitters similar to our most powerful radar installations, it would not be difficult to transmit to a distance of ten or twenty light years. After making some reasonable improvements, one could even reach out to 500 light years.

"One trouble is the considerable amount of static in the galaxy, because all sorts of objects, such as stars and clouds of dust and gases, emit radio waves. However, you can cut down on the static if you receive with a large mirror which is 'looking' at the transmitter. There are two reasons for this. The larger the radio mirror, the more energy it picks up, and also the smaller the area of the sky from which it picks up signals. This cuts down the amount of static, and at the same time increases the strength of the signal. So you see that the larger the mirrors at both ends are, the farther you can expect to communicate.

"Of course, we should not judge everything by our present standards. The largest radio antennas which can be built on earth are of a diameter of a few hundred feet. The technical limitations on size are chiefly the distortions caused by gravity, wind, and changes in temperature, which warp the shape of the mirror as it tracks an object. These, however, are temporary limitations. On the moon, or in outer space, much larger mirrors could be built, possibly miles instead of feet in diameter. Since we are on the verge of being able to build such devices ourselves, civilizations only slightly more advanced than we are would have no difficulties in doing this."

"Well, if all this is so simple, why haven't we started communicating?" asked Mr. Tompkins.

"Because it is only simple if you already know that someone is beaming a transmission at you, if you know the direction the transmission is coming from and the frequency he is using. In fact we know none of these things. The big problem is the first step, which is to discover that a transmission exists. We do know that to overcome static, the transmission band will be very narrow and the transmission rate quite slow. A dot or dash might last several minutes or even hours. Therefore a large number of frequencies will have to be examined in detail, which is very laborious. It has been suggested that for easier identification, 'probing' transmissions will operate at some 'natural' frequency—say, at twice the emission frequency of hydrogen, since this frequency would be known to any scientist in the universe. Even so, there are a large number of possible stars which would have to be examined in detail, about 50,000 of them within a radius of 400 light years. For these reasons it is expensive and tedious to search for the weak signals we might expect to receive. This, of course, would be true for those near a distant star as well.

"Because of these difficulties it is rather unlikely that someone out there is beaming a signal at us unless he is pretty sure we have a radio. We do now, and you might suppose that this someone could tune in to our regular commercial and military transmissions, which are broadcast in all directions, and would discover this. But, as I said, unless we beam our signal, it is hopeless to try to receive such a weak signal through the cosmic static.

"However, there may be a way out using a statistical method which makes it possible to detect the presence of a very weak signal in the presence of a lot of noise. The principle is simple, and can be explained by throwing a die.

"Suppose I want to signal 'six' by loading a die. I can load it so that it always falls with the six up. If I give the die to you, you throw it a few times and find that you always get six, so you are quite sure it is loaded to signal six. The signal is coming through without noise. Suppose, however, that the die is loaded, but not perfectly. An unloaded die turns up six once in six throws, the imperfectly loaded one, only once in three throws. Here the signal 'six' is coming through static. Still you will have no great difficulty in receiving the signal; you will just have to throw the die a greater number of times to be sure. The less the die is loaded, the greater will be the number of times you will have to throw to find how it is loaded. So in theory, at least, you can get a signal through any amount of static if it is repeated often enough, or to put it in another way, if you pay the price of a slower transmission.

"The principle is not just theoretical, but is in use in such applications as radar studies of the sun, moon, and planets. Pulses are sent out at certain intervals. When they are reflected back, they may be too faint to be recognized individually through the static. However, we can analyze the signal to see whether the average intensity corresponding to the interval between pulses is stronger than at other intervals. If it is, we know we have a reflection, even though no individual pulses can be distinguished.

"In the same way it is possible for someone near a distant star to point a radio telescope at our solar system and study the signal, which will be mostly static. If the signal is recorded at two different times, it will be found that at certain series of frequencies, corresponding to the frequencies of our transmitters, the sum of the signals is slightly higher than at others which are only noise, since the noise is expected to vary in a random manner and will tend to cancel out. It is not difficult to show that if a really large radio dish is available to receive the signals, and a large computer to process them for statistical studies, a 'someone out there' could detect that our earth is now transmitting, even if he were many light years distant. Of course, no individual message would be received; it would only be known that we have radio transmitters. But that itself would be a most important message, saying that a planet around our sun is the abode of intelligent life.

"We have now been transmitting significant amounts of energy at high frequencies for more than twenty years. It may be that our signals are now being picked up many light years away, and someone, knowing we are here, will beam us a signal which will start communications between our two solar systems. Such a signal might therefore arrive within the next few decades."

"But how," asked Mr. Tompkins, "could we communicate if we did not know one another's language?"

"This again would not be much of a problem, since to start with we would have one language in common; the numbers. You can transmit one, two, three, and so on, as one, two, three, dots, and then develop a shorthand for them. Once you have numbers, you can do a lot of things. You can, for example, send a picture. Each point of a picture can be represented by a number which signifies whether it is black or white, just as in facsimile transmission. With this or another method, the problem is like cryptography in reverse. You send a message which will be the easiest for a recipient to decode, rather than the most difficult. But you must remember one thing. The distances between stars are so vast that even radio signals traveling with the speed of light will take decades or centuries to arrive. Of course, it is possible that some messages have already been sent some time back, so we could receive them now. But it will certainly not be like an ordinary telephone conversation. It will be more like exchanging books."

"What will we talk about?"

"A good question. What makes us want to communicate is that we might hear from a civilization millions of years ahead of us. In a sense we might therefore travel forward an incredible distance in time, using nothing more than a radio receiver, but surpassing by far the fantasy of Wells when he created his time machine."

"This thought is so startling," said Mr. Tompkins, "that I cannot help asking whether you really believe that we shall communicate with intelligent beings in other solar systems."

"I do, but with one important qualification. I am convinced that life is abundant in the galaxy and that it tends to evolve toward intelligence. The question is, what happens when it does? If a technological civilization usually lasts for millions of years, then of course such civilizations will be numerous, and I am sure that communications between them will be established. But perhaps this is not so.

"Imagine that a space probe of some sort is now circling our earth. It will pick up a babble of transmissions, and if it can decode them it will obtain a most interesting view of what goes on under our cloud layer. From the capitals of the world a flood of invective, hate, and threats of destruction pours forth in an unending stream. The probe would learn that these are not idle threats: the equivalent of many tons of TNT for each inhabitant of the earth is stored below. Not knowing that we are really a kind and gentle race of beings who would not hurt a fly, the builders of the probe would draw the conclusion that the transmissions will not last long. Evolution, they would conclude, has produced an insane and vicious race of maniacs, bent on self-destruction.

"The basic question is whether a technological civilization necessarily carries with it the seeds of its own destruction. It is not difficult to see how this might be true. Our own trouble is that we have discovered methods of changing our environment more and more rapidly, but have mentally failed to adapt to such changes. If we do not adapt, we of course face the fate of the dinosaurs. As one of my astronomer friends has so aptly put it, the driving forces toward technological civilization are competitiveness, which leads ultimately to destruction, and a desire for a life of ease, which ultimately leads to physical and genetic deterioration. We can survive only if we discard these driving forces once they have outlived their usefulness.

"If it is true that all technological civilizations have a short life span, the prospect of communication between them is dim. Few such civilizations will exist at any one time. They will therefore be very far apart, possibly separated by thousands of light years. Even if they succeed in locating each other, two-way communication will be impossible. During the thousands of years that a message traveling at the speed of light would take for the round trip, both civilizations will become extinct."

It was now dark as they rowed home. Mr. Tompkins had caught no fish, but he scarcely noticed it. His thoughts were elsewhere, on some lines from a poem by Heine he had once read:

> . . . Oh solve me the riddle of living,
> That age-old, tormenting riddle,
> That many a head has brooded over,
> Heads in turban and black mortar board,
> Periwig heads and a thousand other
> Poor, perspiring heads of people—
> Tell me this, what meaning has man?
> From where has he come? Where does he go?
> Who dwells up there on starlets golden? . . .

Index